THE SKULE STORY

THE SKULE STORY

The University of Toronto
Faculty of Applied Science
and Engineering,
1873–2000

RICHARD WHITE

Printed for the University of Toronto
Faculty of Applied Science and Engineering
by University of Toronto Press Incorporated

© Faculty of Applied Science and Engineering, University of Toronto

Printed in Canada

ISBN 0-7727-6704-1

Printed on acid-free paper

Canadian Cataloguing in Publication Data

White, Richard, 1952
The Skule story : the University of Toronto Faculty of
Applied Science and Engineering, 1873–2000

Includes bibliographical references and index.
ISBN 0-7727-6704-1

1. University of Toronto. Faculty of Applied Science and
Engineering – History.   I. University of Toronto. Faculty of
Applied Science and Engineering.   II. Title.

T173.T77W55 2000   620'.0071'1713541   C00-901577-9

CONTENTS

Preface vii

Author's Preface ix

chapter one
A PRACTICAL SCHOOL OF SCIENCE 1

chapter two
GALBRAITH'S VISION 39

chapter three
CAUTIOUS PROGRESS 87

chapter four
FROM WAR TO RENEWAL 147

chapter five
THE FACULTY TRANSFORMED 207

CONTENTS

Appendix 269

Notes 279

A Note on Sources 303

Works Consulted 305

Index 317

DEAN'S PREFACE

In 1998, the Faculty of Applied Science and Engineering celebrated its 125th year, having been founded in 1873 as the School of Practical Science (SPS) in Ontario. Many older Torontonians still speak fondly of 'SPS', even though it formally ceased to exist in 1906 when it became the University of Toronto's Faculty of Applied Science and Engineering. This old name lingers on, in part, because the lintel stone of the original SPS building, engraved with the school's name, was preserved when the building was demolished and is now incorporated into the public foyer of the Galbraith Building, but also because our graduates have long been mindful of their Faculty's past and keen on preserving its traditions.

Yet we have long lacked a comprehensive history. A book covering the school's early years was produced by C.R. Young, a former dean of the Faculty, in 1958 under the title *Early Engineering Education at Toronto 1851–1919*. Since then, a collection of articles edited by Robin S. Harris and Ian Montagnes titled *Cold Iron and Lady Godiva – Engineering Education at Toronto 1920–1972* was produced to commemorate the 100th anniversary in 1973, and Barry G. Levine, having just graduated from the Faculty, wrote and published *A Century of Skill and Vigour* in 1985 on behalf of the University of Toronto Engineering Society.

It seemed appropriate, therefore, as we passed our 125th birthday and stood on the verge of the 21st century, that a new, complete history of the Faculty be written based upon a full review of the rich historical record. To carry out this job we obtained the services of Richard White, a historian with a PhD in history from the University of Toronto who had recently completed a study of early Canadian civil engineering. Richard has worked diligently for close to two years to bring *The Skule Story* to fruition, and in doing so has brought to light a good many surprises. I am grateful to him for a job well done.

We have so much of which to be proud; perhaps the most significant is that many of our former students have gone on to leadership roles in business, industry, academe, public-sector management, and independent professional practice, and thereby contributed so much to the current stature of Ontario and Canada. And there is no doubt that they will continue to do so. We have traveled a long way; but the distance yet to cover is far greater.

This book will be of great interest to current alumni and friends of the Faculty, and to the many who will follow as the Faculty continues to grow in size, stature, and international significance.

MICHAEL E. CHARLES

AUTHOR'S PREFACE

I came to the task of writing this history of the University of Toronto's Faculty of Applied Science and Engineering – or 'Skule,' as its students and graduates have taken to calling it in recent years – as an outsider. This, I must admit, had its disadvantages, and might well have caused me to overlook or under-appreciate some parts of the Faculty's past. But it also offered opportunities, for it allowed me to see themes and make connections that an insider might not have seen and made, and to place the Faculty's history into a broader context. I hope I have made good use of these opportunities, and that my outsider's perspective has yielded more insights than oversights, but readers of course will judge this on their own.

The Faculty's history is a rich and fascinating story, interwoven with several interesting themes. The one theme that stands out above all others for me, however, is the strength of the Faculty's traditions. This institutional trait has evoked, and still does evoke, quite different opinions, being viewed by some as a source of valuable stability and by others as a cause of maddening inertia. As the following pages will reveal, for an institution teaching its students the knowledge and techniques needed to further material progress, the school could at times be surprisingly unprogressive. Changes to its structure and programs were usually implemented very cautiously – by 'evolutionary' rather than 'revolutionary' methods, one of its deans explained – and often quite a bit later than advocates of change within its own walls would have liked. Yet one will also see that this was rarely an impediment to success, for there can be no doubt that most of what it chose to do it did well. Caution and circumspection, time and again, yielded well-considered ideas and solid innovation. There is indeed strength in tradition, as *The Skule Story* reminds us again and again.

The chapters in this book are rather long, something that warrants a brief explanation. It has resulted from my coming to see the Faculty's history in terms of 'generations' – periods of roughly twenty-five or thirty years in which a certain set of circumstances or guiding principles prevailed, or in which a particular fundamental change was worked through. It seemed fitting, therefore, to give each of the Faculty's five generations a chapter of its own, in which that generation's key events are narrated and its distinctive features described. The result is that each chapter covers a fairly long run of time, but is to my mind more coherent for doing so.

Looking back now, after being immersed in this very enjoyable work for nearly two years, I am amazed at how much I have been able to learn about the Faculty, the university, and the profession of engineering. It is also clearer than ever to me that I have been able to do so only through the generosity of others, and I happily and gratefully acknowledge their contributions.

To Marty Friedland and Peter Wright I owe a special word of thanks, for the two of them, quite independently, hatched the idea of this project and helped set me upon it. The current dean of the Faculty, Michael Charles, who also played a key role in bringing this book to life, has been everything an author could want from a person who commissions his work – patient, trusting, and open-minded – and this I have appreciated enormously. Many people in the Faculty, more that I can mention, took time to share recollections and opinions with me, and in doing so gave me essential knowledge and perspective. Especially generous with their time and thoughts were Gordon Slemon, Frank Hooper, Ben Etkin, Ian Dalton, and Michael Charles. Several of my historian colleagues – Carl Berger, Terry Reynolds, and Philip Enros – took an interest in this work and kindly agreed to read chapters and offer their comments; Janis Langins (of the Institute for the History and Philosophy of Science and Technology at the University of Toronto) and Harold Averill (of the University of Toronto Archives) read the entire manuscript in draft form and made valuable suggestions. Harold was nothing less than indispensable in the photograph selection. The University Archivist Garron Wells, and her entire staff, provided me with essential support and assistance from the first day of the project to the last. The staff of the University of Toronto History Project, especially Charles Levi, freely shared research materials and ideas, and were a helpful – and suitably dubious – sounding board as my conclusions took shape. My assiduous research assistant Steve Walton has contributed in more ways than I could possibly recall, and for all of them I am grateful.

Despite the fact that this is a commissioned work, what follows are my own words. Many people in the Faculty offered me their thoughts and opinions, but none attempted to influence my thinking in any way. For errors, omissions, or misinterpretations, therefore, I alone am responsible.

RICHARD WHITE

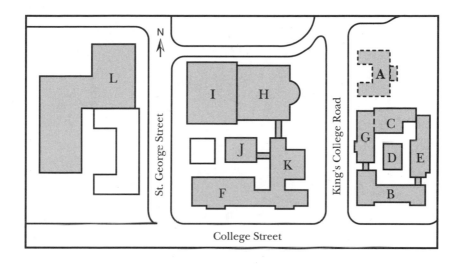

**Faculty Buildings
on the University of Toronto St. George Campus**

A. Engineering Building
   (demolished 1966; site now occupied by Medical Sciences Building)
B. Mining Building
C. Thermodynamics Building
D. Haultain (formerly Mill) Building
E. Rosebrugh (formerly Electrical) Building
F. Wallberg Building
G. Mechanical (incorporating Thermodynamics) Building
H. Sandford Fleming Building
I. Galbraith Building
J. Engineering Annex
K. Pratt Building
L. Site of Bahen Centre for Information Technology

THE SKULE STORY

chapter one

A PRACTICAL SCHOOL OF SCIENCE

People have birthdays – clear, unequivocal dates on which they came into the world. Whether remembered or not, one's date of birth is a simple fact. This is not always so with large institutions, which are often born and reborn as they evolve amid changing circumstances, and such is indeed the case with the Faculty of Applied Science and Engineering at the University of Toronto. Strictly speaking, the Faculty was created in 1900, but the year usually given for its founding is 1873, when its precursor the Ontario School of Practical Science came to be. This earlier date is probably more appropriate, and it has been generally accepted, but it too has its problems, for although the school came to be as a legal entity in February 1873 – on this the legislative record is clear – it did not become a physical entity or begin teaching students its full program until 1878. Prior to this, in 1871, something called the College of Technology, a partial SPS usually considered to be its antecedent, had been established. Complicating matters further still, until 1889 the SPS was really nothing more than an adjunct to University College. So the Faculty's story must begin with a retelling and clarification of this long, and at times rather confusing, institutional genesis.

— ∞∞∞ —

The Ontario School of Practical Science was a provincial project, the creation of a government eager to foster development of its new domain. The first few years after Confederation were a time of expectation and enthusiasm in the halls of power in Toronto.

Not only had the new Dominion of Canada just been created, so too had the Province of Ontario. Freed at last from a forced twenty-six year union with Canada East, during which the Roman Catholic French Canadians and old Anglo-Canadian establishment had thoroughly dominated political life, the leaders of this new province were keen to set a course of progress all their own. And the future looked promising indeed. A faith prevailed among many Ontarians that their province would soon be sharing in the great industrial expansion that much of the English-speaking world had been experiencing for generations. Businesses of all kinds – farms, manufactories, mines, and railways – sat poised for growth and prosperity, and the provincial government stood by ready to foster development any way it could.

This enthusiasm was especially evident in the field of education, over which the province now had complete authority, and in particular in any kind of 'technical' or 'industrial' education that could help advance the province's economic performance.[1] There were moves to increase the overall technical component of public education, to add more vocational or practical courses to the high school curriculum, and to improve the standards of education for the industrial trades. The Ontario Department of Public Works and Agriculture began granting money to the Mechanics Institutes in 1868, urging them to revive their evening classes for working men; (most of the Institutes had fallen dormant after the old Province of Canada stopped supporting them in 1858). The Ontario College of Agriculture would soon be established by the province, for much the same reason as the School of Practical Science.[2] At times the enthusiasm was so great that politicians and educators jumbled together several quite different educational needs, and one wonders if the enthusiasts always properly understood one another. Advocates might call for 'technical' education, for 'practical' education, or for 'industrial' education – sometimes, but not always, meaning the same thing. Or they might talk of 'technical' training for both artisans and scientific professionals as if that training were the same.[3] Specific educational programs might not have been clearly set out, but the desire was there, as were the provincial powers needed to establish whatever was devised.

There was also a university, a provincial university, in Toronto at the time, but few expected it to play much of a role in the province's practical or technical education. For one thing, the province did not fully control the university. As an educational institution, it had been placed under provincial authority at Ontario's creation in 1867, but it was governed by its own independent senate, not by the government, and was sustained not by provincial government grants but rather by a combination of student fees and revenue from the old land endowment bestowed on it at its founding (as King's College) in 1827. This land, scattered about the province, had almost all been sold, and the money thus acquired invested in financial securities now yielding some $60,000 per year.[4] So although the university was a public institution in the sense that it had been established by a generous gift of public land from the Crown and was nominally under the auspices of the province, it ran its own affairs and paid its own bills. The university's religious roots were a troublesome matter too, a vestige of an old world for which the new Ontario government had little sympathy – the province had quickly, in 1868, terminated all the grants to religious colleges that the government of united Canada had been providing before Confederation.[5] The University of Toronto was non-sectarian, and had been since 1850, but it was not irreligious. Residents at University College (the university's only college) were required to 'regularly attend their respective places of worship on Sundays,' and attend morning and evening prayer unless officially exempted. There was also a strict daily regimen, with the evening bell summoning students to residence at 9:00 p.m., and the college gates closing half an hour later for the night. This was all a little monastic for the proponents of new industrial Ontario.[6]

The University Gates on College Avenue (now Street), looking west at Yonge Street, late 1870s. UTA, A65-0004/0.64

Universities throughout the western world were, in fact, at this time undergoing profound changes. Their traditional purpose – protecting the great intellectual traditions of western culture – was being challenged; within a few decades many would be places where knowledge was produced as well as protected, and where students learned what to do not just what to think.[7] Several major universities, no longer content with knowledge for its own sake, had already begun to seek 'utility' in their instruction.[8] This was especially true in the sciences. Both Yale and Harvard had created practically oriented science schools before 1860 (although they were kept separate from the main university). Even Cambridge had considered establishing an engineering program in the 1850s.[9] Old methods of teaching were being questioned, too; some schools were allowing students into laboratories to perform their own experiments, and some professors were adopting a more informal lecturing style. Many institutions were also relaxing their traditional student discipline.[10]

Some of this had begun to appear at the University of Toronto. Since the 1850s students at University College had been able, officially, to study agricultural science or civil engineering. But, in truth, the university had but a tepid commitment to these practical courses. Its chair in Engineering had never been filled, so the Civil Engineering course consisted only of instruction in the standard academic sciences. Only the occasional student had enrolled in the course.[11] Student laboratory instruction was being considered, but the equipment at University College was not yet sufficient for this to be done properly. Student discipline was loosening, but was still officially in place for all students in residence. Reforms, in other words, had begun, but few politicians, or even students, would have seen much evidence of them.

So all things considered – curriculum, governance, pedagogy, and student life – the university looked like an unlikely ally in the province's quest to develop the practical education needed to foster industrial growth. Its teaching might have been important for the province's lawyers and schoolmasters, but most Ontario legislators and educators would not have thought it practical enough to help build Ontario's railways, factories, or mines.

It was in this context, with a good many uncertainties still clouding the matter, that the Ontario government of Sandfield Macdonald resolved in early January 1871 to create a provincial 'School, or College, of Technology,' to provide advanced, post-matriculation study for the scientific professions.[12] Exactly who or what stimulated this concrete move seems to have escaped documentation, but considering how widespread was the wish for this sort of education, identifying its prime advocate might be impossible. Certainly Egerton Ryerson, the province's well-known commissioner of Education, was among its promoters, but judging by the speed with which the scheme went through he was likely not alone. The Macdonald government promptly appointed a commission of two (one of them being J. George Hodgins, Ryerson's assistant) to study and report on a number of such schools in the United States, from their finances and administration to their curriculum and building design, and to recommend a proper course of action. A few weeks later they reported, strongly supporting the decision to create a provincial College of Technology (or 'School of Industrial Science,' as they called it on occasion) for Ontario.

Although not their job to propose a specific program, the commissioners did suggest certain general features of the school. They envisioned an advanced institution, like those they inspected at Harvard, Yale, and Cornell, that would require for admission a minimum age of sixteen to eighteen years and a good secondary education. Students would take a course of several years duration in a wide range of subjects – mathematics, sciences, drawing, and languages – in order to prepare themselves for professional work. The commissioners spoke highly of the absence of strict student discipline and the use of 'conversational lectures' at the schools they visited. For the proposed Ontario school, they suggested that instruction be 'as practical as possible.' One point in their report on which they were particularly insistent was that the school should 'in its teaching, management, and government, be kept entirely distinct from any other institution.' They had learned, especially from the Sheffield Scientific School at Yale and the Lawrence Scientific School at Harvard, where the practical emphasis was being challenged, that such independence was essential. Also, since students at the proposed new school would be expected to perform 'manual effort and physical labour,' and would require 'more constant teaching oversight and professorial supervision than students in Colleges, or Universities,' the typical university professor was obviously not suited for this sort of work. 'Schools of technology are *sui generis*,' they claimed, and thus needed independent administration.[13] The report's authors evidently viewed universities as traditional, unreformed institutions.

The Ontario government followed their advice and promptly requested $50,000 from the provincial legislature to establish the new school – although they proposed no bill – but immediately met with considerable opposition. This was an unprecendented step, providing provincial funds on this scale for advanced education, and it was not going to go unchallenged. The operating costs of such a school with several full-time professors, would be considerable, and Liberal leader Edward Blake attacked the very essence of the commission's report – the school's independence – for this reason, arguing that the expense of a whole new school was unnecessary when the existing university already taught most of the same science subjects. Blake had long been a friend of the university; he knew its affairs well and unlike many other members of the legislature had faith in its teaching capacities. But he was unable to sway the Sandfield Macdonald government. The request for funds was passed, and the government pressed on. Their plan at first was to build the new school on the Normal School grounds at Church and Gerrard streets, but within a few months they changed to the more modest scheme of purchasing and refitting the existing Mechanics Institute building at the corner of Church and Adelaide streets. The province bought the building in September and immediately began the necessary renovations.

For some reason, plans had already begun to change, and what the government now envisioned was something rather different from what the report had recommended only a few months before – it was now to be a curious hybrid of a school replete with all the confusions of the day. The school was to train professional

9

engineers (mining, civil, and mechanical), as well as 'workers in wood, leather, woollen and flax fibres,' 'modellers and carvers in the decorative and industrial arts,' and 'persons desirous of studying chemistry, as applied to our various manufacturers.'[14] It was, one critic later said, a combined engineering college, technical high school, and art school.[15] Whether such a diverse combination could have worked nobody would ever know, for in mid-December 1871, before the scheme could be put in place, the Sandfield Macdonald government fell and Edward Blake became premier of Ontario.

Although no legislation had been passed requiring the school's creation, the project had enough momentum to survive the government's fall. But before it opened its doors Blake and his fellow reformers modified it further still. Blake had, from the outset, thought that creating an entirely new school for professional education was unnecessary duplication, favouring instead establishing such instruction in connection with the university. So, not surprisingly, when the College of Technology opened in May 1872, it was an evening school for working artisans and nothing else. Advanced, post-matriculation education for professionals was not offered. There were no daytime classes. The scheme was further pared down by the Blake government; only two instructors were hired and two subjects taught. W.H. Ellis, a medical doctor with a BA and MA from University College in natural sciences (1867, 1868) who had recently begun teaching chemistry to medical students, taught Chemistry on Monday and Wednesday nights; William Armstrong, an experienced civil engineer and gifted draughtsman who would later gain renown as a watercolourist, taught architectural and mechanical drawing on Tuesday and Thursday nights. The lectures were free, and very popular. Between 50 and 100 men, mostly tradesmen or clerks, attended classes every night right from the start.[16]

The Blake government knew that it had not created an engineering school. Professional education was not offered at night,

University College, 1875, viewed from near the future site of the School of Practical Science. UTA, A65-0004/1.18

for no charge. Despite the frequent confusion about which sort of technical education belonged where, it was widely recognized that professional engineering education was academically more advanced than what this College of Technology now offered. The college took the form it did for several reasons – because both Blake and Education Minister Adam Crooks were friends of the university, and perhaps also because of political and fiscal forces, but not because of ignorance about the engineering profession.[17] In fact, if anything, the exclusion of engineering from the teaching program at the College of Technology shows a better understanding of the needs of professional engineering education than the Macdonald government's plan for an all-inclusive school.

The Blake government – before long the Oliver Mowat government once Blake departed for the federal Liberal leadership – knew it still had work to do to establish professional scientific education. Accordingly, in January 1873, it brought forward a bill to do just that.[18] Going back in some ways to the recommendations of the former government's 1871 report, it called for 'a School for Practical Education in such arts as Mining, Engineering, Mechanics and Manufactures.' But there were some new aspects. It was still to be a provincial institution, sustained and controlled by the Ontario government, with an explicit mission to 'greatly promote the development of the mineral and economic resources of the province, and its industrial progress,' but the Act of 29 March 1873 gave the government authority to make arrangements with the University of Toronto for students of the new school to attend University College lectures and vice versa. Nothing was certain on this front, nor could it be; the university ran its own affairs, so this decision was not the government's alone. But the intention was clearly stated. There were still plenty of details to work out – the site of the school was not specified, nor was whether it would be situated in new or existing premises – but the school that would in time become the Faculty of

Applied Science and Engineering at the University of Toronto had been legally founded.

This new legislation introduced another novelty: the institution was to be named the Ontario School of Practical Science. How and why the word 'practical' entered the name has long been viewed as something of a mystery in need of explanation.[19] But it was in fairly common use; a School of Practical Science had been proposed at Cambridge in 1859, and the term appears occasionally in Ontario government reports, so its use was not exceptional.[20] Exactly what the minister meant by 'practical,' however, does remain a little puzzling, for the word had two rather different meanings at this time. For some, it meant 'serving a useful purpose,' and its antonym was 'impractical'; thus, practical science would include the thermodynamics of steam engines, the chemistry of ore refining, or the statics of bridge building. But to science educators at the time, it referred instead to the new style of teaching by involving students in laboratory work – teaching, in other words, by allowing students to 'practise' science. Which of these two meanings the minister of Education had in mind when he drafted the 1873 bill is unknown. It is generally assumed to have been the former, but the latter was probably more common in educational circles at that time. Perhaps he meant both, and was cleverly doubling support for the school. In any case, enigmatic as it is, the name is perfectly appropriate. It stands as a telling artifact of both the trends and the confusions of the times.

Little changed for several years except that the College of Technology began to call itself the School of Practical Science, which it does not appear to have had to do. The college was certainly not the school that the 1873 legislation called for. As to formalizing arrangements with the university, determining the new school's site, or setting up its courses, nothing was done. The 'Downtown

SPS' as it was sometimes called, continued to give free evening lectures to artisans as the months, and then the years, passed by. The whole project seemed to be getting further from, not closer to, fruition.

There was, however, a new force at work: James Loudon, a young Toronto scholar who would in time play a leading role at the University of Toronto, and who might well be the most important individual in the founding of the School of Practical Science. Loudon was a graduate of University College (1862), where he had studied natural philosophy. He had been appointed mathematics tutor at the college in 1863 and dean of Residence in 1865. In 1873, he had taken on the job of teaching physics at the College of Technology, adding a third subject of instruction to the college's evening offerings. He was also appointed that year to the university senate as a representative of the college alumni.[21] Loudon probably had academic career aspirations by this time, but, being the only Canadian among the staff of a dozen or so British imports he felt he had little chance of a professorship or chair at the college. As a younger man, however, he also had novel, somewhat reformist, ideas about teaching physical science. He was one who favoured a less formal lecturing style than was conventional at the time, and he strongly endorsed the integration of laboratory work into science classes. Loudon also seems to have had some sympathy with real-world applications of science – as evidenced in his teaching at the College of Technology – although there is no sign that he ever did such work himself.[22] Favouring the use of laboratory work in the teaching of science and sympathizing with practical applications of science are not the same thing – practical science teaching, in other words, is not the same as teaching practical science – but they do have a certain commonality, and in James Loudon they went hand in hand.

In 1875, Loudon was appointed to the chair of Mathematics at University College upon the retirement of Professor J.B. Cherriman, and thus became the first Canadian-born man to occupy a

James Loudon, c.1880; Loudon would go on to serve as president of the University of Toronto from 1892 to 1906, but as a young professor at University College in the 1870s he played a critical role in the establishment of the School of Practical Science. UTA, B2000-0024/001 (#10)

permanent staff position at the university. Having established himself as a credible scholar and science educator, Loudon was asked by the minister of Education for a formal opinion on how the government should go about solving its problem of the unbuilt School of Practical Science. Loudon had a ready solution, which he offered to Provincial Secretary C.S. Wood in a letter dated 17 December 1875.[23] In providing his solution, Loudon, perhaps unwittingly, altered the problem. To him, the problem was not just where the School of Practical Science should be established and how it might make use of the University College professoriate; it was also how University College could develop its practical teaching of physical sciences (meaning laboratory instruction), a matter he had been trying to raise in the university senate.[24] In his letter to Wood, Loudon claimed that both of these were stated as goals in the 1873 Act, which is not quite true, although the Act did call for the creation of a museum to house specimens that could be used for the practical teaching of science. In any case, Loudon's reconstituted double problem seems to have been accepted from this point forward. So, too, was his solution.

Loudon pointed out that an entirely new school, with its own staff of five or six professors to instruct the required mathematics, science, drawing, and so on (as had been recommended in the 1871 report) would be prohibitively expensive, and not fully justified given the untested demand for the school's services. With this Mowat's government no doubt agreed. More prudent, Loudon argued, would be to establish the school on the university grounds, and to make use of the existing University College staff for all but the actual engineering courses – for which a single new professor of engineering would have to be hired. Furthermore, and here Loudon's interests are unmistakably revealed, the new building could also be used for University College's science instruction. All students – students of the new school as well as those at University College – would take their science instruction from the college professors at the new school, and the school would, of course, be equipped with enough laboratory space and equipment to allow students to do their own laboratory work.

This is exactly what was done. A year passed without action, but late in 1876 the minister announced plans to sell the old downtown college building and to erect a new structure on the university grounds. Kivas Tully was engaged as architect, the site was chosen by a committeee of the university senate, lectures at the downtown building were terminated, the equipment there put in storage, and the new Ontario School of Practical Science finally began to take material form through 1877–78.

Despite the views so emphatically expressed in the 1871 report, the SPS was not being born as an independent school. It was in fact the 'Applied Science Department of University College,'[25] and was going to be thoroughly under the wing of the college's arts professors. It is true that it would have its own board, distinct from that of University College, and that it was going to be paid for entirely by the government of Ontario (which the university certainly was not). But the 'board' was a somewhat artificial creation. It was to consist of the professors who taught at the school, but of course all but one of these men were the science profesors of University College – the chemist H.H. Croft, the geologist E.J. Chapman, the biologist R. Ramsay Wright, and the mathematician and physicist James Loudon. The single exception was the yet-to-be-named professor of engineering. Croft, the most senior, was to be chairman of the board. Furthermore, the building was to include laboratories for chemistry, mineralogy and geology, and biology under the authority of Professors Croft, Chapman, and Wright, respectively, but there would be no engineering laboratory. Even the school crest, devised by Chapman, was to be a slight variant of the college's.[26]

If there was any deceit underlying this curious conception, we will never know. Was James Loudon fooling the Ontario government? Was the Ontario government fooling the public? In any case, for now, everybody thought they had exactly what they wanted: Loudon had a practical school of science for the university, at government expense, and government promoters of provincial development had a provincial School of Practical Science, at a bargain price.

Construction went according to schedule, and classes were set to begin in October 1878, but there was still one missing piece: the professor of engineering, the man who would carry the engineering instruction that the science professors could not do. In the summer before the school opened, there was a minor dispute over this appointment. Among the nine applicants for the position was William Bell Dawson, son of the eminent McGill University scientist John William Dawson. The elder Dawson was a friend of University of Toronto president Daniel Wilson, a fact that no doubt influenced Wilson in his decision to recommend to Adam Crooks, the minister of Education, that young Dawson be given the job. William Dawson was confident enough that, while in Toronto to view the new facilities, he began making arrangements for his office – much to the dismay of the other professors, who had not even been consulted and who quickly raised a voice of dissent. Crooks, as it turned out, was not yet committed to Dawson, for he subsequently asked for and took the advice of James Loudon to hire another of the applicants – John Galbraith, a man who would devote the rest of his life to the school and whose long, illustrious career is now legendary.[27]

Galbraith, thirty-two years old at the time, had had little experience with engineering education. He was, however, university educated, with both a BA and MA from University College; he was also an associate of the Institution of Civil Engineers in England, and a successful practising engineer of wide experience. He fit well into a program that would attempt to blend the practical and the academic. He was also popular among his peers and perhaps most important of all at a time when engineers had to be men of strength as well as brains, he had been able, since his youth, to 'defend himself on the schoolyard.'[28]

John Galbraith had been born in Montreal in 1846 into a respectable middle-class family, three of his four grandparents being Scottish immigrants. The fourth, his maternal grandmother, was a French Canadian. His father worked as an accountant in a merchant house in Montreal until 1852, at which time he took on a business venture in Port Hope, Canada West. The family moved west with the father and there, in Port Hope, John Galbraith grew up. He excelled at the local grammar school, finishing first in all his classes. In his adolescent years, he met and fell under the influence of a surveyor and aspiring engineer in Port Hope named George Stewart, and through Stewart, Galbraith learned of and quickly took an interest in engineering. Apparently intent on a university education as a preliminary to entering the profession (which, although desirable, was not really necessary at the time) the young Galbraith, after consulting Professor Cherriman at University College, elected to enrol in the arts course there to study mathematics. He arrived in the fall of 1863, the very year James Loudon was appointed mathematics tutor.

Galbraith graduated from the college in 1868, winning the Gold Medal in Mathematics that year, and had the good fortune of embarking on his informal professional apprenticeship just as a railway boom was taking hold. He was able to secure several years of good employment as a railway engineer. When the boom ended in 1874, Galbraith moved back to Port Hope and went into private practice. He also re-established his connection with the university, working as an occasional examiner in Mathematics, and acquiring his MA degree in 1875 (which, at the time, required little formal work).[29] He followed this with a year as a mechanical draughtsman at a locomotive works in Portland, Maine, gaining valuable mechanical engineering experience. When he applied for the professorship at the SPS, Galbraith already had an impressive ten-year professional career, and with his MA and his occasional work as a mathematics examiner, had kept up what he called in his letter of application 'the theoretical part of my profession.'[30]

He was appointed the first professor of Engineering at the Ontario SPS on 28 September 1878. So close to the start of the teaching term was the appointment that Galbraith missed the school's first board meeting on 1 October. But he made the

John Galbraith in his mid-thirties, a few years after his appointment at the school. UTA, B2000-0024/003 (#3)

second, five days later, after classes had begun. One other instructor was appointed prior to the school's opening, as well – W.H. Ellis, the medical doctor who had taught chemistry at the former College of Technology, had been named assistant to the chemistry professor, H.H. Croft. Ellis had studied under Croft while at the college in the 1860s.

The building where Galbraith and his colleagues were to do their teaching was indeed not much more than a 'little red schoolhouse,' as it would later be known. It was a three-storey red brick structure, basically rectangular in plan, only about 30 metres wide and 15 metres deep, with a small wing extending south from the west end. There were two lecture rooms, one seating about 200 and the other about 40. The basement housed the laboratory and specimens of geology and mineralogy. On the ground floor was the main chemistry laboratory and the private rooms of Professors Loudon, Chapman, and Croft. The second storey was used partly for an additional chemistry laboratory and partly for engineering. The attic was given over entirely to Professor Wright's biology specimens, laboratory, and office.[31] The building was modest to the point of austere, costing just $30,000. The inadequate heating, plumbing, and plastering would vex those working there for the next decade. Across the university lawn, some 200 meters to the north, stood the splendid, stone University College, erected at a cost of nearly $400,000 twenty years earlier.[32]

The original School of Practical Science, central as it is in the memory of the many thousands of engineers who would graduate from it, was not, in fact, conceived as purely an engineering school. For one thing, it offered three courses of study (what would now be called 'programs') leading to the three-year SPS Diploma: Engineering (Civil, Mechanical, and Mining), Assaying and Mining Geology, and Analytical and Applied Chemistry. Within a decade or two, engineering became the course of choice; the professions of geologist and chemist never took hold in the late nineteenth century as engineering did, and enrolment in them never amounted to much. But they were distinct from engineering at the time, and were among the nascent scientific professions the SPS was to teach. Students in any of these three diploma programs were classified as 'regular students.' The school also offered a one-year course leading to a certificate in surveying, as well as the option to register as a 'special student' in individual subjects, an opportunity that would be taken (primarily for biology and chemistry) by students of veterinary medicine and by medical students attending the city's private medical

The only known photograph of the front of the original School of Practical Science in the 1880s; unfortunately, small trees have been inked on the glass negative, partly obscuring the building. UTA, A65-0004/6.1

schools.[33] It was a school of practical science, not just an engineering school.

In addition, of course, it was to be used by the University College professors for teaching science to their own students, and by far the majority of the school's early students were of this classification. In its first year, 53 University College students received their chemistry instruction in the school, as did 23 special medical students their chemistry and biology, while a mere 8 students were registered as SPS students proper. The following year, 137 UC students took their chemistry (smaller numbers now took geology and biology, as well), while 38 veterinary and 24 medical special students took classes. Only 12 students, now in two years, were registered as regular SPS students, all of them in the engi-

East side and front of the original School of Practical Science building, 1880s, from John Galbraith's personal album. UTA, B78-0018/#12

neering course.[34] No concern was expressed over this imbalance. All was evidently going according to plan.

The only change in management at the school during the first few years was the appointment of the new university president Daniel Wilson as chairman of the board to replace Croft, who retired at the end of 1879. This was done at the start of the fall term in 1880, at the same time as Wilson's subject, ethnology, was added to the subjects of instruction provided at the school – the latter almost certainly being done as a necessary precursor to the former.[35] The university clearly wanted to keep as much control as it could over this 'school of science,' as it was often called in these years, and the provincial government quite willingly went along.

This curious double-duty of the school, however, did cause its share of confusion. Who, for instance, was to pay the cost of student laboratory equipment at the SPS? Was this to be borne by the college, which was obliged to provide the equipment for teaching its students, or the government, which was obliged to equip SPS 'for practical education as specifically mentioned in the Act.'[36] Professors' duties and salaries were also murky matters. The rules of operation for the school stated that the college would continue to be responsible for paying the salaries of its own professors – Croft, Loudon, Chapman, and Wright – even though they were to do most of their teaching at the school. This was clear enough, and made good sense since nearly all the students they taught were from the college. The SPS was to pay only for Galbraith and Ellis, who taught only the handful of SPS students proper. But the college professors' extra workload brought on by having to teach the SPS students, especially the special, non-diploma students, seems not to have been considered. Ramsay Wright, after only a month of instruction, asked the board's support in requesting from the government an extra $100 as compensation for the work of teaching medical students at the school. E.J. Chapman, two months later, complained of insufficient time, space, and equipment to teach mineralogy and geology to special students at the school.[37]

None of these difficulties was as acrimonious, or as consequential, as a fight between the SPS and the new professor of chemistry at University College, Professor W.H. Pike.[38] Pike was an Englishman, with a recently awarded PhD from Gottingen in Germany (1873), who came to University College to replace Croft. He apparently took the appointment knowing nothing about any teaching responsibilities beyond those at the college itself. When he

W.H. Ellis, c.1880; Ellis was one of the two original teachers employed directly by the school, and its first professor of Applied Chemistry. UTA, B2000-0024/ 003 (#5)

learned that extra work was expected, he balked, informing the board in March 1880 that he had no intention of teaching SPS students in the Analytical and Applied Chemistry course (i.e., program), and asking that the course be deleted from the SPS prospectus. There were, in fact, no students registered in the course – all twelve of the SPS students had elected to study engineering – but it appears the responsibility for the course carried with it the obligation to teach chemistry to the school's special students as well, of which there were many. Meanwhile, however,

Pike's assistant, W.H. Ellis (originally Croft's assistant), had stepped into the breach by agreeing to teach basic chemistry to veterinary students for the Easter term of 1880. In the fall of 1880, however, the course was not taught by either Ellis or Pike, Ellis evidently being unwilling to do the work for which Pike, now settled in, was being paid to do. But the veterinary students needed their chemistry, and the school's mandate required that it provide it; the minister of Education had a troublesome matter to settle.

The minister's initial, and not very well considered, response was that, since Ellis had been appointed to teach at the SPS and Pike at University College, there should be no problem. As long as Ellis was available, Pike need not take on the extra duties. This response pleased the board because Ellis, although not as academically qualified as Pike, was a far more congenial colleague than the supercilious Englishman, to whom nobody had warmed even after a full year. And Ellis had far more experience with practical education. So the board eagerly inferred that the minister's reply 'recognizes Dr Ellis's position as an independent teacher of the School of Science, and Member of the Board,' that Ellis would now be in charge of the Analytic and Applied Chemistry course, and furthermore that he needed full charge of the upper (first storey) chemical laboratory to carry out this duty. To all of this Pike hastily objected – he was losing the laboratory in which he taught his University College students – saying that the minister's reply was being miscontrued. The college council concurred with Pike – intriguing, in view of the overlap in board personnel – claiming quite correctly that the chemical laboratories had been built for their use as well.

On learning of the continuing dispute, the minister took the matter to the premier and cabinet, where, after nearly a year, a resolution was made. By a provincial order in council, Dr Ellis was named professor of Applied Chemistry at the SPS, independent of Pike, and given the upper laboratory in the school. From this point on, all chemistry instruction for SPS students, both regular and special, was Ellis's responsibility. Pike had been relieved of his extra work, but in the process had lost the laboratory that seems to have been the better equipped for teaching purposes. The damage done to teaching was minimal, for the province compensated Pike by fully equipping his lower laboratory, at a cost of $1,100, in time for the start of the 1882 session.[39] More important, the rift between practical and academic, masked by personal relationships between Croft and Ellis and between Galbraith and Loudon, and by the fairly practical inclinations of Ramsay Wright and E.J. Chapman, was opening for all to see.

To the students at the school, these squabbles were probably invisible. The teaching continued, and the school remained heavily used. Fees for SPS students were substantial – $80 per year, including laboratory fees and the cost of books and equipment[40] – but evidently many families could afford such an investment in their sons' futures, because enrolment rose steadily from year to year.

The content of the early SPS courses, devised by the department of education and the school's board, was similar to what was taught at other such schools in the nineteenth century. In fact it was remarkably similar to what engineering students would learn a century later.[41] Students took mathematics, both pure (algebra, trigonometry, calculus) and applied (mathematical analysis of statics and dynamics), certain aspects of physics (hydrostatics, optics, thermodynamics), mineralogy and geology, strength of materials, and chemistry of various types (applied from Ellis, general from Pike). The mathematics and physics classes, both taught initially by James Loudon, were held in the University College building, while all others were taught at the SPS. Two-hour blocks of time late in the afternoon were allotted to field work, primarily surveying, several days a week. The centrepiece of the program, however, was engineering drawing, a subject that was actually a mix of many things – technical drawing, mapping and topography, the study of projections and perspectives, descriptive geometry, and even such practical matters as drawing out stone-cutting patterns. Students spent fourteen of their forty hours a week on this, and were expected to spend any free time at their drafting tables, as well. Instilling the skill of visualizing was, obviously, the heart of engineering education. Free time, however, was unlikely, unless instructors were absent, for every hour of the forty-hour week, from nine to five without a lunch break, was prescribed for all programs in all years.[42]

There was considerable variation in the curriculum among the three courses of study. Students in the Assaying and Mining Geology course took physical geography, paleontology, and geology laboratory techniques that other students did not, while those in the Anaytical and Applied Chemistry course took biology and more chemistry laboratory study than the others. Among the three areas of engineering – Civil, Mining, Mechanical – there was slight variation, but all engineering students, regardless of specialty, spent the same amount of time in engineering drawing, where they were divided by year, not specialty.

No subjects that would today be called arts or humanities were included in the fixed forty-hour curriculum. Students were expected to be able to read French and German on account of the important scientific literature in those languages, and they were permitted to attend French and German lectures at University College, but with no time allotted for these lectures in the timetable, and the requirement that all free time be spent at the drafting table, it is unlikely that many students took either the lectures or the language requirement seriously. There were no language examinations.

In addition to its professional education, the school rather half-heartedly provided occasional evening classes for tradesmen. This had been expected from the start; the original act creating the school explicitly states this feature.[43] The rules printed with the Ontario Sessional Papers in 1879, when the school first opened, say so as well. The rules printed the next year in the school's second syllabus, however, do not.[44] One is inclined to think the board was not keen on offering this service. After two years went by without any evening classes, the minister of Education reminded the board of its obligation; only then were classes introduced, the first being offered by Daniel Wilson late in 1881.[45] Not until 1882, when Galbraith (Engineering) and Ellis (Chemistry) taught them, were they reported to the minister. The classes seem to have been offered only sporadically. Both Galbraith and Ellis were reluctant to take on the extra work without extra pay.[46] Galbraith arranged to have William McDougall, a qualified civil engineer, teach evening classes in engineering starting in February 1884, for which McDougall was to receive all the fees as payment, but no students enrolled and the arrangement was terminated a month later. The following winter the board requested a special appropriation of $50 to pay a Mr F.W. Babington to give eight evening lectures in applied electricity, so this course must have gone ahead. It was a troublesome matter, handling these night classes, and eventually this part of the school's original program faded away. Technical and trades education in Ontario soon evolved in other directions.[47]

Relations between the college and the school remained close and, once everything was fully understood, quite harmonious. James Loudon equipped a fine physics laboratory at University College early in the decade, paid for largely by an appeal to the college alumni, and he used it for students from both the college and the SPS. By 1886 he had installed enough electrical apparatus that the teaching of electrical engineering was considered, and by 1887 the lab included a gas engine and lathes. This was the closest thing the school had to an engineering laboratory – and it was in University College. The university also gave the SPS a 'liberal grant' for the purchase of additional equipment for the school's biology laboratory.[48]

The university senate established a new CE degree in 1884, superseding the old degree that had been on the books since 1851 but which only seven men had ever received. This new degree required a three-year SPS diploma in civil engineering, three years of engineering work experience, and an essay (including drawings) on an engineering subject. It was, in fact, more of a formal professional designation built specifically upon the SPS course than a university degree, but it was awarded by the university nonetheless.[49]

With the close relationship between the two institutions, student requests for transfer from the college to the school came up from time to time. This was usually permitted, but with a loss of at least one year. The teaching at the two institutions, although much of it by the same professors, was different enough that a straight transfer could not be permitted. T.R. Rosebrugh, a man who would later rise to prominence in the SPS, applied for admission to the school in the fall of 1887 with a University of Toronto BA degree in honours mathematics and physics. He was granted admission, but only to second year, his three-year BA giving him just one year of credit at the SPS.[50]

By the latter part of the 1880s, the Ontario SPS was unmistakably a success. Enrolment was steadily rising and the school's graduates were beginning to gain positions of responsibility in Ontario industry and public life; the government could indeed feel, as the SPS report of 1883 had said it should, that investment in the school 'is making some adequate return to the Province.'[51] One consequence of this rising enrolment was that a greater proportion of students using the school were actually enrolled there, although the majority were still University College students. In 1887, 106 UC students took mineralogy and 91 took chemistry – enrolment in science at University College was still strong – but there were now 59 full-time SPS students. Plenty of medical students also took classes there – 124 in 1887.[52] But SPS students,

The interior of the 'large' lecture room that extended south from the west wing of the original School of Practical Science. This photograph was taken in 1966, prior to the building's demolition, but the room had changed little over its nearly ninety years. It was still, in 1966, referred to by old-timers as 'Dr Ellis's lab.' UTA, A72-0045/001(37) for image; A87-0048/001 for identification

almost all of them in the engineering course, were becoming increasingly prevalent.

Another obvious consequence of rising enrolment was that the little red schoolhouse was overflowing. The modest building was simply no longer adequate. Engineering lectures were being conducted in the laboratories and drafting rooms as well as the small lecture hall, often with other students in their midst trying to do laboratory and drafting work. The small library, meanwhile, had been given over to drafting. Even the college's science lectures were beyond their limits. The large lecture hall, used primarily for chemistry lectures, was still adequate – in size at least. But the floor of the room swayed so badly when fully occupied that delicate balances could not be used in the lectures. In the smaller lecture room, built to hold only forty, E.J. Chapman reported regularly giving lectures to upwards of seventy students, leaving many to stand in the halls around the open doorway while he lectured.[53]

The number of teaching staff, at least that based at University College, had been increased fairly early in the decade through the addition of several assistants and fellows, and had thus kept up with enrolment. But the SPS staff, which could only be increased with the provincial government's approval, had been limited to Galbraith and Ellis until the 1884–85 academic year when E.W. Stern, a graduate of the school, was appointed fellow in Engineering to assist Galbraith.[54] Even with Stern's assistance, Galbraith was still overwhelmed with teaching duties as the school's enrolment rose. He was responsible for all engineering instruction, which included a few lectures in applied mechanics along with long hours of drawing supervision and field work. Students were taught separately by year – at least they were supposed to be. Stern was essential for this, for he could supervise the first- or second-year drawing classes while Galbraith did the third. But with Galbraith's many other responsibilities, students must have passed a good many unsupervised hours at their drafting tables.

Shortcomings in equipment were starting to show, too. Loudon's physical laboratory at University College was providing adequate service for the study of electricity, but it was not an engineering laboratory; it had no heavy equipment for testing structural materials and no experimental steam engine. This missing equipment impeded the proper development of courses in mechanical and electrical engineering, the demand for both of which was growing yearly. The school began admitting mechanical and electrical engineering students as 'special students' in

James Loudon's physical laboratory in University College, early 1890s. UTA, A65-0004/1.91

1886–87, allowing them to receive extra instruction in the physical laboratory beyond what the standard engineering course provided, but the equipment was just not up to the job. Three of Galbraith's special students in mechanical engineering left the school in the fall of 1887 for institutions with better facilities: McGill, Lehigh, and Cornell.[55] The provincial minister of Education, George Ross, wanted to expand the laboratory by taking over part of the college residence; Loudon supported the move, but President Wilson would not hear of it.[56] It was time to recognize the school's success and move it on to another level. The building was too small, its facilities inadequate, and its staff overworked. Its dual purpose was interfering with its proper development and the general engineering program was no longer appropriate. There seems to have been complete consensus that something had to be done. '*When* the government is prepared to spend more money on the School...,' the board's chairman, Daniel Wilson, wrote in prefacing his 1888 report to the minister.[57]

As it happened, the university was at that very time undergoing a complete restructuring. After years of debate, several of the province's denominational colleges had finally agreed to federate with the University of Toronto, largely in order to draw funds from the university endowment, which could only be used to support non-sectarian institutions.[58] With the Federation Act of 1887, a process began that would in time bring Roman Catholic St Michael's, Methodist Victoria, Anglican Trinity, and several other colleges under the auspices of the university. In doing so, the colleges, including University College, turned over some of their non-religious teaching – their science instruction especially – to the university, which now became a teaching as well as an examining institution. The university expanded further still by making the private Toronto School of Medicine into the university's Faculty of Medicine, and by establishing a new Faculty of Law. This federation and expansion was a landmark event in the development of the University of Toronto.

It was also an important turning point in the history of the SPS. The school had been built on an arrangement with University College, at the time the teaching wing of the University of Toronto, but now that the college no longer had its own science professors, and was part of a more complex whole, affiliation with the college was no longer appropriate. The school therefore had to alter its arrangement by affiliating with the university rather than the college. Accordingly, the provincial School of Practical Science was formally affiliated with the University of Toronto in the fall of 1889.

This changed the operations of the school very little. Arts and meds students still took their science at the school (although as University of Toronto students now, not University College or spe-

SPS Graduating Class of 1888; John Galbraith, W.H. Ellis, and E.J. Chapman are seated in the middle row, second, third, and fourth from left; C.H.C. Wright is seated in the centre of the front row; Walter MacFarlen, whose photograph this was, is back row, fourth from right. UTA, B80-0022.(44)

cial medical students); the same science professors, now as university staff, taught science to the school's own students. But it did bring about a fundamental change in the school's management. This affiliation is usually seen as a joining together of the previously independent SPS with the university, but, in fact, the opposite is the case. The SPS had never been independent; it had been little more than a branch of University College – a separately funded one, admittedly, but not an independent one. Now, in being made an affiliate of the university, the school was being recognized as a distinct entity, and it was given self-government. John Galbraith was named principal of the newly constituted school. The old board of the SPS, dominated since its inception by University College professors, was now to be superseded by a council

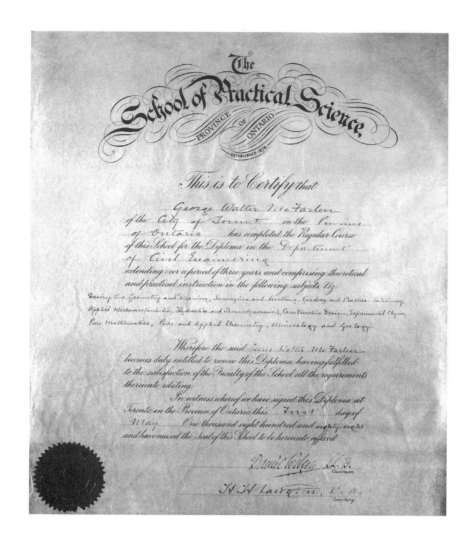

Walter MacFarlen's SPS Diploma, 1888. UTA, B88-0022/001(03)

consisting only of the teaching staff of the SPS itself. Gone were Wilson, Loudon, Chapman, and Wright. Still in place were Galbraith and Ellis, their two teaching fellows, and a new lecturer in surveying appointed in 1888, Louis B. Stewart. The 'practical' scientists were fully in charge of their own affairs. The School of Practical Science had finally become the independent professional school proposed in the 1871 report. Its long genesis was complete.

chapter two

GALBRAITH'S VISION

From 1889 to 1914, the SPS came of age. Although a fully established school by 1889, with a building, a staff, and plenty of students, uncertainty remained about its future. Would demand for its services continue to grow? Should it remain a government-supported school? What would be its relationship to the university? What sort of education would it provide? These questions were on many minds in 1889, but by 1914 they had all been answered. During this, its first generation as an independent institution, the principles and traditions by which the Faculty of Applied Science and Engineering would live for much of the twentieth century were set in place. And the man who played the largest role in accomplishing this was unquestionably John Galbraith. His beliefs and actions were the die that shaped the school.

When Principal Galbraith and his new SPS council convened their first meeting in December 1889, they were facing circumstances better than they had seen in years.[1] The school's greatest need, more space, was at last being met. The first step towards improvement had come not from their sponsor, the Ontario government, to whom they had been appealing for years, but from the University of Toronto. With a growing enrolment of its own, and with a Faculty of Medicine now one of its parts, the university had begun construction of a new Biology Building in 1888, and by the summer of 1889, the eastern portion was sufficiently completed to allow the Biology Department to move from the top floor of the SPS into the new premises. The school was free, once and for all, of its obligation to provide space for teaching biology to the university's arts and medical students. Teaching chemistry to arts and meds, however, remained one of its key functions – 133 medical students and 68 university arts students took their chemistry at the school that fall. No wonder the space freed up by Biology's departure was immediately allotted to Professor Ellis for lectures and laboratory instruction in applied chemistry.[2]

A far greater increase in facilities was imminent, for builders were at work that fall on a large addition that was nearly tripling the size of the school. Although the sounds of construction likely interfered with lectures and meetings, it was a small price to pay to bring several years of overcrowding to an end. There would soon be four new drafting rooms, three new lecture rooms, a cloak room, library, and instrument room, and a large examination hall suitable for public meetings.[3] The original north-facing building, on which the central third storey was being extended to the full width of the building, would now become just the north wing of a much larger structure facing east. Most of Kivas Tully's original design elements were maintained in the new structure, including the use of red brick on the building's exterior – in contrast to the new university buildings still being made of stone – so once the work was completed the old building was barely recognizable within the new.[4] Its informal name, however, would survive. The grand new structure would no longer deserve the label 'little red schoolhouse,' but the name, along with its implications of modesty and practicality, would endure for generations.

One of the main purposes for this expansion, apart from an overall increase in space, was to make room for a full-scale engineering laboratory, something the school had needed badly for several years. Galbraith and the Ontario minister of Education had travelled to Ithaca, New York, in the spring of 1889 to inspect Cornell University's laboratory, and following that had begun

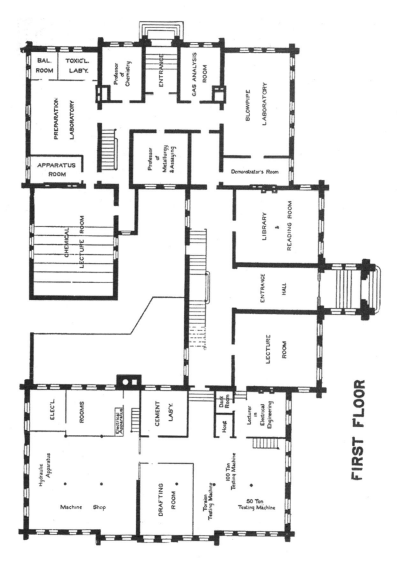

FIRST FLOOR

Plan of the first floor of the new, expanded School of Practical Science, 1896, with its main entrance now facing east. The entrance to the original building, now the north wing, was retained. Plans of each of the building's four floors were included in the school's annual prospectus. UTA, *SPS Prospectus*, 1896/97 planning to purchase equipment for their own. Now, with the new laboratory space soon to be available, the school introduced a distinct 'course' in mechanical engineering in 1889, its first true engineering specialty.[5]

So matters stood – good and getting better – as Galbraith and his associates officially took over SPS affairs. Galbraith, as the school's principal, was now the man in charge. On the old SPS board he had been little more than a junior member, dominated as that board was by older university scholars such as James Loudon and Daniel Wilson. But not one of the other four members of the new council could be considered Galbraith's better. His congenial colleague and friend W.H. Ellis was still at the school and on the council. There was also L.B. Stewart, the newly appointed lecturer in surveying who, although certainly a capable man, had no university degree and had come recommended not by his international reputation but by being the son of G.B. Stewart, Galbraith's professional mentor in Port Hope thirty years earlier. Beyond these two were the two teaching fellows of the school – one in engineering and one in applied chemistry – both of whom, as SPS graduates, had not long ago been Galbraith's students. There could be no mistaking Galbraith's new authority.

The school developed rapidly under Galbraith's guiding hand, as new courses and new staff were added almost every year. The first task was to flesh out the course in mechanical engineering. Although officially offered that fall, the council held off accepting students until the second term because the laboratory was not yet fully equipped, but in January 1890 eight students were enrolled in the new course. The practical part of the mechanical engineer's training was not going to be overlooked; in addition to three years of study at the school, students in the new course needed a full year's work experience in some mechanical trade connected to engineering, 'eg. as a machinist, pattern maker, moulder, steam engineer, etc.,' in order to receive their SPS diploma.[6] There was no need to hire new staff, as overall student numbers were no higher than in past years and the content of the mechanical course was not much different from that of the basic engineering course. Fifty-four students were in the original general engineering course that year, now called 'Civil Engineering (including Mining Engineering).'[7]

In the fall of 1890 a course in architecture was added to the school's offerings. The impetus for this came not from within the school, but from the provincial government, a reminder that the government still saw the SPS as its own and felt free to direct the school's affairs as it saw fit. Two years earlier, in the summer of 1888, Minister of Education G.W. Ross had announced the government's intention to appoint a professor of architecture at the school, and he had subsequently sought the advice of the fledgling Toronto Architectural Guild in developing a program of instruction. The local profession was enthusiastic, and architect S.G. Curry offered, on behalf of the guild, to assist Ross in the task, but nothing came of this connection. When the course was actually introduced in 1890 it was very much an SPS course, with little involvement from the profession. Galbraith had insisted that any lecturer in architecture must also teach strength of materials and theory of construction to engineering students, a requirement that probably excluded most practising architects. Accordingly, C.H.C. Wright, a recent graduate of the school (1888), was hired as lecturer in Architecture in 1890. Wright had worked for a year in Boston as an estimator for a construction company, but he had no architectural credentials and no connection with the local profession. Five students enrolled in the new course in the fall of 1890. It was basically the same as the school's engineering course, but with a small architectural component of a few hours a week that, following Beaux Arts conventions, emphasised the classical orders and the drawing of models and plaster casts of building details.[8]

In the fall of 1891, an optional fourth, post-diploma, year was added to the program. It was not at first envisioned as a university

The architecture room in the SPS building, c.1909, showing plaster casts used for drawing exercises. UTA, A65-0004/6.53

degree; initially, it was described in the school's prospectus as just an 'extra certificate or diploma,' the details of which had yet to be worked out. But Galbraith subsequently reported that 'the students and graduates of the School of Science' were expressing their wish that a university degree in Applied Science be established for graduates of the SPS, and the following year, 1892, the University of Toronto agreed to award a Bachelor of Applied Science (BASc) degree to students who completed a fourth year of study, including a thesis, at the SPS.[9] The school continued to award its diploma to students who completed three years of study, and for a time most students found that sufficient.

The installation of equipment in the engineering laboratory

was finally completed by early 1892, giving the school an impressive and, if one can believe the descriptions of the day, uniquely equipped facility. It housed machinery for testing beams, posts, and shafts subjected to various stresses, a power lab with steam engines, electric dynamos, and hydraulic equipment, and a geodetic and astronomical laboratory equipped with all-new, top-quality measuring and surveying equipment.[10] That fall, the school once again altered its courses, offering a separate Mining Engineering course for the first time; in doing so, it dropped the non-engineering course in assaying and applied geology – without it ever having produced a graduate.[11] It also introduced a sanitary engineering specialty in the Civil Engineering course, and renamed the mechanical course Mechanical and Electrical Engineering.[12]

Underlying all this development, and justifying the province's generous expenditures, was a swelling enrolment. The school enrolled 129 students in the fall of 1892 and 135 in 1893, up from just 68 in 1889. The biggest jump was in Mechanical Engineering – attractive because of the new laboratory – which had 55 registrants in 1893, almost double the enrolment in Civil Engineering. The size of the teaching staff also increased. Wright had been added in 1890 when the architecture course began, and T.R. Rosebrugh had been named demonstrator in the engineering laboratory the same year. Like Wright, Rosebrugh was a SPS graduate (1889), but he also had an earlier BA from University College (and would in time develop into an accomplished applied scientist). A.P. Coleman, added to the faculty in 1892 as professor of Metallurgy and Assaying, had a different background. Coleman was a Victoria College graduate who had gone on to acquire a PhD from the University of Breslau in 1882, and had for some years been a geologist on the staff at Victoria College. But the termination of science instruction at Victoria after federation had set him free, and the university placed him in the staff at SPS.[13] He was, therefore, not Galbraith's appointment. That same year

Rosebrugh was moved from the laboratory into the position of lecturer in Electrical Engineering.

Affairs at the school stayed fairly constant for the rest of the decade. As the courses (i.e., programs of study) became fixed, they began to be referred to in the number format familiar to generations of staff and students: Civil, Department One; Mechanical and Electrical, Department Two; Mining, Department Three (the latter two switched numbers in 1896), Architecture, Department Four; and Analytical and Applied Chemistry, Department Five. Enrolment fell slightly during the mid-1890s, but soon resumed a steady annual rise. The Ontario government kept paying the bills. It bought, among other things, additional testing machines for the school's laboratories and new optical equipment for a photography and photometric workshop, and built a small, permanent observatory on the grounds southeast of the building for the large new theodolite. The teaching staff continued to expand. G.R. Mickle, an SPS graduate (1888) who had done some post-graduate study in Germany, was named lecturer in Geology and Mineralogy in 1895 to bolster teaching in Mining Engineering. His was the only permanent appointment, but the increasing enrolment required that several teaching fellows be appointed in each subject every year. A few names that would become familiar fixtures of the school were among them: A.T. Laing, fellow in Surveying 1895; R.W. Angus, fellow in Electrical Engineering 1897; J.W. Bain, fellow in Mining and Geology 1898. All of these men, fellows and permanent staff, were SPS grads with no further academic credentials.[14]

By the mid-1890s, after only a few years under the new regime, the school had expanded its facilites, diversified its programs, and hired several capable new academic staff. And as steadily rising enrolments made perfectly clear, it was proving itself to be the way of choice for young men intent on entering the scientific professions. The school was quickly dispelling any uncertainties about its future.

It is in the evolving relations between the school and the university, rather than in the affairs of the school itself, that one finds the most crucial developments in the ten or so years straddling the turn of the century. This was by no means a simple, straightforward matter. The two institutions were diverging, as academic study at the university and professional education at the SPS went their separate ways. But in the administrative realm the opposite was occurring; here one finds a convergence that led, in 1906, to the school becoming a part of the newly organized University of Toronto as its Faculty of Applied Science and Engineering. This latter line of development will be considered first.

At the start of the 1895 session, the school was again permitted to expand within its own premises; the university opened a new chemistry building on a site just southwest of the SPS and Professor Pike moved his office and laboratory to the new building. The vacated rooms, in the eastern part of the original wing, were converted into a blowpipe and assay laboratory for mining engineering, while the basement space below them was used for additional electrical equipment. This ended the last vestige of the dual-purpose role of the school; no longer would any University of Toronto students – arts or meds – have to take their lectures or laboratories in the SPS building (although students still could, and a few did). The teaching connection with the university, however, did not cease; SPS students still took their mathematics and physics at the university, and, for the time being, a few still took Professor Pike's lectures on theoretical chemistry in the new Chemistry Building. But the SPS building was from this point on, with few exceptions, exclusively for SPS students.[15]

The University of Toronto's decision to build new facilities at this time was a bold step, but it must have been made with some trepidation. Rising enrolments certainly demanded it, but science buildings equipped with teaching laboratories were expensive. The new chemical building, although designed with an eye to

The new, expanded SPS building, viewed from the east, c.1904. The tall tower above its entrance would be a campus landmark for many years. UTA, A65-0004/6.71

'practical utility, rather than architectural effect' – the exterior had been finished partly in red brick – had still cost $77,000, almost as much as the Ontario government had spent on the far larger SPS expansion.[16] The university simply did not have the income to cover such an expenditure, so to pay for the new building it had had to cash some of its invested endowment, with a corresponding reduction in revenue. Income from fees rose with enrolment, of course, but so did expenses. The university had, in fact, put itself under severe financial strain; what in the 1880s had been annual financial shortfalls had become by the 1890s a near financial crisis.[17]

Yet there sat the splendid new SPS, fully and generously supported by the province, reminding university administrators of the advantages of utility and good political connections. In 1892 the university had won for itself a portion of the SPS's student fees as compensation for teaching services. This seemed only fair since university professors were still teaching much of the SPS program, yet SPS student fees all went straight to the provincial treasury. But this figure, about 20 per cent of the school's receipts, was running at a little over $1,000 per year through the late 1890s, not nearly enough to cover the university's annual deficits.[18]

The Province was being generous to another institution, too, further irking the university. Following a Royal Commission recommendation in 1891 that the province establish a school of mines, the government had begun funding the Kingston School of Mining and Agriculture in 1893, providing $6,000 in the first year and $12,000 in the second.[19] University president James Loudon at the time, and historians ever since, have recognized this as financial aid to Queen's University 'under the cloak of aid to the Kingston Mining School.' But the province was not supposed to be funding other universities; the University of Toronto was legally the only provincial university. Might the province consider additional direct support to its own university as well? Repeated appeals brought very little. Beginning in 1897, the government did provide some *ad hoc* grants to help the university keep its deficit under control, but these were by no means a precedent for future policy. Education Minister Ross suggested in 1897 that the university simply 'cut down expenses and raise the fees.'[20]

Fortunately for the university, circumstances were changing. By 1900 SPS was again running short of space. Enrolment had resumed its customary rise, having increased about 20 per cent per year since 1895 to 223 students by 1900. Drafting tables once again spilled into the hallways; the old chemistry equipment in the original building was by now inadequate and badly out of date. 'The only solution ... is the erection in the immediate future of a new building,' Galbraith wrote in his 1899 report to the Minister of Education.[21] Galbraith had many arguments on his side –

rising government revenue, steadily increasing enrolment at the school, and perhaps most important of all, a public enthusiasm for industrial development. The province did sympathize, but offered no commitment.

At this very time, in December 1900, the university made the SPS into its Faculty of Applied Science and Engineering.[22] Why it did this is not clear. Nothing seems to be on record explaining the action. It must have been done at the university's rather than the school's initiative, for the SPS paid it little heed. It was scarcely mentioned in council minutes, and not mentioned at all in reports to the minister. Galbraith did speak of it with some satisfaction in a speech at a dinner held in his honour shortly after the senate resolution confirming it was passed, but only in his concluding remarks. The school's indifference is understandable, for little seems to have changed, and the school received no evident benefits. Relations with the university were already close – especially since the university BASc degree had been established in 1892 – and most people involved seem to have viewed the action as a formalization of what was already the case.[23] The university, however, had plenty to gain, something that has usually been overlooked. Viewed in the context of the university's struggle for increased provincial funding, it is hard not to think that, by making the SPS one of its faculties, the university was deliberately tying itself to a highly valued and well-funded public institution, one with strong support in the inner circles of the Ontario government. Surely this could not hurt its chances of obtaining greater provincial aid.

As it turned out, this new Faculty of Applied Science and Engineering did indeed play a critical role in bringing more government money to the university. On 6 March 1901 a delegation of about 200 SPS students (as they were still called) marched to the Ontario legislature in Queen's Park. Unhappy that the government had not responded to Principal Galbraith's pleas for additional facilities, they, in the words of the *Globe*, 'stormed the government, asking for enlarged accommodation for the expanding classes of the college.' They presented their case to Premier Ross, Education Minister Harcourt, and others, reminding them of the close connection between the school and the industrial development of the province. Their petition, printed and bound into an impressive, official booklet, referred to the need for skilled men to build the railways, develop the water-powers, open the mines, and expand industrial chemistry – and of the importance of the SPS in ensuring that this essential work be done well.[24] The premier agreed with the school's students that something was needed, but pleaded a shortage of money with which to work. This SPS deputation was followed a week later by a group of university alumni making a similar plea to the government. Once again, Ross was conciliatory, and actually claimed to be pleased that such a visible public demand had been made.[25]

Scarcely a month later, the province took action, and it did so in a way as to provide support for both the SPS and the university. It agreed to build, at public expense, a large new building on College Street to be shared by the SPS and the university's Department of Mineralogy and Geology. The SPS council promptly decided that their portions of the new building would be used for chemistry and mining – the two subjects in greatest need of new facilities – and by 1902 had taken to calling it the Chemistry and Mining Building. A separate one-storey milling building, seventy feet square, would be built behind to house machinery for experiments on the mechanical processing of ores. Excessive noise from heavy milling machinery had been a frequent irritant in the earlier buildings, so the separate structure was thought necessary.[26] The province also agreed to pay for the cost of maintaining the university departments of Chemistry, Physics, and Mineralogy and Geology. This partial step towards public support of the university – in specified subjects – shows more clearly than anything else just how categorically the Ross government opposed funding advanced education that was not 'practical,' or clearly in what

The Chemistry and Mining Building on College Street nearing completion, c.1903. UTA, A65-0004/7.7

they deemed the public interest. Even biology, much to President Loudon's dismay, was not considered practical enough for public support.[27] But it was nevertheless a major public contribution; in 1902, the government paid the university over $30,000 for salaries and maintenance of these departments.[28] One wonders how the university could ever have obtained these public funds without its new Faculty of Applied Science and Engineering leading the chorus of demands.

This financial assistance to the university, telling and important though it is, affected the SPS very little; the government's decision to build the new building mattered much more. The school's instructors craved new space, and they watched anxiously as the building took shape. They had hoped to be able to move in for the start of the 1903 session, but that turned out to be wishful thinking. Not until the summer of 1904 was the interior fitted up and the laboratory equipment installed. Lectures began in the new building in the fall of 1904. Unfortunately, this grand new building, with a total floor space greater than the expanded engineering building, would not end accommodation problems because enrolment was rising at the same pace as the facilities were expanding. Between the year the new building was started, 1901, and the year it was completed, 1904, enrolment nearly doubled and now stood at 475 students. The new building was thus at capacity the year it opened. Furthermore, most of the space vacated in the old building, being in the original wing of the school, was not adequate for new laboratories and lecture rooms, so it had to be left under-used. More space would soon be needed, but for the time being the Chemistry and Mining Building was going to have to do.[29]

The university's financial troubles had been lessened, but not entirely cleared away. It continued to need – and demand – greater support from the province. A new arrangement in which the province paid the university $925 per year for rent of the SPS grounds began in 1902, and the SPS's annual payments to the university for teaching its students now exceeded $1,500, but this was still not enough. The university's shortfall was nearly $15,000 in 1903, and over $30,000 in 1904.[30]

By this time, however, a new force was at work. University support had become a provincial political issue. The university had been joined in its demand for greater support by the Conservative opposition leader, J.P. Whitney, who had openly espoused greater university aid soon after the alumni delegation had argued its case to the government in 1901. When Whitney defeated Ross in the election of 1905, all those close to the university expected a new era, and it did indeed arrive, with little delay. After only a few months, the Whitney government greatly increased its support to the University of Toronto, providing both one-time grants for specific buildings and an annual commitment of $30,000 for new construction. Whitney also established a Royal Commission to study the University of Toronto and to consider a possible new structure and system of governance. The commission reported the following year, strongly in favour of generous public support; it also recommended closer ties between the university proper, with its focus on traditional arts and science studies, and the practical, professional schools with which it had been affiliated, more or less, for decades. The commission report in turn led to the University of Toronto Act of 1906, which transformed the university along the lines recommended by the report into a true publicly funded educational institution.[31]

This was an extraordinary set of policies, implemented over a remarkably short period of time. The Whitney government was taking an enormous and unprecedented step into support of university education, and in doing so changed the provincial university system forever. At the SPS, the consequences were both simple and far-reaching – the school would no longer have a separate existence. In 1906, the SPS became, both in rule and in practice, the Faculty of Applied Science and Engineering of the University of Toronto. The name SPS lingered on in common usage for years – in fact, well into the late-twentieth century – but the school itself, which nominally had continued to exist even after the 1900 resolution creating the Faculty, officially ceased to be.

The smaller school has thus been subsumed by the larger university, and the aspiring upstart legitimized by becoming part of the establishment, or so the story is often told. But once again the events can be misconstrued. The difference in size was not as great as one might think. There were, in 1905, some 1,200 students in Arts, 650 in Medicine, and nearly 500 in Applied Science and Engineering, the three main faculties forming the new university.[32] Certainly arts was the largest, but it was not in a league of its own. More importantly, the SPS already had exactly what the university wanted: secure public funding. Since public support of advanced education still had to be rooted in utility, even to the more generous Whitney government, the SPS's association with the university was critical to the whole project. So the 1906 Act did not really cause the SPS to be subsumed by the university, nor did it make the smaller simply a part of the larger. It created something new: a publicly funded university in which professional faculties were an integral part.[33] The university brought tradition, authority, and high standards of book-based scholarship; the SPS brought utility, connections with the real world, and a thirty-year tradition of provincial government support. Both institutions were essential parts of the new creation.

At the same time that the financial needs of the university and the vagaries of provincial politics were bringing the school and the university together, basic differences in their academic principles were moving them apart. One must not go too far with this, for formal academic ties remained stronger than ever, as the BASc degree signifies. But in the later 1890s, with its fully independent council, and under the personal influence of John Galbraith, the school elected to follow a path quite distinct from that of the university.

Perhaps the most important development in academic life at the University of Toronto in the 1890s was the growing value placed on research, an aspect of the widespread reform movement that swept over nearly all the major universities of the western world in the late nineteenth century.[34] At the University of Toronto, James Loudon was one of the first proponents of what is often called the 'research ideal.' Where and why Loudon adopted his ideas is hard to determine, but he had certainly espoused research as early as the 1880s. His insistence on the importance of laboratory facilities for the university when the SPS was being conceived, although based mostly on his wish to enliven university teaching, was also an early sign of his belief in research.[35]

When Loudon was named president of the university in 1892, development in this direction was nearly assured, and when the university adopted the research-based PhD degree in 1897 research was formally in place. Adding to the world's store of knowledge, not just protecting and teaching what was already known, now formed part of a scholar's job. This was the first such doctoral degree in Canada, and a milestone in Canadian educational history.[36]

It was in this direction, down the road of research, that the SPS would not go. Although there is often presumed to be a connection between scientific research and the practical applications of science, the connection should not be taken for granted.[37] In the minds of some of the school's founders, Loudon especially, they appear to have been closely connected, but right from the start basic differences were evident between the professors at the SPS and those at the university in this regard, and the university's increasing emphasis on research at the turn of the century accentuated them.

Galbraith himself did little that might be called research. He published a philosophical paper in 1876 (likely his University College MA paper) assessing the merits of competing theories of the nature of force, but after receiving his appointment at the SPS, his only publications, with one exception in 1909, were reprints of his public addresses on matters concerning the profession and professional education.[38] Ellis occasionally published papers in the 1880s and 1890s. Some were of a simple observational nature, such as 'Chemical notes on the so-called Sudbury coal'; others were more scientific, and derived from laboratory research – such as a measurement of solids in milk, or of tannin in cloves – but they were of an extremely practical nature and the science in them was quite elementary.[39] L.B. Stewart, once he was hired in 1888, presented and published occasional papers, but they, too, were of a descriptive nature; some concerned his travels and some his instruments, and none were true research publications.

John Galbraith lecturing on heat engines, c.1908. Galbraith was not considered an outstanding lecturer, but he had a rapport with his students that was second to none. He served as principal of the School of Practical Science from 1889 to 1906, when it was made into the university's Faculty of Applied Science and Engineering, and as the Faculty's dean from that year until his death in 1914. UTA, B78-0018/(#7)

Nearly all were published in local periodicals, with a good many of them in the school's own transactions (papers read by and to the school's staff and students, published by the school's student society). Most of the SPS graduates Galbraith hired to the academic staff in the 1890s, such as Laing, Ardagh, and Bain, were not inclined in the slightest towards scientific research. They continued in the tradition of the earlier men, occasionally publishing descriptive articles, mostly in the school's transactions.[40]

The scientists at the university worked in a different world, even in the 1880s, and were far more active in publishing. Chapman, Wright, and Loudon published dozens of scientific articles in the 1880s and 90s, as did Coleman, who, although on the SPS staff for a time in the 1890s, had an academic background and was much more a scientist than an SPS man. It is true that so-called 'scientific' publications prior to the 1890s could also be brief and anecdotal, and often tended towards synthesis rather than original discoveries; nevertheless, the scientific men published much more, and, perhaps more significantly, tended to do so in international journals, an indication that they were part of and had the respect of an international body of peers.[41] But certainly by the turn of the century, university physicists and chemists had moved decisively into advanced research on fundamental scientific principles, and were increasingly members of international scholarly communities.[42]

This was not the case at the SPS. Two of the new SPS men, Rosebrugh and Boswell, did do some fairly advanced scientific research after 1900 in association with Lash Miller in the university chemistry department. Rosebrugh even worked for a time with Miller setting up an electro-chemistry laboratory in the new Chemistry and Mining Building.[43] But this joint work did not last, and the research output of both Rosebrugh and Boswell subsided. The teaching demands of the expanding school, rather than personal interests or abilities, are what likely held back their research, for the quality of their work had been quite good.

W.H. Ellis teaching in his laboratory, c.1900. Dr. Ellis, as he was always known (he was a medical doctor), taught chemistry at the school from the very beginning, and was as much a fixture as John Galbraith in the early years; he served as dean for five years after Galbraith died in 1914. UTA, B78-0001P.02(01)

Research was evidently not what one did as an academic staff member at this busy engineering school. L.B. Stewart moved into fairly advanced astronomy after 1905, but his work remained strictly observational at a time when the science of astronomy was moving towards astro-physics.[44] Peter Gillespie, hired as a lecturer in applied mechanics in 1909, studied the properties of building materials and published extensively, but in construction-industry periodicals, not science journals.[45] So, although the growing academic staff at the SPS was not entirely uninvolved in research – a point to which we will return in the next chapter – neither they nor the school's principal were as committed to it as the new university scientists.

The most striking event in this growing divergence between school and university is the severing of connections between the SPS and the university's Department of Physics. Physics at the University of Toronto was, by the turn of the century, coming under the influence of the brilliant young J.C. McLennan. McLennan had studied physics at University College with James Loudon in the late 1880s, and had been kept on as a laboratory demonstrator after he received his BA in 1892. Several years later, in 1896, after hearing of the recent discovery of x-rays by the German scientist Roentgen, McLennan set about replicating Roentgen's experiments in his Toronto laboratory. He called upon C.H.C. Wright, who had by this time a well-equipped photography laboratory in the SPS building for his architecture teaching, to assist him. The experiment was a complete success, the results being 'even more wonderful than we had anticipated,' McLennan reported. This demonstration of Roentgen's discovery brought McLennan considerable local attention and acclaim. Two years later, he took a leave of absence from his demonstratorship to conduct advanced research at the Cavendish laboratory in Cambridge on the electrical conductivity of gases under cathode-ray bombardment, and the results of this research, published by the Royal Society of London in 1900, were sufficient for him to be awarded the University of Toronto's first Physics PhD that year. With his reputation well established, McLennan attracted other scholars to the university and soon developed the physics laboratory into an internationally recognized centre for the study of spectroscopy.[46]

One of the jobs of the university's Physics department was to teach SPS students their physics, an arrangement that had been in place since the school began. Basic statics and dynamics were taught at the school by SPS staff, but the more advanced subjects of optics, heat, and acoustics – generally called physics – were taught by university physicists. Among them was McLennan. Another was G.R. Anderson, hired in 1899 to assist in laboratory teaching. Anderson had graduated from the University of Toronto in 1893 in honours Mathematics and Physics and, after teaching high school for a few years, had returned to the university to continue his studies. He received an MA in 1898 (not yet a research degree), and then attended Harvard University long enough to be awarded their AM degree in 1899. After four years in the physics laboratory, however, Anderson was let go.[47] He was not up to the standard of the department, which was by now, in 1903, being guided by McLennan and his fairly advanced research program.

Galbraith was dismayed. He had been quite happy with the physics instruction Anderson had provided to SPS students, and he urged Loudon to keep him on in the physics department so that it might continue. But none of the permanent staff in Physics was willing to do so. To this predicament Galbraith responded by hiring Anderson himself as a lecturer at the SPS and, with the full approval of the minister of Education, setting him up as the school's own one-man Physics department. With this bold and unexpected step, Galbraith terminated the school's long-standing relations with the university's physics professors.[48]

James Loudon, as president of the university and professor of Physics, was deeply offended and more than a little incredulous.

Galbraith had been his own student forty years before, and Loudon had played no small part in placing Galbraith into his SPS professorship in 1878. Was it really possible that all the scientific expertise and splendid equipment in the physics laboratory was to be spurned by the school? Furthermore, plans to build a new university physics building with provincial government assistance could no longer be justified with physics enrolment cut in half. Galbraith's move threw everything awry. Loudon protested to the minister of Education, but to no effect. Galbraith had done such a fine job at the SPS, the minister explained to Loudon, that 'I could not be expected to treat lightly his recommendations.' McLennan raised it at the university senate, but found little support there.[49] Loudon was in a weak position as president by this time, having alienated himself from most of the senior university administrators for other reasons, and this likely contributed to his and McLennan's failure to drum up senate support.

Unopposed by anyone else at the university, Galbraith's scheme went ahead. The teaching of SPS students in the university's physical laboratory ceased in the fall of 1904. The connection between physics and engineering – the root of the school's founding, and one of the key academic ties between the two institutions during the 1890s – came to a sudden end. No doubt many factors were at work here, including, one must admit, the pride of the men involved. One cannot help but sense Galbraith finding a little pleasure in playing his trump card of provincial government support. But surely there is more to this than personal rivalry and pique. Galbraith justified his actions on two accounts. One was the ease of timetabling – which McLennan claimed was spurious, and he was probably right. The other was that it would give the school 'better opportunites for modifying the teaching in physics to suit the changing requirements in engineering education than at present.'[50] This latter point, although it could be better put, cannot be easily dismissed. What Galbraith meant by 'changing requirements' is uncertain; Loudon found no sense in it. It seems more likely that what Galbraith wanted was not for physics to change along with him, but for engineering not to change along with physics. Galbraith's man of choice, G.R. Anderson, had completed his studies ten years before; he had no enthusiasm for advanced laboratory work, but plenty of teaching experience. This, evidently, was what Galbraith wanted for physics instruction at the SPS.

The SPS was going to be, above all, a professional school. This was what it had been conceived as, and this was what it would remain. Its curriculum would impart the knowledge and skills needed to practise engineering, and in such a curriculum the frontiers of knowledge played no part. SPS students would receive 'advanced mechanics dating from 1850 or so,' as the physicist E.F. Burton dismissively commented some years later.[51] Nor would expanding those frontiers be part of the job of an SPS professor. The academic staff of the school would be chosen primarily on their ability to teach and guide students, not on their reputation as scholars. This meant falling out of step with the developing university, but to Galbraith that was by no means anything to regret.

The newly created Faculty of Applied Science and Engineering carried on after 1906 much as it had as the SPS. Galbraith, who was a faculty dean now, not a school principal, no longer reported directly to the provincial Minister of Education, but there is no sign that this change made much difference to the school's operations. Nor does the closer formal connection to the university seem to have brought about any new emphasis in programs or teaching. The new university governing structure called for five representatives of the Faculty to be named to the university senate, but although the number was greater, the connection itself was not new; W.H. Ellis had sat on the senate since at least 1901.[52]

The Faculty was, nevertheless, changing through forces at work both within its own walls and in the world outside. The first new course in over a decade appeared in the fall of 1905, prior to amalgamation, with the introduction of Chemical Enginering, a response to the rapidly expanding chemical industry. The course – added to the Faculty's offerings as Department Six – was not meant to replace Analytical and Applied Chemistry (still Department Five), which continued, although rarely with more than three or four students. The chemists held firm to the notion that theirs was a distinct profession, and the curriculum in Chemical Engineering was fairly different from that of the old chemistry course; students in Chemical Engineering took more drawing and applied mechanics than those in Analytical and Applied Chemistry, while the latter took lectures in mineralogy, biology, and geology that the Chemical Engineering students did not.[53]

As had been the case before, and would be again, the Faculty was experiencing a rapidly rising enrolment that it had to meet with an equally rapid increase in space and staff. Ontario's growing population, its expanding industrial economy, and its rising standard of living, along with the greater proportion of adolescents attending Ontario's high schools, all contributed to an unprecedented jump in attendance.[54] From 1900 to 1908, the number of students rose from 223 to 754, a more than threefold increase in just eight years.[55]

The critical need was laboratory space. So much equipment had been added to the 1892 laboratory that there was simply no longer enough room in the lab for the proper teaching of either thermodynamics or hydraulics. The solution proposed was a large new building with extensive laboratory space and one wing of classrooms and offices. Designs for such a structure, to be built directly south of the engineering building, were produced by the Toronto architects Darling and Pearson and approved by the university board of governors in June 1908. In the course of construction, however, the university found itself unable to pay for the entire building. Since the laboratory was the most pressing need,

Steam, Gas and Hydraulic Laboratory Building of the University of Toronto   Darling & Pearson, Architect

This shows the building as it will appear when completed.   At present the whole laboratory part is completed which comprises all of the building to the left of, and including, the first window to the right of those protected by awnings.

Faculty of Applied Science and Engineering

The Thermodynamics Building, as designed in 1908 and printed in *Applied Science*, February 1910. The front portion shown here on the right was in fact never built. UTA, A78-0008/008(02)

the western front of the building, which was to house the class-rooms and offices, was omitted and only the large high-ceilinged laboratory was built[56] (a temporary front was built, with access from the north, and the permanent front was not built for another forty years). The big laboratory was finished and open for use at the start of the fall session in 1909. Referred to at the time as the Thermodynamics Building, it housed all the steam, gas, and hydraulic power equipment, as well as equipment and offices for the Mechanical Engineering staff. The laboratory was laid out and its installation co-ordinated by R.W. Angus, who had, since 1907, been the Faculty's professor of Mechanical Engineering.

New staff appointments came every year to meet the rising enrolment, nearly all of whom were products of the Faculty's own halls. H.W. Price, W.M. Treadgold, T.R. Loudon, J.R. Cockburn, and C.R. Young, among others, had all joined the staff by 1908. As the staff increased in number, they began to be grouped into administrative 'departments,' which were usually based on the various engineering specialties that the Faculty taught, such as Mechanical Engineering or Mining Engineering. Thus the word department, already in use for the courses of study, began also to apply to administrative units of staff. In order to distinguish between the two, the terms 'teaching department' (applying to the newer use) and 'graduating department' (departments in which students could graduate) were introduced. This was con-fusing enough on its own, but matters were further complicated by the fact that staff teaching subjects like drawing or applied mechanics, and who taught students in all courses, were in 'teach-ing departments' which did not have corresponding 'graduating departments.' The Department of Skule of Physics, created by Galbraith in 1904, would turn out to be the longest lived of these, but there were others, such as Engineering Drawing. This puzzling arrange-ment would continue until the 1960s, perplexing outsiders and newcomers time and again.

The most notable appointment in these years was undoubtedly

H.E.T. Haultain to the position of associate professor of Mining in 1908. Haultain was an extraordinary man, one of Canada's most outstanding and influential engineers. It was he who, in 1924, led the move to establish the 'iron ring ceremony' for graduating engineers, and he would remain a force in the Faculty – often a bothersome one, by his own admission – until the Second World War. Haultain had attended the SPS in its early years, and received his SPS diploma in 1889. The school had no separate Mining Engineering course, but knowing that mining was his calling he had specialized in it as much as possible within the general engineering course. After graduation, he had embarked on a world-wide career, working in Ireland, Bohemia, South Africa, and the western United States, and doing post-graduate studies at the School of Electrical Engineering in London, England, and the Royal School of Mines in Freiburg, Saxony. He ended up in the Kootenay district of British Columbia early in the 1900s, working as a consultant to a number of different companies. He had stayed in touch with Galbraith, offering his former professor some valuable advice on the mining program at the school in 1901. When G.R. Mickle resigned his position as professor of Mining in 1908, Haultain, at Galbraith's urging, applied for and was given the position.[57]

Haultain's pride was enormous, and his temper legendary. When he learned, after his first year on the job, that he had been given an increase in his associate professor's salary, he wrote to the university president refusing the increase. To accept it would imply acceptance of the inferior position, he explained. Instead, he was expecting promotion to full professor. President Falconer wrote back assuring him that accepting the raise would not harm his position or reputation, and that he would be reviewed and considered for a professorship, as they had agreed, after the following year.[58] This was not the last such exchange that Haultain would have with his colleagues.

In the fall of 1909, the Faculty carried out its most substantial

Students in the heat laboratory of the new Thermodynamics Building, c.1909
UTA, A65-0004/6.45

curriculum revision since the school began. First Electrical and
Mechanical Engineering were separated, with the former going
on the books as Department Seven. Electricity, with its many
applications in lighting and power, was fast developing into a distinct field, and now that the mechanical laboratory was in a building of its own, separating the two made good sense. The change
had little immediate impact – the courses remained identical
until third year – but the departments and the courses could
now develop according to their own needs and wishes.[59] T.R.
Rosebrugh, who had been the school's professor of Electrical
Engineering for several years, became the head of the new
department.

Another fundamental change was the introduction of the
four-year course, and the corresponding end of the three-year
diploma. This had been under consideration for several years –

most students were by now taking the optional fourth year and receiving their BASc – but as it had meant an increase in the total number of students at the school, the Faculty had held back until the Thermodynamics Building was completed.[60] Successful students who enrolled in the fall of 1909 would graduate in four years with their BASc in 1913. There was no true class of 1912.

This extension of the program offered an opportunity to expand the subjects being taught, and council ventured, for the first time, into the realm of non-engineering instruction. All students starting at the school in 1909 were required to take one hour of English per week in their first year, as well as one hour per week of either French or German in both first and second year. They were also required to take one hour of business instruction per week, in all four years. The business subjects differed by year, and in fourth year they differed by course (Civil Engineering and Architecture students took Contracts and Specifications, while all others took Cost-keeping), but business was mandatory for all students.[61] Foreign languages had always been an informal part of the curriculum, so putting them in as proper classes was not a break from the past. The concern with English composition – and that is what it was, for there was no literature taught – was something new, however, and it reflected a growing recognition by both students and staff that, since engineers were being called upon to read and write quickly and effectively in their professional work, some sort of instruction in these skills was needed. It was the dawning of a concern that, as many later deans could attest, would have a long life. The English course was dropped at the start of the 1911 session, against the wishes of students, but was revived after the First World War.[62]

The only further change in the curriculum in these years was the introduction, in the fall of 1913, of a course in Metallurgical Engineering, designated Department Eight. George A. Guess, with an MA from Queen's University, was appointed professor in the subject. There was talk of a new building for Electrical Engineering, but nothing was done, partly, no doubt, because enrolment had stopped rising. After a peak of 793 students in 1911, it began a slow decline in the years leading up to the war. There was a sense that the curriculum needed further change in some subjects – Haultain was particularly concerned that the curriculum in Mining Engineering contained too much science and not enough engineering – and the students in Architecture requested that their degree be changed to BArch, but action on all these was deferred.[63]

For students at the SPS in these years, as for most students at the university, life was filled with hard work, expanding horizons, and plenty of good fun. This last experience was something new. Fun was not something that students had much of at university before the 1880s. But student life in these turn-of-the-century years was indeed changing, as the old discipline of college life, kept in place for years by small student numbers and traditional respect for authority, was lost once and for all. Students began to organize and take part in extracurricular activities as they never had before, to socialize away from the eyes and rules of authorities, and, perhaps most striking of all, to demand a say in the affairs of the university. Out of this flourishing student culture emerged many of the traditions of the 'old school' that were to remain a part of engineering-student life for much of the twentieth century.[64]

The academic side of life for SPS students remained much as it had always been. The day was full from nine to five all week. In fact, at the request of L.B. Stewart, who wanted more time for field work, the program was extended in 1898 to include Saturday mornings from nine to noon.[65] The timetable was still fixed; students had no need to puzzle over electives, or what the most convenient time would be for certain subjects. It was all laid out for them. There was increasing variation among the courses – Mechanical and Electrical students, for example, took several engineering drawing hours on their own, while chemical engineering and chemistry students spent extra time in the chemical laboratory – but one's course and year fixed one's timetable. Rigid as this was, there was ample opportunity to slip behind. As the alumnus A.G. Christie (SPS Dip. 1901) recalled, it was common enough for students to do little beyond attending their lectures and labs through most of the year and then slave day and night for several weeks at the end of the year, an acceptable scheme when grades in most subjects were based entirely on final examinations.[66]

New courses and new specialties were added, but the overall thrust and organization of the curriculum remained the same. Students still took their lectures in the morning and their labs in the afternoon, many subjects being offered in the same time slot year after year; engineering drawing remained the heart of all the courses, occupying from ten to fifteen hours per week; and the faculty members, once installed in permanent positions, never left. There was some restructuring between 1908 and 1912 as the four-year program was introduced, but the fourth year had already existed for years as an option, and the new non-technical courses took only one hour per week each, so basic changes were not needed. Practical experience was still required for degrees in all courses. Students in Mechanical, and later also Electrical, were explicilty required to have eight months of experience working in industrial production (work in sales was not permitted) 'under commercial conditions' in order to receive their degree.[67]

Nor did the make-up of the student body change appreciably over the years. Its size did, of course, but the type of student did not. SPS students remained overwhelmingly young men from the towns and cities of old Ontario. Farm boys, judging from students' homes listed in the calendars, were few, which might be expected with high school matriculation less easy to obtain in rural areas.[68] Of the hundreds of students attending in any given year, only one or two might be from the United States or else-

Students attending the Faculty's annual dinner in 1910. Large enrolments and almost total student participation made for huge (and exclusively male, it appears) school dinners. *Applied Science*, Feb. 1910, 158

where in Canada. This changed somewhat from the 1890s to the 1910s with respect to western Canadians. Just 2 of the 150 students attending the school in 1898 were from western Canada; in 1913, 74 of the 626 students (12 per cent) came from the west. But since these young men's families were almost certainly newly arrived westerners, probably from Ontario, they could hardly be said to be bringing a different regional perspective to the student body. Among those of Ontario origin, Toronto was by far the most common home, at the beginning and the end of this period; Toronto residents usually accounted for slightly under half the students. No doubt Toronto families, with no room and board to pay, found using the school much cheaper than did those from elsewhere, and this likely led to Toronto residents being over-represented at this supposedly provincial school.[69]

There were, needless to say, no women among the SPS students. There are occasional references to women applying to the school, but no evidence of any being admitted before 1912. At four consecutive meetings in 1895 and 1896, faculty council considered whether to admit Miss E.M. Curzon, a woman with a BA in natural sciences from the university who had been working in Professor Ellis's laboratory for six years, but never did decide. She probably found other avenues to follow, for the matter disappears from the record.[70] The first and for some years the only woman to graduate from the school was Hildegarde E. Scott, who received a BASc in the non-engineering course in Analytical and Applied Chemistry in 1912, but since she did not receive an SPS diploma prior to her BASc and appears to have done her preliminary study as a student at Trinity College, the extent to which she actually attended the school before 1912 is uncertain.[71] The situation was quite otherwise in the university at large. Women, having gained legal admission to the University of Toronto in 1884, were enrolling in the arts faculty in rapidly increasing numbers; by 1911, 653 of the 1,895 registered students were women.[72] In engineering, however, such changes were generations away.

The first, and for a while only, student association at the school was the Engineering Society. This had been founded very early, in 1884, when the school had just a few dozen engineering students. At the beginning, SPS students had been expected to join the existing University College student society (the UC Lit); two positions on the Lit's executive had been set aside for this purpose. After a few years, however, the engineering students found this arrangement unsuitable and instead formed their own society, naming Professor Galbraith their first president.[73] The purpose of the society was primarily academic; the fortnightly meetings were used for the presentation and discussion of technical papers, occasionally given by notable guest speakers, many of which were then printed in a pamphlet for distribution. Galbraith gave the society his full support, and even allowed student papers presented at the meetings to be considered in awarding honour standing. The society played an important part in life at the school; the annual compilation of published papers read before the society was, by the 1890s, sometimes over 200 pages long.[74] Another important Faculty organization that would have a long and influential life, the Engineering Alumni Association, was founded a little later, in 1909.[75]

With rising enrolments and a growing enthusiasm for student life through these turn-of-the-century years, student associations of other kinds began to take shape. Students formed an SPS Athletic Association in 1890 to coordinate the organized sports that students were playing in increasing numbers, football and hockey being the first. By the early 1900s, separate clubs had also been formed for rugby football, association football, hockey, and track.[76] Students set up clubs for most of the engineering specialties taught at the school; an Industrial Chemical Club, Architectural Club, and Electrical Club were all active by 1912. The two other great organizational passions of the age – Christian associations and military drill groups – both appeared, as well; early in the century, students established a Faculty branch of the YMCA and the Officers of the 2nd Field Company Canadian Engineers.[77]

There was much more to student life than clubs. The school held its first formal dinner in 1890, and this immediately became an important annual event. Dancing was not permitted at the university until 1896, but the SPS students requested permission from council to hold an 'At Home' in November 1895. Council had to ask the provincial minister of Education for his permission before they could reply, the outcome of which is not recorded, but the school appears to have begun holding occasional dances nonetheless. The first official 'At Home,' however, was not held until 1911.[78] Students at the school also took avid part in the increasingly popular university tradition of Hallowe'en theatre nights, in which groups of students from various faculties paraded through the city streets to a prearranged gathering at a public theatre where they all made a nuisance of themselves. It was at one such event, in 1897, that the cherished 'Toike Oike'

'On Friday evening, Feb. 9th, the coldest night in seventeen years, the Engineering Society held its second annual At Home. The most striking feature of the decorations was a model, one-fiftieth size, of the new Quebec Bridge. It was suspended from the ceiling by sixteen wires one-sixteenth of an inch in diameter. On the floor of the bridge a double-track railroad was laid, on which a miniature train was operated by means of electricity. The structural parts of the model were designed and constructed by the fourth year students in Civil Engineering, with some assistance from students in other years. The railroad and lights were installed by the mechanical and electrical students.' Applied Science, Feb. 1912, 173–5 yell is said to have been introduced (the 'forty beers' couplet is said to have been added, spontaneously, after a University of Toronto rugby victory in 1905). The words 'Toike Oike' were apparently what the old Irish caretaker 'Prof' Graham seemed to be saying when he told lingering students to 'take a hike' at the end of the day when the building was closing.[79]

There were also the notorious 'hustles' or 'scraps' that live so vividly in the memories of those who experienced them. Ritualized acts of aggression called 'hazings' – usually directed at an individual student as a consequence of some sort of misdeed – had been a part of student life for generations. But the fracases of the turn-of-the-century years were of a different, and to the university authorities more alarming, sort. Inspired perhaps by the fad of organized sports, these struggles began to resemble organized brawls, with hundreds of young men fighting hand to hand outside the university buildings.[80]

The fights usually occurred at initiation time, as the sophomores exercised their newly gained status by sticking it to the frosh. There was a predilection for paints and dyes in the Faculty, and especially for shoe polish. In one well-recorded initiation in October 1911, when the incoming first-year class was among the highest yet seen at 275 students, the sophomores attacked the freshmen as they filed out of a morning lecture behind the engineering building. 'The Sophs were armed with some 15 dozen boxes of polish, which they began to use with good effect,' *The Varsity* reported. 'Soon there was a struggling mass of about two hundred students, all of whom quickly began to appear like black men.'[81] Elections for the Engineering Society executive provided another occasion for merriment. Great pandemonium usually erupted in the large drafting room, where crowds gathered to hear the results. One year, those who made the mistake of sporting proper dress had their ties and collars torn off, and those with moustaches had their upper lips shaved with the scant lubrication of an apple core rubbed on the hair and skin. As the night wore on, the assembled students indulged in indoor broomball on roller skates, and the apparently hilarious sport of blindfolded boxing. It was at one of these election gatherings, in 1912, that the 'Brute Force Committee' had its genesis, formed to intimidate voters into supporting a certain candidate. The *Toike Oike* newspaper, first produced in 1911, also began life as part of an election run-up.[82]

Little harm was done. University property was occasionally damaged in these scraps, and reports of minor injuries were heard but, since most of the participants were willing, complaints were few. The university, however, did not take these fracases lightly and began to impose fines and even expulsions on the instigators. The authorities were especially unforgiving when liquor was involved, as it often was at the election-night parties. Penalties grew harsher as the years passed. In 1897, the SPS council imposed $5 fines on four students found drunk on election night, but in 1905, five SPS men 'caught red-handed putting ink of that colour on medical students' were suspended from the university.[83] The senior academic men in charge at both the SPS and the university had, of course, come of age in a different sort of institution. Galbraith and Ellis had attended University College in the 1860s, when actions on such a large scale were unheard of, and probably even undreamed of. It is no wonder they and others were so alarmed. The university made the scraps illicit – and in doing so made them less appealing to some students and more appealing to others – but could not stop them.

What is especially noteworthy about these activities is that the engineering students were not unique. They were simply taking part in the university-student culture of the age. All faculties indulged in these shenanigans. Hallowe'en theatre nights, for instance, were a university-wide event.[84] On the day in 1911 that the engineering sophomores polished the faces of the frosh, dentistry sophomores later did the same. The Brute Force Committee of the Faculty was modelled after a long-standing tradition of election coercion at University College.[85]

The Faculty's students showed themselves to be part of the university around them in other respects, too. Students throughout the university in these years were awash in a confidence that older staff members found close to contemptuous. The most outstanding illustration of this was the student strike of 1895, prompted by the university's suspension of James Tucker, editor of *The Varsity*, for criticizing the hiring of Professor George Wrong, and by the university's refusal to allow a public speech on the campus by a well-known labour sympathizer. The upshot was a few days of boycotted class, almost unanimously respected, followed by a Royal Commission to investigate this startling transgression.[86] SPS students did not, in the words of the *Globe*, 'feel called upon to abstain from lectures in their own institution,' although they did refuse to attend their University College lectures for the duration of the strike.[87]

Yet the engineering students were not above radical collective action of their own. In response to the 1905 suspension of the students caught applying red paint to meds, the entire second-year class, and then the first-year class, boycotted lectures and demanded that the suspensions be lifted. This strike lasted a week, eventually being resolved by Galbraith's personal intervention. The suspensions were withdrawn – there had never been any suggestion that they were permanent – and all the striking students were made to sign a document 'acknowledging their guilt and giving a guarantee for the future.'[88] While this appears to have been the only conflict that reached the point of a strike, students at the school made their influence felt in many other ways. They petitioned council to have annual examinations spread over a longer time in the spring (rejected), sought permission to publish examinations from previous years' courses (allowed), called for Christmas examinations 'of a less formal nature' in all subjects (rejected in 1903, but allowed in 1911), and asked for permission to assemble and sell lecture notes from various courses (rejected). The Engineering Society even went so far as to suggest

"Toike Oikestra," 1913-14

The Toike Oikestra, 1913–14; Professor C.H.C. Wright sits in the centre. UTA, A79-0060/011(06)

'On Monday evening I went to the first practice of the Toike Oikestra in the C&M building. There are about 15–18 fellows in it. They seem decent enough, though some of them smoke. We sawed off the ragtime from 7:30 till nearly 10.' UTA, B94-0001, 28 Oct. 1914, Kent Duff to his mother

to council specific changes in certain professors' courses, some of which were agreed to and some not, and it asked for and was given a role in setting punishment for students found guilty of breaching rules.[89]

Although most features of engineering-student life in these years were not unique to engineering, certain customs had by the end of the period taken on a distinct engineering form, or had come to be claimed by the engineers as their own. The Toike

Oike yell might have been born as part of a university Hallowe'en caper, but it was firmly fixed as the engineer's own yell. So, too, had the Brute Force Committee (1912), the *Toike Oike* newspaper (1911), the School Dinners (1890), the Toike Oikestra (begun in 1911), and the miniature cannon (stolen from the Military Institute by some SPS men one night about 1900, and coveted by the meds as soon as word got out) become set as Faculty institutions.[90] By 1914, engineering students had a set of traditions all their own. They had also developed an identity of themselves as a practical, unpretentious lot, distinct from the students of the Faculty of Arts – an identity that found its image in the spartan little red schoolhouse. And they had come to value the camaraderie, almost a team spirit, they felt with fellow students of one's year and course, something that came from taking all classes together in a fixed timetable. 'We are, we are, we are the engineers,' truly meant something to the young men who chanted it.

The year 1914 marks the end of an age at the school, as it does in so many aspects of Canadian life. The outbreak of the First World War is, of course, the main reason for this, but it is not the only one. In July 1914, after several months of failing health, John Galbraith died.[91] The loss left a great hole in the fabric of the school, and a deep uncertainty in the minds of the men now left to run it. It was, in the words of his old colleague W.H. Ellis, 'a loss the greatness of which cannot be overestimated.'[92] For thirty-six years, Galbraith had been the man in charge – a somewhat tentative advocate in the early years under University College control, but an increasingly confident principal and then dean in the years that followed. The school had never existed without him. The mark of his hand was everywhere.

In the short term, the solution was simply to put another professor in charge, and the deanship naturally fell to W.H. Ellis. Ellis had been at the school as long as Galbraith – he was, in fact,

about a year older – and at nearly seventy had no intention of settling into the job for long, but he agreed to take it on until a permanent replacement could be found. This, as it turned out, was
several years away, for war broke out in the fall of 1914 and the
decision on a permanent replacement was postponed as long as
the war lasted. Ellis remained in the deanship until 1919. It is
probably correct to say, therefore, that Galbraith was not fully
replaced until C.H. Mitchell took over the deanship after the war,
but Galbraith himself was gone when the war began.

John Galbraith was, above all, devoted to the school – one is
tempted say 'his' school, so deep was his commitment. He rarely
missed a meeting, and readily took on whatever administrative
tasks needed to be done. His dedication was to the school, not
the profession; in all his thirty-six years of service, he accepted
just one offer to work personally as an engineering consultant,
and that single job was for the Royal Commission on the Quebec
Bridge disaster in 1907, a duty Galbraith took on only because of
its great importance.[93] He taught every year, and did so with such
devotion to his students that many alumni considered him a personal friend, something with which he was quite comfortable.
'Johnny,' they called him among themselves. One student
recalled Galbraith personally tutoring him in preparation for
the French matriculation examination – something the student
already should have passed before being admitted to the school
in the first place. Another recalled Galbraith permitting an entire
class to pass their year without writing a chemistry examination.
They had taken their chemistry from Professor Pike (not one of
Galbraith's favourites), but on being presented with Pike's examination at the end of the year, they had refused to write it, feeling
that he was examining them on material he had not taught, and
had left the room en masse. Galbraith never did make them sit
for a chemistry examination.[94] He was a friend and advocate of
his students, as well as the dean of the school.

Galbraith's main guiding principle in engineering education

was that a school, on its own, was not enough to train a professional engineer, and that a young engineer's education had to continue beyond his schooling into his early years of employment.[95] In Galbraith's own words, 'It is plainly impossible within the short space of three or four years, and under academic conditions, to turn out an engineer, architect, or chemist fit for the full responsibilities of his profession.'[96] An engineering school's curriculum, it followed, should be designed with this limitation in mind, and should include only those subjects that suited school instruction: the principles of science, the skills of drafting and reading drawings, the qualities of materials, the ability to read and assess technical literature, and the capacity to recognize (but not necessarily do) skilled work. Practical work experience was also essential, but Galbraith maintained that it did not truly belong in a school or university curriculum. Only in commercial conditions could one acquire true experience, so a school shop, Galbraith thought, had little value; students were better off gaining their experience in the real world. It was thus because of his respect for practical work that Galbraith kept it out of the school curriculum.

A good many engineers in 1900 were dubious of their profession ever being properly taught at university, for about half of the engineers in Canada at that time had learned their profession through apprenticeships, not at school.[97] It was these doubters whom Galbraith had to win over to legitimize the school, for they would be the employers of his graduates, and it was to them that he addressed his public statements. Galbraith was, of course, one of these men himself in a sense, for although he had studied science and mathematics at university, he had acquired his professional education on the job; he was thus more credible among practising engineers than a man with purely academic training would have been. So when Galbraith argued the advantages of university education for engineers while readily acknowledging the limitations, he was believable. And, evidently, he was believed, as the rising number of students attending the school attests.

Galbraith was, admittedly, not a pioneer in this movement, nor was he unique in his accomplishments. Throughout North America and much of Europe, engineering was becoming a university subject. Nor was his way the only way; other engineering schools had closer ties to university science departments, greater international connections, or more commitment to engineering research. But his achievement was real nonetheless. By respecting the practical, while advocating the academic, he succeeded in carving out a niche for professional engineering education at the University of Toronto. Such an outcome was not predestined in 1889.

Despite his wish to have engineering education closely allied to the university, he clearly did not advocate research at his engineering school, neither for staff nor for students. This was an important tenet of Galbraith's, one that would have fairly lasting effects. His opposition, however, was more a matter of pragmatism than principle. He knew what some science educators took years to recognize: that practical science was a particular kind of science, not just pure science applied to practical things. He saw the need for research by engineers or practical scientists to build up this body of knowledge, 'with which the investigators of pure science are more or less unacquainted.'[98] But Galbraith felt that, since employment for such researchers would never amount to much, research would always have to be subordinate to teaching. He opposed research, therefore, because of his commitment to serving the practical needs of his students, not because he opposed engineering research *per se.*

As for resistance within the university to having engineering students at an institution of higher learning – something that MIT was facing at this very time as it considered joining Harvard University[99] – Galbraith had little to contend with. Perhaps some haughty scholars somewhere at the university objected to having an engineering school – or any professional school, for that matter – in their midst, but if they did they left no obvious evidence.

The official policy of both the province and the university was quite the opposite. The university took an unequivocal position during the provincial enquiry of 1906: professional schools would comprise one of its parts; and on this rested much of its claim to public support.[100] Resistance to having engineering education in the university, if it came from anywhere, came not from the university but from those in the profession who had done well without it.

Relations between the Faculty and the university were not always harmonious, but Galbraith appears to have brought this on himself. He set a very bad precedent right at the start when in 1890, the first year of his tenure as principal, he had refused to permit University College the temporary use of an SPS classroom the day after the college was badly damaged by fire. Only if given written permission from the minister of Education, he maintained, could he allow such a thing, and he taped the door of the desired room shut to show his resolve. University College President Daniel Wilson was outraged, and his respect for Galbraith, already declining, was lost from this point on.[101] Overplaying his government connection, evident in his handling of the physics dispute with James Loudon, as well, was something of an obsession of Galbraith's, and at times it did more harm than good.

One notable feature of Galbraith's accomplishment was that he formed the school to his vision with next to no dissent, at least within the school itself. This harmony is easy to explain. The academic staff were all Galbraith's men. Of the eighteen permanent staff in 1913, all but four had been Galbraith's students; of those four, two, G.R. Anderson and L.B. Stewart, owed their appointments entirely to Galbraith, and one, Ellis, had long been Galbraith's friend and associate. Only G.A. Guess, the metallurgist from Queen's just appointed that year, was not a true Galbraith man. Galbraith was unapolgetic about this. 'Our practice results in much greater smoothness and consequent efficiency in the work of the school ... and much less risk of selecting poor teach-

John Galbraith on the front steps of the Engineering Building, c.1908. UTA, B78-0001P.02(01)

ers,' Galbraith explained to the minister of Education.[102] No doubt this was true; men from elsewhere might well have caused disharmony. They might also have brought new ideas, but as the minister of Education told President Loudon, one cannot argue with success.

John Galbraith was a product of the nineteenth century in both his educational vision and his paternal feelings towards the school's staff and students. He had fought his battles well, no question, and in doing so had found a place for his engineering school within the university, the profession, and the industrializing Ontario economy. But these battles were now over. One might even say they had been over for several years, and that Galbraith's vision was showing its age well before he died. That is not to disparage his accomplishment. Galbraith had led the school from an ill-defined concept in the minds of government and university administrators into a flourishing school of engineering with a place, a mission, and a tradition of its own, a success that should not be taken lightly. It was now up to others to carry the school into the twentieth century.

chapter three

CAUTIOUS PROGRESS

The years from 1914 to 1939, from the start of one world war to the start of the next, were a time of surprisingly little change at the Faculty. This is especially striking in comparison with the previous generation, during which the school grew and evolved so fast, and when one considers how quickly technology was developing in these interwar years. Not that the Faculty faltered or fell badly behind. It remained a successful and popular institution, by far the largest engineering school in the province; every year, up to a hundred or more of its graduates moved on to work in the growing industrial economy of the region, some to public and some to private institutions, and some, as always, to careers of great distinction. There were a few important changes in the Faculty's curriculum and there was an unmistakable increase in research activity among the academic staff. Nevertheless, when change came it came slowly, and usually resulted from committed individuals swimming hard against the tide of tradition. Galbraith's vision of engineering education far outlived the man himself.

Of the two calamaties that struck in the summer of 1914, the death of Galbraith in July and the outbreak of war in August, the former sent a greater shock through the Faculty. But looking back, the latter clearly had more damaging effects. Although Galbraith's death shook his colleagues badly, it disturbed the school's affairs very little. Galbraith's legacy was secure. The war, on the other hand, undermined almost everything. Enrolment fell, student life lost its spirit, space in the school was given over to war work, and the academic staff devoted much of its time to organizing the war effort rather than teaching engineering. The war years were close to lost years for the Faculty.

When the academic session began at the end of September 1914, some eight weeks after the outbreak of war, the Canadian government had already fully committed the country to a part in the conflict. Some of the first contingent of Canadian forces, recruited and trained, were by then on board ships heading down the St Lawrence River to the Atlantic Ocean. The war must have been on everyone's mind. In his formal greeting to the students, President Falconer spoke about 'the greatest of moral struggles' in which the country was embroiled, and he urged students to 'live a life of sacrifice this winter, and thereby contribute something to help the nation in relieving its suffering.'[1] Such gravity might have seemed a little overwrought to the assembled students, for the war was, after all, far from the Toronto campus. In the Faculty of Applied Science and Engineering, enrolment, which had been falling slightly for a few years, remained solid at 556 students. Social and athletic activities were planned as usual. There was no immediate sign of campus life being disturbed. How quickly this would change.

The first of what would turn out to be many consequences came in just two weeks with the formation of the Canadian Officers Training Corps. This program had been conceived in August, just after war broke out, when a delegation from several universities had met government officials in Ottawa to discuss how universities might contribute to the war; they had decided that a corps of student volunteers who would undertake regular military training while still pursuing university studies would be best. Such a corps would provide a pool of partly trained young men from which officers could be recruited as needed.[2]

In the Faculty of Applied Science and Engineering, where sym-

Lantern slides produced during the First World War. Who made these slides, and for what purpose, is not on record. UTA, A65-0004/052, #10-25 and #10-26

pathy with the British cause, as well as with military matters generally, abounded, students enrolled in the COTC in impressive numbers. Within weeks, some two-thirds of the Faculty's student body had joined, the more ambivalent being carried along by the fervour of the committed. 'With the President and profs and fellows all urging you to join I could scarcely do otherwise,' one first-year student, rather cool towards the war, wrote his mother.[3] Student participation in the COTC was so great throughout the university that the president ordered all classes and labs to finish by four o'clock, at which time the campus would be given over to military drill. Engineering and forestry students were organized into a company, and every Thursday and Friday, from 4:00 to 6:00 p.m., several hundred of them went through their paces on the university field. Occasionally, they even marched off to city ravines to practise traversing bush and fording rivers.[4]

The Faculty fully supported the COTC. C.R. Young, then an assistant professor of Applied Mechanics, and two professors from Architecture, A.W. McConnell and H.H. Madill, took on the job of training the Faculty's company, all three being assigned the rank of captain and reduced to half-pay by the university.[5] Professor of Architecture C.H.C. Wright, with the rank of lieutenant, served as quartermaster for the entire university corps.[6] The Faculty also gave over space in the Mining Building for the COTC. To encourage its students to enrol, the Faculty gave all those who did, and who performed their military activities satisfactorily, a 10 per cent bonus on their grades. Students in the Faculty were also encourged to, and did, volunteer for active service. In early 1915, faculty council resolved that students who enlisted would be granted their year provided they stayed in attendance until 15 February.[7] By the end of the session, in addition to the hundreds in the COTC, seventy-seven students had volunteered for overseas service.[8]

This was just the start of the disruption. In the fall of 1915, as Dean Ellis put it, 'the full effects of the war began to be felt.' This was so throughout the university, as intercollegiate sports were suspended, fraternites closed, and social activities curtailed. Enrolment in the Faculty fell to 341. Incoming first-year numbers were down, but so, too, were the intermediate years as students continued to enlist. One student who had begun his studies in 1914 reported that, by the end of his second year, only 51 of the 130 who began with him were still in the school.[9] The Engineering Society fell into financial crisis with such a low enrolment, and had to cease publishing its journal of papers and addresses, *Applied Science*. By the completion of the 1915–16 session, another 134 students had volunteered for active service. Faculty were also being drawn away – J.R. Cockburn, T.R. Loudon, and A.W. McConnell of Architecture all volunteered.[10]

By the following year the situation at the university had worsened further still. The pressures of war were intensifying throughout the country; manpower of all types – enlisted men, farm workers, industrial labour – was in short supply, and the public, many of whom had by this time lost at least one relative or friend, was growing increasingly skeptical and unforgiving towards those who avoided enlistment. Slackers and evaders were sought out everywhere. The university responded by conducting its own military registration in January 1917 – as a public relations move of sorts – requiring students to report their physical health and their willingness to do national labour service. Adding to the sense of emergency, the university ran short of coal to heat its buildings in the winter of 1917. Since industrial use of all fuels was given priority, nothing could be done to alleviate the shortage, and for three weeks, from 14 February to 5 March, the university had to keep its main buildings closed for lack of heat. Enrolment at the Faculty fell further still that year, to just 194 students. One thing that was plentiful at the university was unused teaching space, allowing the Royal Flying Corps to establish a training centre on campus in the spring of 1917; parts of the Engineering Building were given over to this, as was much of Devonshire House, forcing students to double up in the one residence dedicated to professional school students. The few students left in the Faculty must have had their minds somewhere other than on their studies.[11]

The staff felt pressures of their own. When the students of the Royal Flying Corps first arrived, but their teachers from England had not, several staff gave volunteer instruction. In June 1917, H.E.T. Haultain volunteered to coordinate the retraining and rehabilitation of returned, wounded mining students. Shortly after this he was appointed vocational officer for Ontario under the Invalided Soldier's Commission, in which capacity he arranged technical education for returning soldiers capable of learning trades – much of which was done or coordinated by his colleagues at the Faculty – as well as occupational therapy for the seriously disabled confined to institutions. For the latter, the commission hired and trained women to teach the soldiers woodworking, basketry, book-binding, and other such skills. Managing this

A group of airmen from the Royal Flying Corps in front of the Engineering Building, c.1917. The Corps operated a School of Military Aeronautics in the building during the later years of the war; academic staff from the Faculty voluntarily taught the fundamentals of internal combustion engines, wireless telegraphy, and photography. UTA, A65-0004/6.62

work turned out to be extremely demanding; by the time Haultain withdrew from the position in 1919, he had a staff of 375 in his Toronto office.[12] Others in the Faculty were engaged in work with a much lower profile. In some cases this involved formal employment, such as J.W. Bain, who in 1918 was seconded to work as a chemical advisor to the Canadian War Mission in Washington. But in others, staff served while still in their capacity as members of the Faculty; E.G.R. Ardagh and J.H. Parkin were among several who tested shells and materials in their laboratories.[13]

Not surprisingly, there were no developments in the Faculty's teaching offerings. The university did decide in 1917 to establish a Department of Aerodynamics, but at the time it meant nothing more than construction of an experimental wind tunnel in the hydraulics laboratory. It was, however, the first such tunnel in Canada, and it allowed J.H. Parkin and R.W. Angus of Mechanical Engineering to conduct some aerodynamic research.[14] With enrolments so low, no new academic staff were appointed. This was no time for anything or anyone new.

Nor was there much research by the staff in connection with the war effort. Some of the work done by the Faculty's chemists might be considered research. Bain's work in Washington led him into 'investigations on the manufacture of picric acid' for a company in New Jersey that supplied picric acid to the French government. M.C. Boswell worked for the same company on the manufacture of synthetic phenol. But when President Falconer was called upon to list the scientific contributions of the university staff, all he could provide for the Faculty of Applied Science and Engineering were Bain's and Boswell's work, some investigations done on magnesium manufacturing by J.T. Burt-Gerrans, a lecturer in electro-chemistry, and a number of other men, most of them sessional instructors, working on shell testing.[15] The university's biggest scientific contribution to the war effort was probably J.C. McLennan's work on helium extraction from natural gas, but this had no connection with engineering.[16]

The war did, however, affect the institutional development of research in the Faculty, for it played a role in the genesis of the School of Engineering Research. The SER appears to have originated in response to two quite separate initiatives. One was an attempt in 1915 by the Royal Canadian Institute in Toronto to set up a Bureau of Scientific and Industrial Research modelled on the Mellon Institute in Pittsburgh. The Institute had approached the University of Toronto before the war, seeking cooperation in this scheme, and the university was still considering their proposal when war broke out.[17] At the same time, as a result of lobbying by industrialists and educators early in the war, the Canadian government had begun to explore how it could best encourage and contribute to industrial research. Germany's astounding success in state-fostered industrial research offered a vivid demonstration of how effective such an approach could be. The government at first considered providing money to universities, since they already had laboratories and skilled scientists. To explore this the minister of Trade and Commerce, Sir George Foster, held meetings in Ottawa in May 1915 with a dozen university scientists and administrators, including President Falconer and Dean Ellis.[18] As it turned out, neither of these efforts came to have a direct bearing on the Faculty. The university elected not to participate in the Royal Canadian Institute's plan, and the Canadian government chose not to provide funds for university research but, rather, to set up an independent research council that would engage its own scientists and conduct its own research. About one year later, when the government founded the body that would later be named the National Research Council, it appointed two of the University of Toronto's leading research scientists, J.C. McLennan and A.B. Macallum (Biochemistry), to an advisory council of this body. Dean Ellis, however, was no longer involved. Engineers were not generally excluded; Frank Adams, dean of Applied Science from McGill, and R.A. Ross, a prominent Montreal consulting engineer, were named to the advisory council. But no engineers from University of Toronto took part.[19]

Nevertheless, all of this activity had its consequences. It seems to have made Dean Ellis into an advocate of increased engineering research, for at this very time he began calling on the university to provide funds for this purpose. President Falconer was already on his side, so he took little convincing. The breakthrough came when the Ontario government, which had been watching these developments with interest, agreed in 1917 to provide the university with $15,000 for scientific and technical research. This in turn led to the university offering the Faculty some of this money, and on the strength of this, in April 1917, the

Faculty founded its School of Engineering Research, and the university agreed to provide $5,000 for its first year of operation.[20] Although born in wartime, research undertaken with its funds in 1918 did not all have a direct connection to the war. The main projects funded that first year were on voltage regulation for high-tension transmission lines (Rosebrugh), plant growth enzymes (Boswell), heat insulation qualities of various building materials (Angus), electrolytic methods of nickel refining (Guess), and a new type of reinforced concrete for the construction of large buildings (Gillespie).[21] It was, nevertheless, wartime urgency that made applied science research seem worthy of public support, so the SER – the Faculty's first step into institutionalized research support for its academic staff – can be counted as a product of the war.

When the war finally ended in November 1918, the Faculty of Applied Science and Engineering was in a badly disrupted state. Its student enrolment was lower than it had been for decades, many of its key academic staff were away involved in war work, and its aging temporary dean, having now served for four years, was anxious to retire. There was plenty of work to do to put affairs back in order. But there was also plenty of energy and enthusiasm. Most people associated with the Faculty could, and did, feel a considerable sense of accomplishment at their contribution to the war effort. More than half of the Faculty's students and graduates, and nearly one-quarter of its staff, had served overseas.[22] Many, of course, had lost their lives, and many others their good health and physical abilities. Yet these losses were a source of pride, not regret, and they served as an inspiration to the staff and students facing the task of re-establishing the school.

For the first two years of the war, the question of who would replace Dean Ellis had remained unsettled. The academic staff of the Faculty offered no obvious candidates, at least not in the mind of

President Falconer. Immediately after Galbraith's death, in the fall of 1914, Falconer had begun writing colleagues at other universities asking for recommendations, but without success.[23] Then, in October 1916, Falconer found his man: Lieutenant-Colonel C.H. Mitchell, a Canadian officer serving on the headquarters staff of the British Second Army in France.

It was an odd choice, and no doubt a surprising one to many, for although a competent practising engineer and an SPS graduate, Mitchell had no experience as an engineering educator. Charles Hamilton Mitchell, the son of a Petrolia, Ontario, clergyman, had received his SPS diploma in 1892 and his BASc in 1894. After graduation, he had worked as a municipal engineer in Niagara Falls, New York, then Niagara Falls, Ontario, during which time he developed expertise in hydraulic and hydroelectric power engineering, the 1890s being the years of several large hydro-power developments in the region. With a growing reputation, he set up a Toronto-based consulting firm in 1906 in partnership with his brother Percival, and took part in developing hydroelectric facilities in several parts of the country. He also entered university affairs, first as a member of the senate in 1901, then as president of the local alumni branch in 1909 and, in 1913, as a member of the board of governors, by which time he had become a close associate of President Falconer.[24]

When war broke out, Mitchell had enlisted immediately and gone overseas as a general staff officer with the First Canadian Division. Falconer wrote Mitchell at Valcartier, prior to his sailing, to commend him for enlisting and to express regret that he would not be present at the board meetings to help find the Faculty's new dean.[25] Once overseas, Mitchell soon proved himself exceptionally skilled at spying across enemy lines and compiling reports about enemy positions. He was awarded the Distinguished Service Order in June 1916, after which he was seconded to the Imperial Second Army and appointed its chief of Intelligence.[26] It was after this award and promotion that Falconer ceased seeing Mitchell as an advisor and began considering him a potential dean. Falconer offered him the job in October 1916, and Mitchell accepted in December. He would take up the job when the war ended – 'if I am spared,' he reminded the president. He did have one proviso. His consulting career had brought him great satsifaction, and he was not prepared to give it up. He would take on the deanship, therefore, only if permitted to devote one-third of his time to his private practice during the teaching session and 'a portion of my summer holidays as well.' To this Falconer agreed, and the Faculty set about waiting for the war to end and their new dean to return.[27]

Mitchell was subsequently transferred to Italy with the British Forces, and he continued to distinguish himself with further honours and awards. Then, shortly after the war, before being discharged, he was promoted to the rank of brigadier general.[28] Thus, when he finally took up his new job with the Faculty in mid-1919, Mitchell came with a stellar war record. It was on this, much more than on his engineering accomplishments, that his apointment rested – not an uncommon turn of events at the end of the Great War when, as the historian A.B. McKillop has written, much of university life 'took on the character of a sustained memorial service.'[29]

Into the excitement and confusion of the Faculty's post-war affairs Mitchell stepped, along with hundreds of young men returning from the war. Named honourary president of the incoming first-year class, Mitchell marched with them from Queen's Park to the old Engineering Building for their initiation.[30] This new mission was a good deal safer than anything he had undertaken in the war, but it was no simple task. Several critical matters had to be dealt with immediately: special conditions for returning soldiers, the big jump in enrolment, the need for a new building, and alterations in the school's program. To these Mitchell and the professoriate now gave their attention.

The handling of returned soldiers (as they were usually called after this war) had already been partly addressed. The Faculty had set up a special session to run from 1 February to 30 June

1919 to allow servicemen to establish themselves in preparation for the regular session of October 1919. The session offered first-, second-, and third-year instruction, and thus served those who had enlisted while part way through their course as well as those wishing to begin their studies. The work was, as one of the instructors later recalled, 'somewhat simplified and abridged,' but it served its purpose well enough.[31] Seventy-seven returned soldiers registered. Then came the great influx of students in the fall of 1919. Enrolment rose from 241 to 819 students, about half of whom were first year and more than half of whom were ex-soldiers. The Faculty had seen this many students before, but never had it seen such an enormous first-year class, and never, of course, had it seen so many war veterans. Special concessions were made to ex-soldiers who had already completed a portion of their studies. Those twenty-five or over who had finished third year prior to enlisting, and who had 'a creditable war record over a long period,' could be granted their degree upon completion of a short course, part of which could be taken extramural. Those twenty-four or over who had completed second year could obtain their degree after just one year of study.[32]

As for the space and professors to accommodate the incoming mass of students, the Faculty was reasonably well prepared. It reclaimed space in the old Engineering Building and the east wing of the Mining Building that had been given over to war work; it also reclaimed its staff from war service, one by one. But it did have to make some special arrangements. The large enrolment necessitated doubling up at drafting tables and laboratory benches, and the offering of several first-year lecture courses in the afternoon as well as the morning. The Faculty also took over the gymnasium in the campus YMCA building – no longer needed with Hart House open to students – for large classes in drafting.[33] No permanent staff appointments were made in this first post-war year, although the teaching staff was supplemented by several new sessional instructors.

The Electrical Building (later the Rosebrugh Building) from the south-east, March 1921, shortly after completion. UTA, A65-0004/20.6

The large enrolment finally spurred into being a new building for Electrical Engineering, something that had been considered for years but which the war had made impossible. Electrical was the one new specialty remaining in the old building, and as it was clearly a field of the future – and the most popular choice of the incoming class – it needed new facilities badly. There was next to no time to plan for it. Just after the war ended, in early February 1919, the provincial government informed the university that it would contribute $350,000 towards a new Electrical Engineering building, but only if construction began at once. The government wished to alleviate rising post-war unemployment with this expenditure, so it would tolerate no delays. The architects Darling and Pearson were hastily engaged, and excavation of a site east of the Thermodynamics Building began immediately. Excavation was finished in fact before the building's design was complete, causing a delay that summer, but by the fall of 1919 construction was fully underway. The new Electrical Building, closely resembling the Thermodynamics Building, which Darling and Pearson had also designed and to which the new building was attached, was in use by the fall of 1920 and officially opened the following November. Intended primarily for Electrical Engineering, it also housed a new laboratory for testing structural materials and so was used for the offices of the Applied Mechanics teaching department.[34]

Mitchell moved immediately to improve the Faculty's internal management. As a memo on the subject stated, 'the growth of this institution has been like that of a small village growing into a prosperous city.'[35] Yet it was still being run like a village; all the professors attended regular council meetings, where all matters were raised. These meetings were taking up so much time that important business, such as planning for the future, was not being tended to. A committee was struck to study the problem, and in January 1920 it proposed sweeping reforms: the formation of ten committees of council, each of which would be responsible for a specific matter, and an executive committee consisting of the dean and the senior professors to handle routine matters not needing full council. This move should have been made years before, but Galbraith likely had seen no need to change a system that had been serving him well for so long. Mitchell, on the other hand, with his experience as a commanding officer during the war, saw such administrative matters differently.

Another pressing problem was the Faculty's relations with Architecture. Architecture had been something of an undernourished black sheep in the Faculty for years, and had never had many students, rarely more than twenty or thirty in all four years. At the time the program began at the original SPS in 1890, architecture education was in a rather early stage of development; most architects learned by professional tutelage, and there was no widespread consensus on how, or even whether, their education

Miss Rose Cave, stenographer in the office of the Faculty secretary, 1920. UTA, A65-0004/6.63

belonged in the university. Nor was it clear where in the university, if it was to be there, it belonged. Engineering schools seemed as good a place as any, since drawing and the elements of structural design were being taught to engineering students. The earliest schools of architecture in the United States in the 1860s and 1870s had been connected to engineering schools, one of them being Cornell, a model for the SPS course. By the turn of the century, however, architecture education, and indeed architecture itself, was changing both in its increasing connection to universities and in the content of its training. Architecture programs now included the teaching of design, a skill previously acquired through apprenticeships in local studios, often added at the expense of science and mathematics. At most universities, such changes had spurred the administrative separation of architecture and engineering schools. Cornell's curriculum changed in 1897, at which time its school was made an independent College of Architecture, as did Columbia's in 1902.[36]

At the University of Toronto in the early 1920s, architecture had still not made this transformation, and as a result the program was flirting with irrelevance. Its only full professor, C.H.C. Wright, had neither studied nor practised architecture (although he did have some expertise in the strength of materials).[37] The architects of Ontario thought this wholly unacceptable, and a deputation from the Ontario Association of Architects presented itself to Falconer in March 1919 to tell him so. Since they had come at the urging of the premier of Ontario, Falconer had little choice but to listen as they expressed their complete dissatisfaction with the university's course. They demanded a broader program, separate from engineering, that included instruction in design and the arts, the hiring of a quality professor of architecture from overseas, and the extension of the program into town planning, for which another professor should be hired.[38] Falconer sympathized, and wrote to Mitchell, not yet back from England, to sound him out. Mitchell replied that he thought their criticism quite valid. He agreed to look for a suitable man in Britain or France, and to address the whole problem more thoroughly when he returned.[39]

As it turned out, nothing fundamental changed in these post-war years. Only one of the Association's recommendations was followed: the hiring of a proper professor of Architecture, Adrian Berrington, who arrived from Paris at the start of the 1920–21 session. Architecture remained part of the Faculty, and the students continued to take much of their instruction from engineering professors. There were occasional lectures in town planning, and a course in Town Planning and Civics was offered through the Extension Department, but instruction in the subject did not formally enter the program at this time. Under Berrington, however, the program did begin to develop a different focus – the BArch was established as a distinct degree in 1922 – and this gradual divergence continued in the years to come. In 1928 the course was extended to five years' duration; and the following year the department's name was changed to the School of Architecture, although it remained part of the Faculty.[40]

The post-war rebirth of the Faculty also gave impetus to another full revision to the school's curriculum. The first change, small but noteworthy, was the cessation of the course in Applied and Analytical Chemistry, effected by Dean Ellis on the eve of his retirement in December 1918. With a chemistry department in the Faculty of Arts carrying on nearly identical work and attracting more students, Ellis thought it 'poor policy to have this duplication of work within the university.' Starting in the fall of 1919, the course in Chemical Engineering, run by a department of that name under the headship of J.W. Bain, would be the Faculty's only course directly relating to chemistry, although the twenty-some students in the later years of the old course were allowed to continue until graduation.[41] Thus ended the last of the original non-engineering courses at the school. At the same time the Faculty's teaching department of Applied Chemistry, a loosely defined department that handled most of the Faculty's chemistry instruction, and of which Ellis had been head, ceased to be, and the lecturers from this department were moved to the Chemistry Department in the Faculty of Arts. With them, however, went the responsibility for teaching general chemistry to the Faculty's students, something J.W. Bain claims he would have opposed had he not been still away on war work. Here again was the old problem of the Faculty's chemistry teaching being handled by professors outside the Faculty, reintroduced by none other than W.H. Ellis. But since the individuals involved now got on well – unlike Pike and Ellis in 1880 – the arrangement was accepted for the time being. (Later, in 1931, by which time Chemical Engineering had more staff and was sharing chemistry teaching with Chemistry in the Faculty of Arts, it would add the words 'Applied Chemistry' to its name; this move to ensure that its wider teaching responsibilities were reflected in its name was in response to a suggestion by the Chemistry Department that, to avoid duplication, all basic chemistry teaching for engineering students might be returned to Chemistry.)[42]

Another small but important innovation, one that would have enduring importance to generations of students, was the inauguration of the Gull Lake Survey Camp on land near Minden in northern Ontario, purchased for the Faculty by the university. Beginning in August 1921, third-year students in Civil and Mining Engineering started their school year at a six-week surveying course at the camp. This freed up time and space during the academic year, and allowed students to be introduced to surveying in real-life circumstances. Judging by the countless surviving photographs of young swimmers and divers, it also provided ample opportunity for outdoor fun.[43]

Revisions of a much more fundamental nature were being considered, but deciding exactly what should be done was no easy task. Like engineering educators elsewhere, the Faculty's professors were having to contend with several currents of change. It was clear, for one, that science was becoming an essential part of engineering; this was especially so in electrical and chemical engineering. Students in these fields had to be allowed to receive more science instruction in their specialty. Yet at the same time specialization was something that older engineers looked at with suspicion, for it seemed to represent a trend that could well undermine the profession's identity. There was also a growing recognition that engineering graduates, in all fields, were finding their way into management, whether as corporate employees or independent consultants. Engineering work now involved presentations at meetings, management of complex industrial plants, and the analysis of financial accounts much more than just inspecting the site or the works, yet the curriculum offered little to prepare students for such work.[44] The Faculty had moved in this direction before the war, but some of the new courses had since been dropped and a general feeling prevailed that more ought to be done. A related, but different, concern was that engineers needed a more rounded education. Unlike other professions, which were beginning to build their professional training on top of a few years of general university studies, engineering students took all their university education in engineering. Was it not important, therefore, for engineers to have some arts courses in their program as well? This last concern was a favourite of Dean Mitchell.[45]

These considerations all contributed to the introduction of a new curriculum for the 1922–23 session. First, and perhaps most important, admission standards were raised. Prospective students now needed full matriculation, not just junior matriculation. This allowed the Faculty to drop some of its basic science and mathematics from first year, such as elementary trigonometry and algebra, and to move some second-year courses to first year, making possible advanced instruction in fourth year. It also permitted some specialization in first year; until now, all engineering students had taken a common first year. Several changes were also made in non-technical instruction. Technical English was reintroduced, as was accounting. A full-year course in banking and finance was reduced to half a year, allowing for it to be paired with another half-year course in economics; similarly a course in limited companies was halved and made part of a wider course in commercial law. In both these cases, more general humanistic subjects were replacing the purely practical, raising the basic question of whether the purpose of the non-technical curriculum was to impart polish and sophistication or to teach non-scientific but practical skills. These two would compete for space in the curriculum for years.[46]

In the spring of 1923 the large class that had begun their studies in the fall of 1919 graduated, and with them went the Faculty's direct connection to the war. Of the 253 graduates, 60 per cent were ex-soldiers. The members of this 'Class of 2T3' had carried a

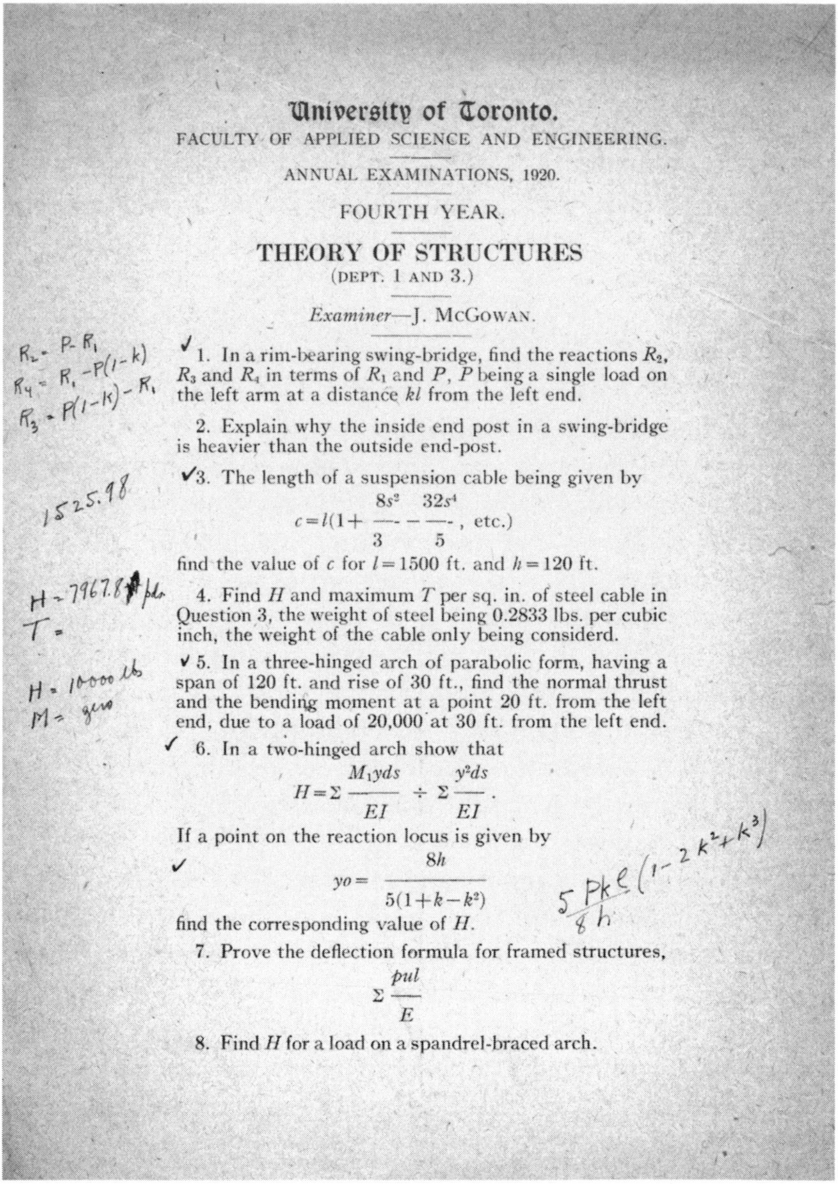

University of Toronto.

FACULTY OF APPLIED SCIENCE AND ENGINEERING.

ANNUAL EXAMINATIONS, 1920.

FOURTH YEAR.

THEORY OF STRUCTURES
(DEPT. 1 AND 3.)

Examiner—J. McGowan.

[handwritten: $R_2 = P - R_1$]
[handwritten: $R_4 = R_1 - P(1-k)$]
[handwritten: $R_3 = P(1-k) - R_1$]

1. In a rim-bearing swing-bridge, find the reactions R_2, R_3 and R_4 in terms of R_1 and P, P being a single load on the left arm at a distance kl from the left end.

2. Explain why the inside end post in a swing-bridge is heavier than the outside end-post.

[handwritten: 1525.98]

3. The length of a suspension cable being given by

$$c = l\left(1 + \frac{8s^2}{3} - \frac{32s^4}{5} - , \text{ etc.}\right)$$

find the value of c for $l = 1500$ ft. and $h = 120$ ft.

[handwritten: $H = 7967.8$ # per]
[handwritten: $T =$]

4. Find H and maximum T per sq. in. of steel cable in Question 3, the weight of steel being 0.2833 lbs. per cubic inch, the weight of the cable only being considerd.

[handwritten: $H = 10000$ lbs]
[handwritten: $M = $ zero]

5. In a three-hinged arch of parabolic form, having a span of 120 ft. and rise of 30 ft., find the normal thrust and the bending moment at a point 20 ft. from the left end, due to a load of 20,000 at 30 ft. from the left end.

6. In a two-hinged arch show that

$$H = \Sigma \frac{M_1 y ds}{EI} \div \Sigma \frac{y^2 ds}{EI}.$$

If a point on the reaction locus is given by

$$yo = \frac{8h}{5(1+k-k^2)}$$

find the corresponding value of H.

[handwritten: $\frac{5\,Pk\ell}{8h}(1 - 2k^2 + k^3)$]

7. Prove the deflection formula for framed structures,

$$\Sigma \frac{pul}{E}$$

8. Find H for a load on a spandrel-braced arch.

A final examination in Theory of Structures for fourth-year students in Civil and Mechanical Engineering, 1920. UTA, B96-0032/007(12) certain distinctiveness with them through their four years at the school; the Great War had been a nearly sacred cause in Canada and all things associated with it were by now imbued with its sanctity. They had worn this mantle proudly, and would continue to do so in the years ahead. They would remain a cohesive graduating class for years, and an influential one too as long as Dean Mitchell remained in office. But they were gone now, and with their departure the post-war transition ended.

The mid-1920s, despite an expanding Canadian economy, saw surprisingly low student enrolments at the Faculty. The large class of 1923 had kept overall numbers fairly high – above 700 every year since the war – but once gone they were not replaced. Enrolment fell to around 500 students for the next five years. The Faculty had not seen so few students, apart from the war years, since the start of the century. The war and post-war experience had evidently stirred an interest in engineering that normal circumstances did not sustain. Not until a few years in the early 1930s, and again in the late 1930s, this time for good, did student enrolment exceed that of 1919. Nevertheless, this was not a time of total stasis. At least one fairly fundamental change was beginning to work its way through the academic life of the Faculty: the rise of research.

The key stimulus of this was the School of Engineering Research, formed in the Faculty in 1917. This 'school' was, in fact, nothing more than a committee of senior academic staff in the Faculty that distributed a set amount of money, granted by the university, to academic staff undertaking research. Researchers applied to the committee, which reviewed the applications and awarded funds to those deemed worthy of support. There were ample funds. The $5,000 given in the first year of operation rose steadily until 1929, by which time the annual grant had reached $22,800. The money went to support ten or twenty small research projects each year, and was used primarily to cover the cost of research assistants and equipment. SER grants funded research in sewage disposal (Gillespie), road foundations (Laing), ore-crushing techniques (Haultain), aircraft design (Parkin), steam-flow through orifices (Angus), gasoline engines (Allcut), the chemical composition of rubber (Boswell), automatic frequency control in electrical networks (Price), and the malleability of steel (O.W. Ellis), among others.[47]

The results of this research were not usually published in academic journals, for there was not yet a fully developed system for academic publishing in all fields of engineering; but there is little doubt that results were disseminated to people who could use them. The structural engineers in Civil Engineering (Young, Gillespie) tended to publish in industry or professional journals such as *Engineering and Contracting* or *Canadian Engineer*. The same was true to some extent for the Mechanical Engineers, whose research (Angus, Allcut) was published in the *Journal of the American Waterworks Association* and *Canadian Engineer*. But Angus and Allcut also reached a wider, international audience. By the 1930s, Angus was publishing his hydraulics research, and Allcut his work on internal combustion engines, in the *Transactions of the American Society of Mechanical Engineers* and the English *Proceedings of the Institute of Mechanical Engineers*. The Chemical Engineers, especially M.C. Boswell, published in well-established international journals as well, such as the *Journal of the American Chemical Society* and the *Journal of Physical Chemistry*. The highest profile researcher was no doubt H.E.T. Haultain. In association with his junior colleague F.C. Dyer, and using slow-motion photography, Haultain analysed the paths taken by steel balls flowing through a model rock crusher, and was thus able to establish the optimum size and flow rate for crushed ore particles. Originally published in *Transactions of the Canadian Institute of Mining and Metallurgy* in 1922, this work brought Haultain considerable renown in mining circles throughout the world.[48] The Faculty also published its own

Bulletin of the School of Engineering Research, a follow-up to the old *Applied Science* of the pre-war years, in which research results were often reported. Although it is hard to track its distribution, records of requests for copies show it to have been much more than simply vanity publishing.[49]

Much of this research would not, by late twentieth-century standards, be considered either scholarly or scientific. It was concerned with identifying what worked best, rather than with the fundamental science of why this was so. The research usually took the form of trials, or tests, for which reporting was observational rather than analytical. This was not usually true of the chemical engineering research, much of which was concerned with scientific fundamentals, a fact reflected by the journals where M.C. Boswell published his work. But most of the research funded by the SER was of a very practical nature. 'Useful,' it was often called. Haultain's work, for example, important though it was in improving the efficiency of ore crushing, uncovered no fundamental mathematical model of fluid dynamics applicable to the process.[50] Such an approach was not unusual for engineering at the time. At several of the Engineering Experimental Stations in the big U.S. land-grant universities, researchers were conducting, and publishing, similar research.[51] This research work was not confined to a small, select group. Of the fifteen full and associate professors of engineering in 1924 (excluding those in surveying, drawing, and architecture), nine regularly published significant research and four occasionally did; only two did not. Research had clearly entered the Faculty. Dean Mitchell was quite correct when he referred, in 1922, to a 'research movement within this Faculty.'[52]

While research grew in importance among the academic staff, it also gained popularity among students. The origins of graduate study and its connection to research lie in the previous generation; the research-based PhD and MA degrees were both established at the University of Toronto before the war. But with little financial support, few students could pursue graduate studies. In 1920, only about eighty students at the entire university were enrolled in MA and PhD programs.[53] The Faculty had established its own MASc degree in 1913, and to encourage graduate study two research scholarships had been set up by the Faculty's Alumni Association the following year. During the war, only a few students took the degree: four in 1914, one in 1915, and none in 1916. After the war, however, interest reappeared, and ten students registered for their MASc in 1921. Small though this was, the dean felt it deserved mention in his annual report. And time would show that it was a lasting change; graduate enrolment stayed at about this level for the rest of the decade, and then began to rise in the 1930s. Graduate study had arrived at the Faculty to stay.[54]

The connection between graduate studies and the concurrent rise of research among the academic staff was unmistakable. On one level, that which the dean and senior staff occupied, research activity among the professoriate appeared to be engendering a 'spirit of research' that encouraged students to conduct original investigations. At least so the dean reported. On a more mundane level, which the graduate students probably knew better, research among the academic staff meant financial support for graduate students; most students worked part-time as research assistants on SER-supported projects while they pursued their studies.[55] School of Engineering Research grants were, in fact, graduate 'research assistantships' of a sort.

Most graduate students were working towards their MASc. The PhD was another matter. It began gaining popularity at the university after the war, but the Faculty was not sure how to fit itself into this growing trend. Beginning in 1919, and continuing for several years, Faculty council considered whether it might offer doctoral degrees, and, if so, whether it should award its own degree (as it did with the MASc) or the standard university PhD. Not until 1926 did a committee finally take a definitive position: there would be no separate degree, but students of the Faculty could work towards the university PhD.[56] There appeared to be a demand for it. Galbraith's old opinion that there would never be work for applied science researchers was being proven wrong; there was work, in both government and industry, and students felt that, in Dean Mitchell's words, 'possession of the degree PhD carries with it considerable monetary advantage.' But there were problems meeting the university's requirements. These called for study in one major and two minor fields within one's chosen department, yet the Faculty's departments were so specialized that they could not offer three separate fields. Engineering students were thus unable to pursue the university's degree, and instead were going off to American universities where PhD requirements were less strict. There was also some question of whether research directed toward utilitarian goals warranted an advanced scholarly degree.[57] So the PhD was slow to take hold. Only Chemical Engineering, which arranged for three distinct fields of study in 1930, began to develop doctoral studies at this date. The Faculty's first PhD, in Chemical Engineering, was awarded to R.K. Iler in 1933;[58] Iler would go on to an outstanding career as an industrial chemist with Dupont in the United States.

Research had certainly entered the Faculty by the end of the 1920s, among both students and staff, and the Faculty would never be without it from this point on. One must be cautious about carrying this too far, for in comparison to research in the Faculty two generations later, the work of the 1920s looks meager. Graduate student numbers were miniscule compared to undergraduate. Even in the early 1930s, when graduate enrolment peaked, it was barely 3 per cent of undergraduate enrolment. As for the staff, research had become a part of their work, but their main job was still undergraduate teaching. As would become evident when SER money ran out in the 1930s, without financial support to hire research assistants, there could be no research, and the Faculty itself lacked the means to provide this. The Faculty of Applied Science and Engineering was still an undergraduate school. That would not change for another thirty years.

The 1920s saw another noteworthy development in its academic staff, one which, while having no connection to the rise of research, deserves mention. As the number of staff increased, which it did despite low enrolments, Galbraith's old custom of hiring only the school's graduates passed. The appointment that broke the pattern was that of Adrian Berrington as associate professor of Architecture in 1920, and the force behind this was the architects of the province, with the full support of President Falconer. The same year J.H. Parkin was appointed assistant professor of Hydraulics. Parkin was a graduate of the Faculty (BASc 1912) who had worked as a lecturer during the war. But then the following year two Englishmen with advanced degrees from Birmingham were appointed: E.A. Allcut as Associate Professor of Thermodynamics and O.W. Ellis as lecturer in Metallurgical Engineering. Allcut was already well established in England, and was recruited to the university by President Falconer.[59] The next year, after the unexpected, premature death of Berrington while on leave in England, E.A. Arthur (BArch from Liverpool) was hired as a Lecturer in Architecture. In the two following years, the Faculty appointed four more professors; two were Faculty graduates (W.G. McIntosh in Machine Design and W.B. Dunbar in Engineering Drawing) and two were not (E.A. Smith, MA McMaster, in Chemical Engineering, and J.A. Newcombe, BSc London, in Metallurgical Engineering).[60] So, of the nine new appointments from 1920 to 1925, only three were the Faculty's own graduates. Although far short of a revolution – the existing staff all remained in positions of influence – it was a break from the past, and shows the influence of the university in shaping the Faculty's development.

Engineering student life, both in class and out, remained much as it had been a generation earlier. A few new traditions were born, and a few of the old ones recast, but for the most part the 1920s and 1930s saw the continuation of customs and activities begun in the burst of student culture at the turn of the century. What did begin to change, however, was the position of the Faculty's students within the overall university student body. In the 1930s, student life elsewhere in the university began moving away from many of the old customs and rituals, especially the rough, physical ones. In the Faculty of Applied Science and Engineering, however, this did not occur, with the result that a rift started to form between engineering students and those in the rest of the university. The student newspapers of the day leave the distinct impression that by the end of the 1930s, engineering students were being viewed as a breed apart, known more for their ability to demolish forty beers than for their efforts to improve the nation's material life.

In the first year or two after the war, a tone of seriousness pervaded student life at the Faculty, as it did all aspects of the university. One such manifestation was the introduction, in the fall of 1919, of university-wide compulsory physical training for students. Young Canadian men, even its scholars and professionals – so the thinking went – must remain vigorous and fit, capable of defending themselves should the call come again. Dean Mitchell readily supported this tendency. He announced that two late-afternoons per week, starting at four o'clock, would be given over to student physical training, and he advised professors to alter their teaching schedules accordingly.[61] Mitchell also initiated a move to ban smoking in the school at the first council meeting of the new session in October 1919.[62]

This did not preclude the reappearance of student social life, and soon students reactivated their many associations. The Engineering Society, the clubs in each specialty, the Debating Club, the Athletic Association, and the Student Christian Movement all became active again. *Toike Oike* resumed publication in 1920. Engineering Dinners started up again, as did freshman initiations.[63] One of the first new traditions to appear was School Night, a night of humourous, irreverent skits poking fun at the Faculty and its customs. 'Follies' or 'stunt nights' had long been a tradition of college life, and engineering students had held them from time to time. But in the spring of 1921 the Engineering Society held its first formally organized nonsense revue, called 'Ngynrs in SPaSms,' at Massey Hall, and a school tradition was born.[64] These shows, 'Skule Nites' they would be called after the Second World War, moved to Hart House a few years later, and remained a popular annual diversion for decades. Another tradition that took form in these years was the cult of the school cannon. Cannons had had something of a special place in life at the school for years, for reasons that nobody has fully explained. By the 1920s, engineering students were often firing a small cannon at important school functions, sometimes damaging property in the process. To avoid detection, and probable confiscation, those who fired it always quickly hid it away – and so its mythic qualities grew. In 1936, a machinist in the civil engineering laboratory, W.H. Kubbinga, fashioned an eight-inch cannon from axle stock and a small block of cast iron, and the tradition was set. This cannon began making appearances at important Faculty events, and was soon coveted by students in other faculties.[65]

The 1919 freshmen initiation was a sombre affair, but that of 1920 was as outrageous as any.[66] New wrinkles began to appear, most probably just formalizations of older customs. The year 1921 looks to have been the first in which frosh were officially banned from entering the old Engineering Building through the main door, and of the ritual attack by the frosh to do that very thing. The same year also saw the start of frosh being forced to wear distinctive college or faculty ties or caps – engineers wore green ties, while the dreaded meds wore red – a seemingly benign tradition that, in fact, led to some fairly rough inter-faculty scraps.[67]

In their academic life, students did mostly what they had always

The Faculty's first School Night – 'Ngynrs in SPaSms' – at Massey Hall in March 1921. UTA, A65-0004/140.42

done. They still surveyed the front campus. They still spent more hours at their drafting tables than anywhere else, although this was slowly being reduced. Days were full, and timetables fixed. Engineering students thus had little time for extracurricular activities during the school day, although some did find time to work on the university newspaper.[68] The curriculum revision of 1922 provided no relief, for in order to add non-technical courses the number of contact hours had to be increased by about 10 per cent. It did shift the balance away from lectures towards laboratories, especially in the later years, so this might have loosened up the routine a little, but overall demands were as heavy as ever. Students were still expected to commit themselves fully to their chosen career; shop or field work, and regular reports of all vacation work, were still required for degrees.[69]

Academic relations with the Faculty of Arts remained as they had been since early in the century when Galbraith had withdrawn his students from university physics. Engineering students still received most of their instruction from engineering professors. The only complete exception was mathematics, which was taught entirely by mathematics professors in the Faculty of Arts. Arts professors also taught languages, mineralogy, and geology to the students who needed them, and some of the more advanced chemistry courses. The Faculty of Arts, rather surprisingly, played almost no role in the non-technical subjects introduced in 1922. In 1924–25, only one of thirteen non-technical courses was taught by an Arts professor; C.R. Fay, professor of Economic History, taught Economics and Finance, but this was taken over by Dean Mitchell in 1930.[70] Business management courses were taught by engineering professors (mostly Allcut and Young), and more specialized courses, such as Engineering Law and Technical English, were taught by the Faculty's own sessional appointments. W.J.T. Wright of Engineering Drawing took over the latter in 1928.[71] The Faculty of Applied Science and Engineering remained, by choice, academically apart from the university.

As the decade wore on, the Faculty's students increasingly came to be seen as socially distinct from the rest of the university as well. This was not something deliberately, or even consciously, done, nor does it seem to have been connected to their academic distinctiveness, which was not new. At the heart of it was the engineers' tendency to carry their scraps and initiation rituals to new levels of rowdiness, a trend about which university authorities grew increasingly concerned. A particularly outrageous initiation occurred in late October, 1922. The school's freshmen were expected to present themselves at the university gymnasium for their ritual 'running of the gauntlet' under the authority of the sophomores. The first-year president, who had seen real combat not many years before, took the defence of his company with unexpected seriousness. In a well coordinated attack, the frosh arrived earlier than expected, cut power to the gymnasium where the sophomores waited, barricaded the doors, and lobbed a vessel of liquid ammonia (apparently a stronger mix than expected) through a skylight into the gymnasium. The gasping sophomores were soon allowed out, but just one at a time, the final few apparently being dragged out unconscious. Such action naturally called for a counterattack, and the more numerous sophomores promptly beat up the frosh quite maliciously.[72] Then followed the initiation itself, complete with electric shocks, sawdust, and 'such sports as shoving an onion along in lamp black.' All the while the frosh were subjected to the blows of barrel staves 'wielded by vengeful sophs.' The event drew immediate criticism from both students and staff at the university. Some students began to call for the end of such rituals, deeming them 'childish, useless, and motivated only by revenge.' Although a poll conducted by *The Varsity* in 1923 found students almost ten to one in support of initiations, opposition was rising.[73]

In the fall of 1925, after another run of troublesome initiations, the university took action. The Caput issued orders prohibiting violent or degrading ceremonies and requiring that students obtain university approval for any initiation before it occurred. Later that year, they ordered that any special dress requirements for frosh – often the cause of fights – be approved by the students' faculty or college.[74] The effect of these restrictions was minimal at first. In fact, the dress restrictions appear only to have made matters worse as the custom took hold of forcing frosh to wear ties, only to clip them for being contrary to regulations. Thus the tie-clipping fad, and its associated hand-to-hand struggles, was born.[75] But by the late 1920s, voices opposed to rough initiations were heard more and more often, whether a result of the university's regulations or of changing attitudes among the students themselves, one cannot be sure.[76]

Among the engineers, however, the tradition persisted. In November 1928, some 200 engineering students, after a downtown soph-frosh banquet, forced their way into Shea's Hippodrome on Bay Street where they marched up and down the aisles disrupting the vaudeville show until police arrived and imposed order. The theatre let the affair drop, but the university was not so forgiving. The episode brought a severe censure from the Students Administrative Council, and prompted a nasty editorial in the student newspaper about supposedly 'civil' engineers harming the reputations of proper students.[77] The November banquet the following year was even worse, with Loew's theatre the chosen venue. '500 Rioting Students Storm Downtown Show,' announced the *Toronto Mail* the following morning. This turned out to be something of an exaggeration, but the affair was shameful enough. The following week, Dean Mitchell cancelled all future soph-frosh banquets.[78] In October 1931, engineers once again drew attention to themselves when, after 'all the horrors of the worst initiation yet on record,' a large group forced themselves through the front door and up into the women's residence rooms at Whitney Hall.[79] The following fall, when a scrap broke out between the frosh and sophs in the halls of the old Engineering Building, Dean Mitchell personally intervened, only to find himself being 'subjected to some rather severe handling' by the scrappers. The dean was livid. He dispersed the crowds and, together with faculty council, banned such affairs from the Faculty for good. 'Examination Hall may never again be the temporary madhouse which for years it has been ...,' wrote a reporter in the student paper.[80]

Standards had clearly changed. Shenanigans such as this were no longer acceptable to either the academic staff or many students at the university. By continuing to engage in them, which they did despite the dean's edict, the Faculty's students set themselves apart from students elsewhere in the university. Increasingly, stories about crude initiations and associated scraps were stories about engineering students. The secretary of the Women's Undergraduate Association, Freddie Chapman, conceded that perhaps these scraps created 'a happier atmosphere in such an institution as SPS,' but for other students, she thought, university life would be better without them.[81] The Faculty's reputation was firmly in place – a product, it appears, of their unwillingness to change.

The Faculty of Applied Science and Engineering was distinguishing itself in another aspect of university life between the

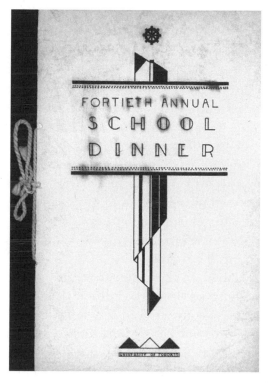

Program and menu of the Annual School Dinner, 1929. UTA, A74-0008/008(02)

wars: in the absence of women students from its halls. Enrolment of women at the university, which had begun before the war, became one of the most striking developments of the age. By 1929, some 45 per cent of the students enrolled in the Faculty of Arts, and 35 per cent of all students at the University of Toronto, were women. At Victoria College, women comprised over 50 per cent of the students that year. Even the School of Graduate Studies (29 per cent) and the Faculties of Medicine and Dentistry (about 10 per cent), had a significant female presence. That same year, 4 of the 697 students at the Faculty of Applied Science and Engineering were female. Although an upward trend did begin in the late 1930s, women's enrolment never reached 1 per cent of the Faculty's enrolment in the interwar years.[82]

This caused no concern among the men in charge. Engineering was man's work. It required physical strength; it demanded periods of absence from home at mines and construction sites; engineers needed authority over working men. Women might well be attaining higher education and entering other professions, but engineering was not for them. So the thinking was at the time. And for the most part, women must have concurred. There is no obvious evidence of women wishing to become engineers being deterred by unwelcoming professors or a threatening student culture. The few who did attend, such as the remarkable Elsie MacGill (BASc 1927), seem to have found their experience in the Faculty quite acceptable.[83]

Nor does this absence of women from the Faculty mean that engineering students wanted to keep their distance from women. Young men in the Faculty enjoyed the companionship of young women just as young men elsewhere on campus did, and like most other students they were experiencing that companionship more than ever before. Engineering students joined the 1920s dance craze along with the rest of the university, holding regular Saturday night dances.[84] They also moved their School Nights to Hart House, because it gave them an opportunity to bring their women friends into the House; women were excluded from Hart House for all but 'special' events, which these evening musical performances were deemed to be.[85] In the social mixing of young men and women, the Faculty was probably not much different from the rest of the university. Even in the faculties with high female enrolment, male and female students had minimal contact with one another in classes, and socializing was usually confined to specific organized events.

Through the 1920s and 1930s, the routine business of the Faculty carried on. Programs were modified, staff hired and promoted, and hundreds of students taught. In the fall of 1924, the two teaching departments of Applied Mechanics and Surveying were made into the two halves of a new teaching department of Civil Engineering, one called Civil Engineering: Municipal and Structural and the other Civil Engineering: Surveying and Geodesy.[86] The change was slight. Each sub-department had its own head – P. Gillespie and L.B. Stewart, respectively – and staff in each department continued to teach students in all courses, but it was one more step towards organizing the Faculty around professional specialties rather than teaching subjects, a trend that would continue for decades. A new, and rather unique, program was introduced in the fall of 1924: a course in ceramics engineering. Instruction in this field had been considered off and on for years. Faculty council had approved its introduction in 1907, but the university's board of governors had turned it down, one member of the board declaring that it was 'not necessary for a man to attend university for four years in order to learn how to make bricks.'[87] The subject was considered again at least once, in 1913, before being proposed and finally accepted in 1924. The force behind it, in all three cases, was the Ontario clay products industry, makers of brick, sinks, ceramic tiles, and other such products, which was dissatisfied with the lack of skilled engineers in their field. Their 1924 proposal came with an offer of financial assistance, and this, together with an Ontario government offer of funds for summer research projects to help sustain a new professorhip, made the plan acceptable. R.J. Montgomery, a graduate of a well-regarded program in the subject at Ohio State University, was appointed to the staff, and the course began as an option in Metallurgical Engineering.[88]

A few years later, in the fall of 1928, the Faculty introduced its first instruction in aeronautical engineering. Research in this field had been occurring in a modest way for several years. The university had paid for the installation of a small wind tunnel in the hydraulics laboratory during the war, in 1917. Then, in 1923,

The Faculty's first wind tunnel for aerodynamics research, and the building to house it, under construction in front of the Thermodynamics Building, October 1923. UTA, A65-0004/6A.6

when additional hydraulics equipment crowded the wind tunnel out of its home, the university built a new, larger wind tunnel, along with a new building to house it, adjacent to the Thermodynamics Building. The Department of National Defence, through the National Research Council, paid for this new facility, but the man behind it in the Faculty was J.H. Parkin, a newly appointed assistant professor in Mechanical Engineering, who used the facility regularly for his research. In the spring of 1928, the Department of Mechanical Engineering proposed an aeronautical option for its third and fourth years, which was readily accepted. It included new instruction in advanced calculus, aircraft design, and considerable laboratory work in aerodynamics.[89]

By the end of the 1920s, the Faculty was once again experiencing rising enrolments, and in 1930/31 finally surpassed the postwar years. This put pressure on buildings. Dean Mitchell alerted President Falconer to an impending problem in April 1928, and in January 1931 wrote him of 'serious and pressing problems of accommodation.'[90] The trouble was not only the large number of students. This many, or at least almost this many, had been taught before – although nobody wished to endure the post-war crunch again. The greater difficulty now was a changing distribution of students. The departments with the oldest facilities, Mining and Chemical (both still in the 1904 Mining Building), were attracting more students; enrolment in these two courses had nearly doubled over the last half of the 1920s. To make matters worse, Chemical Engineering was now enrolling graduate students, who, although few, needed well-equipped laboratory facilities for their research. Enrolment in Mechanical Engineering had also jumped, and the limits of its 1909 Thermodynamics Building had been reached. Civil Engineering enrolment, meanwhile, had grown very little, and even showed signs of possibly declining. With the help of the Ontario Department of Mines, money was found for an expansion and re-fitting of the Mill Building in 1931, but beyond that the university would not go. The Faculty undertook a thorough study of its current and future needs in 1932, producing a huge, detailed report recommending completion of the unbuilt west front of the Thermodynamics Building and a large new building at the corner of College and St. George streets.[91] But nothing could be done, for by now the Depression had taken hold and the university faced sharply falling revenues.

The Depression of the 1930s did not affect university life to nearly the extent it did the economy overall.[92] Toronto's middle class, from which most students came, continued to find money for its sons and daughters to attend university. Enrolment at the Faculty of Applied Science and Engineering makes this perfectly

The single-storey Mill Building in September 1930, prior to the addition of several storeys. UTA, A65-0004/7.60

clear. With a peak of 914 students in 1932/33 (the worst year of the Depression), enrolment stayed around 800 for the entire 1930s. Perhaps, as Dean Mitchell commented, it showed a faith in the future development of Canada, and a corresponding faith in the role engineers would play in it. But one need not resort to such lofty explanations. For those who could afford it, engineering school was a good choice even in the short term, because job prospects for graduates remained reasonably good. They were not what they had been in the late 1920s, when nearly all graduates had found work immediately, but in the early 1930s more than half of each graduating class was finding jobs upon leaving school.[93]

Fee-paying students were, however, only one source of university revenue. The other source, the Ontario government, did indeed start to cut back. The government reduced its university grant substantially in 1932/33, which necessitated a cut in staff salaries, and put any new buildings out of the question.[94] It also caused the university to cease providing funds for the School of Engineering Research in 1933. Only the research of W.H. Price survived this cessation of university funds. His work on electric frequency control appears to have been supported to its conclusion by the Ontario Hydro-Electric Power Commission. The year 1933, however, brought some extraordinarily good news that must have partly made up for what was lost. Ida Marie Wallberg, sister of the late engineer-industrialist E.A. Wallberg, died that year, and in her will bequeathed $1 million to the Faculty for, if possible, construction of a new building as a memorial to her late brother. This huge bequest appears to have come from out of the blue. E.A. Wallberg, who had died just four years before, leaving his sister some $4.2 million, had had no direct connection to the Faculty or the University of Toronto, nor had his sister as far as anyone can tell. He had studied engineering at the University of Iowa and at MIT. But he had built his fortune from numerous central Canadian mining and manufacturing ventures, so he likely worked with Faculty graduates through the course of his career.[95] All in all, the Depression certainly brought nothing like the damaging consequences of the Great War a generation earlier.

In the mid-1930s, the Faculty introduced something new in its curriculum that would prove to be of utmost importance: a course in Engineering Physics. This course was nothing less than a fundamental break with the Galbraithian tradition that had guided the Faculty since the 1880s. Such articles of faith as a reliance on shop or field experience, engineering drawing as the centrepiece of all instruction, a balance between 'professional' and 'applied science' subjects, and keeping engineering students away from the university's pure science instruction – all these essential elements of Galbraith's vision were up-ended in the new course. This would be no fleeting change. In the decades that followed, Engineering Physics would gradually move to the heart of the Faculty, and the tenets on which it was based eventually became the Faculty's new guiding principles.[96]

Galbraith's 1904 decision to withdraw engineering students from university physics had stunned the physicists. They had had no choice but to live with the decision, but it had never sat well with them. J.C. McLennan and his younger associate E.F. Burton both occasionally sought to mend this rupture, but without success. They had proposed a new joint mathematics/physics/engineering program in the later years of the war, but the Faculty thought it would be too difficult to administer and timetable, and had opposed its creation.[97] Still, the physicists had persevered. On 19 January 1921, Dean Mitchell had been astonished to read in his morning paper that the university was about to inaugurate a new course in 'Physics-Engineering' under the joint auspices of Physics and the Chemical and Electrical Engineering departments. Mitchell knew of no such thing. He quickly sent off letters to McClennan, named in the article as the course initiator, and President Falconer to bring a quick end to the plan.[98]

There were several reasons for the Faculty's reluctance to move in this direction. As an institution of professional education, its prime responsibility was the training of engineers, and its programs were devised to accomplish this. A reduction in the amount of engineering instruction for its students, something that would have been inevitable in a joint program, was therefore not a simple matter. T.R. Rosebrugh explained the Faculty's position to President Falconer in these words: 'As our course is intended to train men for professional work, there is a minimum beyond which it cannot be reduced.'[99] There was no such thing as a partial engineer, so the notion of a joint program, to a professional school, was hard to accept.

There was also the matter of the Faculty's own physics department, created in 1904 by Galbraith himself in the person of G.R.

Anderson. This department, so-called, had never amounted to much. Its only other permanent staff member was K.B. Jackson, a man evidently cut from the same cloth as Anderson. Jackson had no graduate training beyond his Toronto BASc, did next to no research, and had gradually evolved into his position under the tutelage of Anderson, whose retirement was imminent. The department, the name of which had been changed in 1911 from 'Physics' to 'Technical Physics,' and in 1922 to 'Engineering Physics,' was strictly a teaching department, offering instruction to students in all the various graduating departments. Its services, however, had shrunk over the years. Anderson had taught fundamental physics to all students at first, but by 1924 he was teaching only two courses that could be called physics – hydrostatics and optics – along with a single-term course in heat for civil engineering students and specialized practical courses in illumination, photography, and building acoustics. Fundamental physics had pretty well disappeared from the curriculum, except insofar as it was taught within courses on electricity, applied mechanics, and aerodynamics.[100] Yet at the same time, Anderson, and Jackson after him, were integral to the Faculty. Their courses, few though they were, had evolved according to the Faculty's needs. Their photographic work, in particular, was valued by all, so much so that the department was often called 'Engineering Physics and Photography,' although it was never named that in the calendar. Senior men in the Faculty would not hear of Anderson or Jackson being disparaged or supplanted, let alone discarded.

Underlying all of this, unmistakably, rests the lingering legacy of John Galbraith. He had been gone for twenty years, but his influence lived on. The heads of all departments but Metallurgy were still, in 1934, Galbraith's appointments. All, again excepting Metallurgy, were Toronto graduates with no further academic degrees, and all were, both by inclination and respect for Galbraith's legacy, wary of the pure scientists at the university.

With such views, McLennan and, increasingly, Burton had little sympathy. They knew that engineering had changed, that such subjects as spectroscopy, electronics, and geophysics, and the complex mathematics that went along with them, were now part of the world of engineering. They even saw their own physics graduates going into practical work. And as for the courses taught by Anderson or Jackson, Burton had little good to say; he had seen students' notebooks from these courses and found the course content badly lacking.[101] They also knew that other engineering schools had not been so fearful of this development. McGill had introduced a course in Engineering Physics in 1920/21, as had the University of Alberta in the 1920s.[102]

In early 1934, Burton appealed again to the Faculty, this time with the full support of new university president, H.J. Cody. How and why this initiative began, and why Cody was involved, is not clear; Cody seems to have started it in an effort to reduce the cost of teaching duplication. In any case, Burton held discussions with the engineers in April 1934 concerning physics instruction in the two faculties, at which was raised once again the possibility of a joint course in Engineering and Physics. Burton's reaction to the meeting was disappointment. 'I can conjecture pretty safely,' he wrote to Cody after the meetings, 'that all of our suggestions – even the one for a course in Engineering Physics – will be stubbornly opposed and delayed, and finally, defeated, just as our two former attempts ... [were] thwarted.' C.R. Young had suggested that K.B. Jackson be given a year to try to develop something new, an idea Burton dismissed outright. Burton was reacting not only to the meeting but also to a Faculty of Applied Science and Engineering report he had recently seen on the future role of its Department of Physics and Photography. The report had concluded that 'appreciative of the soundness of the policy in accordance with which the Department of Engineering Physics was established ... the present arrangement be continued.' The report, Burton concluded dismissively, and quite correctly, was 'just a claim to maintain the status quo.'[103]

Being unfamiliar with the inner workings of another faculty, and not recognizing the historical importance of the Faculty's own physics department, Burton was taking their cautious position a little too literally. The Faculty had in fact, for several years, been coming to terms with this from another angle, and was about to show itself more receptive than Burton thought. Two changes had recently taken hold: higher admission standards were yielding a greater number of advanced students, and the teaching of applied mechanics and aerodynamics was requiring fairly advanced mathematics. So late in 1932, at the initiative of T.R. Loudon, professor of Applied Mechanics, the Faculty had struck a committee to investigate how it might offer advanced mathematics and physics instruction to its top students, and the following spring put in place a new scheme for students with excellent marks on their first year Christmas examinations to take an option in advanced mathematics.[104]

So Burton need not have been so surprised when, a little over a month after his meeting with the Faculty in 1934, C.R. Young asked if a new committee consisting of himself, Angus, and Bain could meet Burton and Lachlan Gilchrist, a notable geophysicist in the physics department, to go over the same ground with a more open mind. Burton in the meantime had come up with a clever compromise plan: change the name of the Faculty's teaching department of Engineering Physics to Applied Physics, but leave it intact under Jackson, then form an entirely new graduating department (i.e., 'course') of Engineering Physics, to which no academic staff would belong but in which students would enroll.[105] This, he felt, would both preserve the old and begin the new. To this approach, Young and Angus readily agreed (Bain did not attend), the only point of dispute being how quickly it could be put into place. Burton won Young and Angus over with his wish to start immediately. Within ten days, the Faculty of Applied Science and Engineering approved the course and proposed its content for the first two years, which Burton, finding it surprisingly close to their own pro-

The Faculty's first graduating class – six students, all seated – in Engineering Physics, spring 1938; staff standing at back are, left to right, T.R. Loudon, Lachlan Gilchrist (Dept. of Physics, Faculty of Arts), John Satterly (Physics), C.R. Young, V.G. Smith, and E.F. Burton (Physics). UTA, A65-0004/140.1138A

gram in Physics and Mathematics, fully endorsed. Burton wrote McLennan, retired and then in England, full of satisfaction. 'The members of the Applied Science Faculty, of their own accord, are going almost further than we have thought possible, in adopting what we have always stood out for.'[106]

Beginning in the fall of 1934, a new course called 'Engineering Physics,' given the unused number Department Five, was offered at the Faculty of Applied Science and Engineering. It was clearly intended for students who excelled at mathematics; to gain admission, an applicant needed at least 75 per cent in the mathematics matriculation examination, as well as the basic Faculty admission requirements. Although more than half of the instruction would be provided by arts professors, and the committee administering it included Beatty from Mathematics and Burton from Physics (along with Jackson, Loudon, Price, and Young), it was an engineering, not a joint, course. Graduates would receive a BASc. The course description declared that 'an effort is made to maintain the practical point of view in the theoretical instruction.'[107] But there is no masking the fact that with a large part of its teaching done by the Faculty of Arts, with only a few hours of Engineering Drawing in first year (and none in subsequent years), and with no requirement for shop or field work, this course was breaking new ground. That is not to say that the Faculty was foresaking its mandate of providing a practical, professional education. The senior men of the Faculty had finally concluded – rather cautiously, for the course was an addition not a replacement – that advanced mathematics and physics now should form a part of that practical education.[108]

Through the second half of the 1930s, the Faculty began to show signs of a more general renewal. This was partly due to the easing of the Depression, the consequences of which, although never very severe, were now passing: enrolments rose steadily from 1935, grants to the School of Engineering Research resumed, new academic staff were appointed, and hopes of a new building were revived. But in other ways, unconnected to the improving economy, new ideas were beginning to take root.

Slowly but surely, the academic staff was being renewed. Apart from the promising civil engineer Peter Gillespie, who died unexpectedly in 1929 at the age of only 56, the early staff members had remarkably long careers. Many continued at the Faculty until the 1930s. The first of them to retire was L.B. Stewart, in 1931. C.H.C. Wright and G.R. Anderson both retired in the summer of 1934, Wright passing the headship of Architecture to H.H. Madill and Anderson leaving the newly named teaching department of

Applied Physics in K.B. Jackson's hands. T.R. Rosebrugh retired in 1936, and H.W. Price took over as head of Electrical Engineering; Price had carried a large part of the department's administrative load for years.[109] Haultain retired in the summer of 1938, although he kept an office in the Mill Building for a time.

Galbraith's imprint on the academic staff was starting to fade, albeit only slightly; Angus, Bain, Young, and Treadgold remained Heads of Mechanical, Chemical, Civil: Municipal and Structural, and Civil: Surveying and Geodesy, respectively, and all still wielded influence. Price and Jackson, the two new heads, although not appointed by Galbraith, had both graduated from the school while Galbraith presided. Yet there were also new men with more varied experience and academic training moving in. C.F. Morrison, with a BA from Saskatchewan and an MSc from McGill, was appointed lecturer in Civil Engineering in 1928 and assistant professor in 1937. R.R. McLaughlin, a schoolman with an early PhD in Chemistry, became a lecturer in 1930 and assistant professor in 1931. G.R. Lord, a BASc with a subsequent SM from MIT, was appointed lecturer in Mechanical Engineering in 1933 (he would receive a PhD from the Faculty in 1939). Several new appointments were made in 1939, among them R. Leggett (MEng, Liverpool) in Civil Engineering and G.F. Tracy (BASc, and MS, MIT). The following year, D.N. Cass-Beggs (BSc, Manchester) was appointed lecturer in Electrical Engineering. Still, however, old traditions endured. Many of the other appointments in this period were products of the Faculty's own halls; V.G. Smith in Electrical, W.G. McIntosh and R.C. Wiren in Mechanical, W.B. Dunbar and A. Wardell in Engineering Drawing, and C.G. Williams in Mining all had no formal academic training beyond their Toronto BASc.[110]

A few minor changes to the curriculum were effected, the most important being the reintroduction in 1936 of teaching in the growing field of aeronautics, under the direction of T.R. Loudon. Aeronautics instruction in the Faculty had ceased in 1930, when

Faculty Gymnastics Team, 1937/38. Although the School of Practical Science had not formally existed since 1906, the name SPS remained in use for years. UTA, A65-0004/140.1151

J.H. Parkin, the subject's only instructor, had resigned to take a job with the National Research Council.[111] Mechanical Engineering's aeronautics program, begun with such high expectations, had thus lasted only two years. The wind tunnel laboratory still stood next to the Thermodynamics Building, and students could apply to do graduate research at the facility, but no undergraduate instruction was offered through the early 1930s. Loudon, however, who had been on the staff of the Faculty since 1906 and an assistant professor of Applied Mechanics since 1919, had become enchanted by flight. He received his pilot's licence in 1936, at the age of 53, and even began to carry out some basic aeronautical research, an unusual turn for a man not trained in the complexities of aerodynamics and advanced mathematics. Loudon was a unique character; although a product of the old system (BASc 1906) he could be an advocate of the new. Beginning in the fall of 1936, aeronautics taught by Loudon was offered as an option in the final years of both Civil Engineering and Engineering Physics.[112]

In the fall of 1937 the Faculty introduced a course in Mining Geology, which it designated Department Nine. Described by Dean Mitchell as an 'applied science' rather than an engineering course, it was in some ways reminscent of the old Mining Geology course at the early SPS in its heavy geology component. The course, Mitchell hoped, would train 'geologists to co-operate with mining engineers in the fast-growing mineral industries of the country.' That same year the Metallurgical Engineering program was moved a step towards the more general subject of materials engineering when its ceramics option was expanded into a new program called Ceramics and Non-Metallic Industrial Minerals. Students could take their full four years in this course, now to be identified as Department Eight(a).[113]

One aspect of Faculty work that the Depression had seriously hampered was research, but as the worst of the economic crisis passed, the university re-established its grants to the SER and research revived. Amounts were meagre compared to those of the late twenties – $3,300 in 1935 and $4,400 in 1937, for example – but they were enough to stimulate new work.[114] Angus and Allcut in Mechanical Engineering continued to be among the most active – Angus in hydrodynamics, and Allcut now in heat transfer and the fundamentals of heat insulation. Haultain was as tireless a researcher as ever. After years of study, he and various research assistants developed two valuable devices for separating and concentrating ores in small batches at the mine site: the superpanner (in which gold particles are dissolved and separated by specific gravity) and the infrasizer (which separates by microscopic differences in particle size). These devices were in use around the world within a few years, and were without doubt major contributions to the field.[115] In Chemical Engineering, several graduate students, among them W.H. Rapson, were conducting research under Bain and Boswell on the chemistry of cellulose and lignin. H.W. Price in Electrical Engineering completed his developmental work on automatic frequency regulators about 1934, after which his device was put into use by the provincial Hydro-Electric Power Commission, but he continued studying the actual operation of these devices. E.R. Arthur of the Department of Architecture drew SER funds to begin his inventory and analysis of historic architecture in Ontario, and in doing so laid the foundation of a long illustrious career in architectural history and preservation.[116]

As had been the case in the 1920s, this research tended to be concerned with how things worked rather than with fundamental physical principles, a fact that needed no apology. It might not have been pure science, but it was considered valuable research nonetheless; its utility was, in fact, what justified the public expense. Such thinking was also common at the Engineering Experimental Stations in the United States, where a public-spirited progressivism ruled. There were, however, signs of change. In the United States, a few academic engineers were by this time moving towards greater use of advanced science and mathematics in their research, especially in hydraulics and aeronautics; most of them had educational roots either in the pure sciences or in the more science-oriented European engineering schools.[117] This new trend was beginning to show at the Faculty, as well. It is certainly evident in R.W. Angus's 1935 paper on the hydromechanics of water hammer, in which he discusses an advanced mathematical model developed by a German engineer/scientist, and in E.A. Allcut's 1935 paper on building insulation.[118] Fairly advanced mathematics is also apparent in the work of T.R. Rosebrugh and V.G. Smith in Electrical Engineering.[119] Although this new work was more scientific and

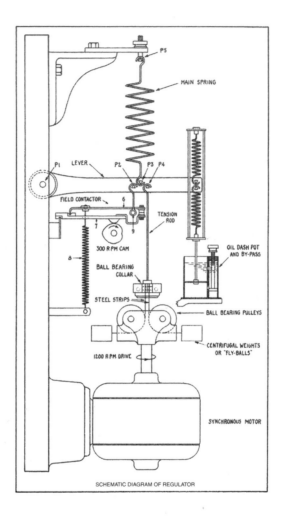

PS

MAIN SPRING

P1 LEVER P2 P3 P4

FIELD CONTACTOR 6

TENSION ROD

300 R.P.M. CAM

OIL DASH POT AND BY-PASS

7

9

8

BALL BEARING COLLAR

STEEL STRIPS

BALL BEARING PULLEYS

1200 R.P.M. DRIVE

CENTRIFUGAL WEIGHTS OR "FLY-BALLS"

SYNCHRONOUS MOTOR

SCHEMATIC DIAGRAM OF REGULATOR

The automatic frequency regulator created in the 1930s by Professor of Electrical Engineering H.W. Price, with ongoing financial support from the School of Engineering Research, was one of the most celebrated devices produced by academic staff at the Faculty before the Second World War. Although the technology was relatively simple for the time, the device was useful and reliable; one was installed by the Ontario Hydro-Electric Power Commission at their large Queenston plant in 1934, and it gave years of service. For his accomplishment, Price was awarded the McCharles Prize by the governors of the University of Toronto in 1935. *Electrical News and Engineering*, 15 June 1935 and 15 June 1938

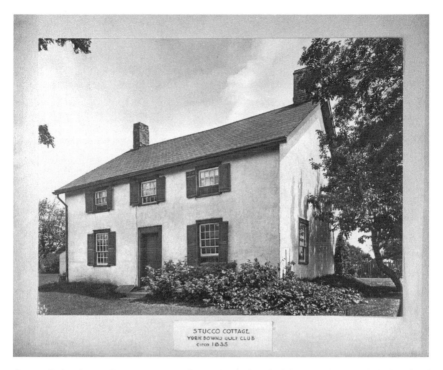

STUCCO COTTAGE
YORK DOWNS GOLF CLUB
circa 1835

One of the lesser-known research projects funded by the Faculty's School of
Engineering Research in the 1930s was Professor of Architecture Eric Arthur's
inventory of Ontario historic buildings. He was especially interested in vernacu-
lar styles. This is one of several dozen buildings identified and photographed by
Arthur himself in the early 1930s, and mounted for display, c.1934. UTA, A79-
0044/002(04)

mathematical, it remained closely tied to problems concerning
devices, processes, and man-made materials – that is to say, to
engineering. It is thus a good early example of what historians
have taken to calling 'engineering science,' the fundamental
science of man-made things, a field that would completely
dominate engineering research a generation or two hence.[120]
But while notable as a harbinger of the future, advanced
research of this sort was still uncommon in the Faculty.

Graduate studies continued as an important but small part of the Faculty. Apart from SER grants to the staff, and a few scholarships, there was still no financial support. The number of students pursuing the MASc degree stayed steady at about twelve to fourteen, with the exception of 1938/39, when enrolment suddenly jumped to twenty-four. PhD students were still rare, and most of the few were still in Chemical Engineering. The Faculty granted twelve PhDs in the 1930s, eight of which were in Chemical Engineering.[121]

These were years of deep uncertainty in the North American engineering profession, as changes in science, technology, and industry – and in engineering practice itself – raised questions about the direction engineering education should be evolving. Such matters as whether advanced science belonged in the basic engineering curriculum, how much time should be given to arts and humanities, and whether practical work should remain a formal part of engineering study were subjects of repeated debate. Schools seemed to be under pressure to make their programs both more general and more specialized, more scientific and more humanistic. In the United States, several studies had been carried out in the 1920s on the current state and future prospects of the profession, and in Canada the rhetoric produced by engineering schools and professional associations reveals a similar quandary.[122]

The Faculty of Applied Science and Engineering at the University of Toronto had not suffered too badly from this plague of uncertainty. Its leaders had remained fairly confident they were doing things right. In 1926, the Society for the Promotion of Engineering Education (SPEE) in New York had published the preliminary findings and recommendations of their extensive study of engineering education (in which the Faculty had participated). Canada's engineering schools had immediately picked up on this Wickenden Report, as it became known, and in 1927 had formed a committee to study the report's recommendations, with Dean Mitchell as one of the eight members.

This had prompted Mitchell to produce a long policy statement of his own in which he set out his vision for the Faculty's future; first delivered as an address to faculty council, it was subsequently printed and privately distributed. Very little needed to change, he had concluded, for most of the SPEE's recommendations did not apply to Canadian engineering. The only concrete recommendation he had made was the establishment of a new course in 'general engineering' for students who intended to go into business careers, something quite consistent with the Wickenden Report, but nothing had ever come of his suggestion. This U.S.-based reform thrust had then disappeared from Faculty affairs.[123]

Now, more than ten years later, the Faculty encountered it again, this time in a person, not a report, and with somewhat farther-reaching results. In 1939, at the initiative of the Faculty alumni and university President H.J. Cody, the eminent engineering educator Dugald C. Jackson, recently retired head of Electrical Engineering at MIT, was invited to review and report on the Faculty's affairs. The full story of why Jackson was brought in appears to have escaped documentation, but in June 1939, after a brief exchange of letters with Cody, Jackson took on the task.[124] Jackson was a reformer of sorts, but a moderate one. He was well into his seventies by this time, winding down a long career in engineering practice and teaching; his active years in the SPEE had been early in the century. Like many of his colleagues in the SPEE, he advocated keeping university engineering education closely tied to professional practice, and even moving it in the direction of business management; he thus favoured a curriculum with good but basic sciences, and a solid component of humanities and social sciences to teach aspiring engineers how to comprehend the non-technical side of the work world. He was no advocate of advanced science instruction, and research, although important, was always to be closely connected to real industrial problems. One of his best-known accomplishments was MIT's cooperative program with General Electric, which he introduced in 1907 and ran successfully until 1932. He also favoured academic staff maintaining consulting practices to keep them in touch with the profession. These ideas had been current in the 1920s, but by 1939 they were rather out of step with the coming trend of increasing science and research. As early as 1929, the final Wickenden Report had taken the position that U.S. engineering schools were intellectually far behind European schools, and that something should be done to boost the level of science instruction. But there is no sign of this idea in Jackson's thinking in 1939.[125]

After six months of study, Jackson reported his conclusions to Cody. He had found plenty of room for improvement. He thought, above all, that the curriculum was too complex and too heavy. The practice of teaching different first years to all the departments he thought unnecessary and overly demanding for the teaching staff, and he thought the amount of fixed class time should be reduced to permit students time for study and reflection. And why not simplify things further by using physicists and chemists to teach basic sciences? He thought a much greater commitment was needed to teaching English and economics, and he recommended that professors in the Faculty of Arts, not engineering professors with an interest in the subject, teach these courses. He could make no sense of the confusing distinction between teaching and graduating departments. He also criticized the excessive inbreeding of the Faculty, and recommended more exchange and communication with other engineering schools.[126]

It was gentle, but well-informed criticism. And it met with firm, well-organized defence. A committee of faculty council went into the recommendations in depth, consulting with a number of U.S. schools in the process, but in the end concluded that little change was needed. This disappointed those in the Faculty who agreed with Jackson, and who felt the school did have deficiencies needing attention.[127] But by now, February 1940, something else was on the minds of the men who guided the Faculty. Canada had declared war on Germany in September 1939, and although the war's initial effect on the home front was minimal, by early 1940 the focus of Faculty affairs had shifted to the war. Resolving these pedagogical disputes would have to wait.

Just as it had in the early years of the First World War, the Faculty soon lost its dean. In the spring of 1941, Dean Mitchell's health and energy suddenly began to decline and he retired rather hastily at the end of that academic year. Retirement brought no relief. He died in late August, the nature of his ailments never made public. The soldier was stoic to the end.[128]

Dean Mitchell's legacy is harder to see than Galbraith's. This may be because, although dean for almost as long, he did not preside over the formation of the school as Galbraith did, and so he lacked opportunities to mold anything to his vision. Nor was it a period of much expansion, where his hands could have left their mark on new programs or facilities. But that is not all there is to it. If one considers the few critical developments of the period, such as the birth of Engineering Physics or the growth of the School of Engineering Research, one is struck immediately by Mitchell's absence. This was not enirely due to circumstances. Mitchell was an engineer from an earlier age, a generalist and a practitioner, not a man in touch with new ideas.

Even in the few cases where Mitchell proposed new initiatives, such as his course in General Engineering, he rarely saw them carried out. He seems to have had little influence over the department heads. This was due mostly to his never having been – indeed never being – an engineering professor. He could not therefore lead by example. He did begin teaching Economics and Finance in 1930, but the course ran only one hour a week and his lectures were fully scripted.[129] In research, Mitchell never even dabbled; that was for others. This absence of true professorial work in the Faculty's dean irked H.E.T. Haultain to no end. Haultain grew obsessed by Mitchell's failings, and even went so

Students setting off their beloved cannon on the steps outside the Engineering Building, election night, 1939. *Transactions and Yearbook of the University of Toronto Engineering Society*, 1939, 60

far as to state that the dean had no claim to authority because the University Act gave governance to a Faculty's professoriate, of which Mitchell should not be considered a member.[130] Haultain seems to have been alone in this obsession, however, and the truth is that there is no evidence Mitchell ruled poorly because of his inexperience. In fact, since he knew he lacked the experience of men like Angus, Rosebrugh, Haultain, and Bain, he deferred to them much of the time, and one important piece of Mitchell's legacy is thus powerful department heads (of which Haultain should not have been one to complain). Mitchell could perhaps be criticized for lacking an overall vision, but not for forcing bad decisions on his senior academic staff.

What Mitchell did have experience in was consulting. His freedom to continue in private practice was one of the terms of his engagement, and Mitchell kept up a practice through his entire career. This is something Galbraith never did, and would not have countenanced; engineering education was a vocation to Galbraith, not one aspect of an engineering career. There was, and still is, something to be said for Mitchell's approach. As educators in all professional schools recognize, keeping academic staff in touch with professional practice yields benefits for both staff and students. Mitchell occasionally made this argument. Yet there were disadvantages. His time spent on non-Faculty business further weakened his authority. And the custom of doing professional work 'both for experience and remuneration' seems to have taken hold during the late years of Mitchell's tenure, with him as a model.[131] This in turn helped establish the notion that professorial salaries were for part-time work, something that impeded later moves towards expanding research in the Faculty.

Dean Mitchell's strong suits were his professionalism and his loyalty. He greatly improved management, introducing committees to council and generally improving the recording of Faculty business. He was also an impressive, highly regarded public figurehead; he kept the Faculty's reputation sound and its profile

Dean C.H. Mitchell in his study, c.1940. Mitchell served as dean of the Faculty for twenty-two years, from 1919 to 1941. UTA, A74-0008P.15(04)

high. Mitchell stood by his men at all times, even when, as in the case of Haultain, they were openly attacking him. Although he did not initiate curriculum reforms, neither did he discourage them when they came fully supported by the professors, and although he himself did no research, he repeatedly called for funds for the School of Engineering Research and proudly trumpeted the fruits of this financial support. He might not have been responsible for the Faculty's successes, but he did facilitate them.

When this generation came to an end with the outbreak of war and the retirement of C.H. Mitchell, the Faculty stood much as it had when the generation began. Granted, there had been some important changes, but they had not yet reached the core of the Faculty. Student enrolment in 1940 was only slightly above what it had been in 1920. The students themselves were still overwhelmingly the boys of British-Ontario families of the middle, or perhaps lower-middle, class.[132] There were next to no women in the student body. Relations with the university's scientists remained untrusting; advanced mathematics and science instruction had been adopted, but for only a minority of students and without a full commitment from Faculty leadership. Academic staff still conducted some research, but they did so with less institutional and financial support than they had had in 1920. New fields like electronics and aeronautics had barely made a mark. C.H. Mitchell, by almost any definition of the word, was a conservative man, but he alone was not responsible for innovation's absence. The school was working well as it was. Why change what works? For those who advocate reform, that is a hard position to assail.

chapter four

FROM WAR TO RENEWAL

If the generation from the early 1940s to the late 1960s can be categorized, the most apt label might be years of unrelenting challenge. The Faculty seems never to have been able to escape from pressures of one kind or another; just as one set of problems was resolved, a new and even more troublesome set appeared. First came the stresses of wartime, then the great task of accommodating huge post-war enrolments, and then the anxieties of planning for and implementing both an expansion of the Faculty and a reorientation of its staff and students towards engineering research. At the same time, this generation, more than any other, defies categorization. So different were the concerns of the Faculty in 1941 from those of 1967 that it is hard to see the two years even belonging to the same generation. Giving the period a single label, then, is somewhat misleading. One thing is certain: the challenges were met and answered. By 1967, the Faculty was a larger and more important place than it had been in 1941, with a thoroughly renewed academic staff, a growing commitment to research, a thriving graduate program, and an increasingly international outlook.

For students and staff at the Faculty of Applied Science and Engineering, as indeed for many Canadians, the Second World War brought experiences quite different from those of the First. The naive, old-fashioned militarism that had carried the country into the Great War was rarely seen in 1939. Canadians certainly supported the new war, but they did so with a different, more pragmatic mindset. At the Faculty, this meant relentlessly heavy enrolments. Not only were military enlistments low among the Faculty's students; the demand for engineers steadily rose as the technical nature of the war became clear. One could serve one's country in this war by studying engineering, and many thousands did just that. Unlike the First World War, when the Faculty coped with falling enrolments and unused buildings, the Second World War brought crowded classrooms, heavy teaching loads, and the stresses of providing an essential part of Canada's war effort.

The first year of the war brought little disturbance to the campus. The university quickly re-established its Canadian Officers Training Corps at the start of the term, and the Faculty, as it had done before, encouraged its students to enrol in it by granting academic credits to those who participated. A little more parsimonious with its gifts this time, faculty council decided to allow *up to* a 10 per cent bonus on grades, the actual amount being based on reports from students' commanding officers (in fact, it gave out few such credits).[1] But there were not many other immediate effects of the war. Students held their annual School Night and continued publishing *Toike Oike*. Intercollegiate sports went on as planned. Being much less enchanted by dreams of war-time adventures this time around, students were not inclined to enlist. The dean gave no figures in his annual report, but stated that students were not tending 'to rush off to enlist as they did in 1914.' That is not to say the war had no presence. C.D. Howe, the guest of honour at the annual School Dinner in November 1939, spoke about 'preparedness and transportation' in the war, and by the end of the academic year most of the 338 engineering students registered in the COTC were attending classes in uniform. One saw and heard plenty about the war. But as the writer of that year's engineering entry in the university year book saw it, 'life at the school passed in much the same way as in previous years.'[2]

By the beginning of the next academic year, in the fall of 1940,

Ten of the twelve women enrolled in the Faculty, 1939/40.

'Girls have invaded the University of Toronto's School of Applied Science with a rush. Since 1920 there have been only 10 women graduates in engineering; this year there are 12 registered in architecture, engineering, and applied chemistry. They're completely feminine, too; just as enticing in an evening gown as the next girl, but they're in love with things like carburetors and aeronautical design.' Toronto Star, *10 Feb. 1940.* Photo and clipping courtesy of Ailsa Doggett

the war in Europe had taken a disastrous turn for the Allied side. France had fallen and Britain was under heavy aerial attack. The alliance of which Canada was a part was now truly, almost desperately, at war. The Canadian government responded to the new circumstances in several ways, but the response with greatest effect on the university was the passing of the National Resources Mobilization Act in June 1940. This act, together with subsequent Orders in Council, compelled all single men between the ages of 21 and 45 to register for military service and to receive 30 days of training. University students were allowed to take about half their training on campus, on Saturdays and late afternoons, provided that they spent a full thirteen days in military camp after the academic term ended in the spring. Responsible now for training nearly all its students, the university set up a new branch of the COTC, the Training Centre Battalion, for this purpose in September 1940. As it had in the previous war, the Faculty took on its share of the university's military duties. The new battalion, in which 1,400 young men were soon registered, was commanded by Lieut-Col W.S. Wilson, secretary of the Faculty, while the original COTC, now the Officers' Training Battalion, was under the authority of Lieut-Col H.H. Madill, professor of Architecture. One of the six companies in the Training Centre Battalion was led by Major W.J.T. Wright, Professor of Engineering Drawing. Students could also train in the University Naval Training Division or the University Air Training Corps, the latter commanded by T.R. Loudon of Civil Engineering.[3]

The special training arrangements granted to university students reveal that, even at this early stage of the war, it was recognized that students could contribute better to the war effort by completing their studies than by enlisting. This was considered especially true in technical and scientific fields, for military leaders could now clearly see that science and technology were going to play a decisive part in this war and that trained engineers were a far greater asset than unskilled recruits. Improvements in chemical explosives, radio navigation and communication, and radar were all being avidly sought by the British in the summer of 1940. So there would be no urging students to enlist, and no promises of degrees for those who left without completing their course. The Faculty did, in the spring of 1941, hold its third- and fourth-year examinations during the academic term rather than after it so that students could leave early for work in war industries, but this was as much of a concession, formally at least, as it would make.[4]

Just as the severity of the war was starting to become clear, the Faculty learned that the burden of coping with the strains of war-

Engineering cadets construct field works on the university campus (Devonshire Place) as part of their compulsory military training during the Second World War, c.1941. UTA, A68-0003/004

time would be the job of a new dean. Dean Mitchell announced his retirement in the fall of 1940, to be effective at the end of the academic year in 1941. The responsibility of finding his replacement fell, as it had during the First World War, to the university president, now H.J. Cody. With several months to consider the matter, Cody turned to Dugald Jackson, the MIT professor who had recently examined the Faculty and with whom Cody had quite warm relations. Jackson's central piece of advice to Cody was to look beyond the Faculty for its new dean, even though, he admitted, 'there are members of the faculty who are of competent dean material.' He recommended two men: A.G. Christie, a SPS graduate (Dip. 1901), who had gone on to an outstanding career in the United States and was now a professor of Mechanical Engineering at Johns Hopkins University, and T.H. Hogg, another SPS grad (BASc 1907), who was at the time head of the Ontario Hydro-Electric Power Commission. Both, however, proved unavailable. Cody then approached C.J. Mackenzie, the dean of Engineering at the University of Saskatchewan, currently serving as acting head of the National Research Council in Ottawa. Jackson knew Mackenzie only by reputation, but thought he would make a fine choice. Mackenzie asked for two months to make his decision – pressures at the NRC prohibited his giving the matter immediate attention – but in June he, too, declined Cody's offer.[5]

An informal understanding seems to have prevailed that, whoever became the dean, C.R. Young would be given the job of assistant dean. At least one alumnus, however, had written Cody to say that he had heard these rumours and thought Young deserved the job himself, and A.G. Christie, in turning down Cody's offer, had suggested Young as an alternative.[6] By early June, with Mitchell's departure imminent, no other prospects in sight, and a capable candidate in the Faculty, Cody agreed. Clarence Richard Young was appointed dean of the Faculty of Applied Science and Engineering in June 1941, the fourth head of the school in its more than sixty-year existence. An alternative would have been to make Young an acting dean, as had been done with Ellis in 1914, and to continue the search, but the pressures of wartime made such a course undesirable.

C.R. Young was a perfectly good choice. Although certainly not a young man at the age of 62, nor a man of the new way – he had no degrees beyond his Toronto BASc, and his research was unmistakably of the practical rather than the scientific variety – he did have a good reputation in all he had done. As a consulting civil engineer, an educator, and a researcher, he had done excellent work. He was not averse to novelty, and had a knack for finding compromise among competing parties; his leadership in bringing Engineering Physics into the Faculty stands as a striking example of both.

The central problem Young had to contend with was coping

with the growing demand for the Faculty's services and graduates. The Canadian government's recognition that engineering students, on account of the importance of their skills, should complete their courses before going into war service, had, by 1942, evolved into calls that engineering students should be sped through their courses and made available to the war effort sooner. The Department of National Defence wrote Young early in 1942 asking him to consider early release of electrical engineering students for work with the Royal Canadian Corps of Signals. Recruiting officers even appeared on some university campuses looking for enlistments. Students, too, were asking for early release. This was just what the original policy had been established to avoid. Young and the rest of the Faculty stood by their belief that speeding up instruction or offering early release did nobody any good, especially since the last term of fourth year was a critical part of all programs. After several exchanges of correspondence with the Department of National Defence and the government's Wartime Bureau of Technical Personnel, the matter was settled. Courses would not be shortened, and any students who did leave before completing their work did so without any promises of special consideration at war's end.[7]

This was not the end of it. By late 1942, the government had decided that the shortage of scientifically trained personnel was so severe that special control of advanced science students was necessary. It passed an order in council, University Science Students Regulations (PC 9566), prohibiting such students from enlisting in military service or entering the workforce without permission from the minister of Labour.[8] It, in effect, compelled students to remain at the Faculty; even those who wanted to leave and were willing to accept the consequences could not. This was in line with the Faculty's wishes, and would have been acceptable had it not been for another product of the war – several academic staff had volunteered for or been seconded to war service and the Faculty did not have enough instructors to teach the large and growing enrolment. With the cooperation of various employers in the Toronto area, twenty-eight practising engineers were secured for the 1942/43 year as part-time instructors, but this was an unreliable and imperfect solution.[9] The Faculty addressed the problem the following year by prohibiting failing students from repeating first year – thus lowering enrolment somewhat – and by obtaining permission for its own graduates to defer military service in order to work as instructors.[10] Such were the administrative challenges of providing an essential war-time service, engineering education, without the freedom to hire enough staff to do the work.

In 1940, before he had retired, Dean Mitchell had described the war as 'an engineer's war,' for he, too, had seen that science and technology were going to play a crucial part. Yet claiming the war for the engineers, suggesting that they were the experts who applied the science and developed the devices, overstates the profession's contribution. It was scientists, much more than engineers, who performed this task. Whether in Britain, the United States, or Canada, it was physicists, mostly, who made the critical contributions – in radar, proximity fuses, and ultimately atomic weapons. There were engineers at the highest levels – C.J. Mackenzie and C.D. Howe being the best-known Canadians – and also in some of the research laboratories, but the leaders of the essential scientific research were the scientists. At the University of Toronto, it was the Physics department that conducted radar research for the NRC, and that trained Navy and Air Force men in radar techniques.[11] It was the university physicist Arnold Pitts who did important research on proximity fuses.[12] And it was the chemist George Wright who led the research team investigating new production methods for the explosive RDX.[13]

Nevertheless, although engineers cannot claim ownership of these important university researches, members of the staff at the Faculty of Applied Science and Engineering were certainly involved. Their diversion into war researches was one of the causes of the Faculty's inability to handle its large enrolment. R.R. McLaughlin and J.G. Breckenridge of Chemical Engineering worked on Wright's explosive research, and probably also on the manufacture of synthetic rubber.[14] R.J. Montgomery, the ceramics engineer, who had worked for Bausch & Lomb in Rochester, New York before coming to the Faculty in the 1920s, and who was known to be an expert on the manufacture of optical glass, was seconded to Research Enterprises Limited in July 1940 to work on the development of glass for artillery range finders.[15] L.M. Pidgeon, a noted specialist in magnesium refining who was appointed to the staff in the Department of Metallurgical Engineering in the fall of 1943, continued his magnesium research in association with the NRC.[16] Some staff members worked for private companies under war contracts – M.J.C. Lazier and R.B. McIntyre did work for Massey-Harris's Aircraft Division – and others for government or defence agencies – T.R. Loudon went off immediately to serve as chief technical officer for the RCAF in Ottawa, and E.A. Allcut was assigned work in 1941 by the NRC on heating and insulating aircraft. And the School of Engineering Research continued to provide small sums for research, almost all of which was war-related. So, while the academic staff in the Faculty might not have been the leaders of the most visible research projects of the war, they did contribute their time and skills.[17]

In 1943 Dean Young undertook, on top of everything else, two substantial revisions to the Faculty's curriculum. One might think such an effort ill-timed, since just keeping the school together with its existing curriculum was troublesome enough. The associate dean, H.W. Price, thought Young was overstretching himself, and demanded in a personal letter that he 'take a protracted rest' in the summer of 1943.[18] But Young could not be dissuaded. These curriculum revisions – the introduction of a new graduating course in Engineering and Business and the expansion of humanities instruction – were close to Young's heart, and he would not rest until he had carried them through. Both were rooted in Dugald Jackson's 1940 report, the recommendations of which C.R. Young had fully supported.[19]

Young brought the matter to faculty council in September 1943, at which time two sub-committees were struck, one on 'Humanistic-Social Studies' and one on 'Engineering Administration.'[20] Both reported early in 1944. The former, of which Young was chairman, recommended introducing two hours per week, in all years and all courses, of either English, history, philosophy, or political economy. Added to the existing practical courses such as contract law and industrial management, which were to be kept, non-technical instruction would then total 8 per cent of teaching time, but this, the committee pointed out, was far below the 25 per cent that the Society for the Promotion of Engineering Education was suggesting for non-technical subjects in the United States. The other committee recommended a new four-year course called Administrative Engineering, quite similar to Mechanical Engineering but with more practical instruction in management and business in the final years. Council endorsed the recommendations of both committees and moved them on to the university senate for approval, along with a proposal to remove the aeronautics options from Civil Engineering and Engineering Physics and to create, instead, a new four-year course in Aeronautical Engineering (this was feasible because T.R. Loudon had returned from his work with the Air Force).[21] The increase in humanities was approved by the senate, as was the new Aeronautical Engineering course – which went in the 1944/45 calendar as Department Ten – but the Administrative Engineering course was not. Several of the Faculty's own alumni in the senate objected, so Young thought it proper to withdraw the proposal from the senate without a vote.

Over the next year, committed as ever, Dean Young laboured on. In an effort to bolster his case that engineering graduates were, in fact, heading for administrative work, he prepared and distributed questionnaires to several thousand alumni asking about the nature of their jobs. He also exchanged letters with dozens of alumni holding senior positions in industry to ascertain their views on the proposed course. Then, with its content changed somewhat, and with the new name Engineering and Business, Young brought the course back to the senate in early 1945.[22] Pitched this time as a desirable choice for returning veterans, a claim which had the support of the SPEE in the United States, the new course was readily approved. Engineering and Business appeared the following year as Department Eleven.[23]

By the time this new course was in the calendar, the war in Europe was over. It had been a stressful five years, but, again unlike the previous war, the Faculty had been strengthened by the ordeal, not only by high enrolments, but also by a widespread enthusiasm for engineering and applied science that grew out of the wartime experience. Newly devised technologies were ripe for refinement and development, government support for applied science research was plentiful, business opportunites were numerous, and science and technology were held by the public in the highest regard. This enthusiasm would soon manifest itself in the biggest administrative challenge the Faculty had ever faced. Returning veterans, aching for a stable and productive life after years of war, and with government-granted free university tuition part of their resettlement package, would soon be applying to the Faculty by the thousands. Carrying the Faculty through post-war reconstruction would be the biggest war-time task of all.

A boom in post-war enrolment had been expected by university officials for several years; as early as October 1941, the Canadian government had announced its intention to provide ex-servicemen with free university education, and the implications of this to the University of Toronto were obvious.[24] In the fall of 1943, the university senate struck a special committee to study the matter, and their recommendations had gone out in a report to faculty councils the following winter. The council of the Faculty of Applied Science and Engineering had immediate reservations. In particular, they opposed the senate committee's suggestion that ex-servicemen be treated as a separate group, and that 'an alternative first year be set up to provide the necessary instruction' for the veterans.[25] Faculty council preferred mixing veterans in with all its other students, thinking that, if a group of students had to be taught elsewhere, which seemed likely, the segregated group should be the entire first year.[26] And this was, in the end, what the Faculty did.

In the fall of 1944, council settled on its plan. There would be two distinct special programs. First, the Faculty would hold a summer session on the main campus for returning veterans, from April to September 1945, at which instruction would be offered in all years of all courses; applications for admission were already mounting up even in November 1944, and Dean Young felt that 'Ex-service men cannot be held out of college till September, 1945.' Then, in September, the Faculty would teach the entire first-year class, now predicted to be about 1,500, at a site off-campus. It was simply inconceivable that such a huge first-year class could be fit into existing facilities, already at capacity. What and where this off-campus facility would be, nobody had yet determined, but that it would be needed was now certain.[27] In April 1945, the special summer session began as planned, with 135 veterans enrolled, but the off-campus first-year session was as yet unrealized. No suitable site had been found. The Faculty had investigated several possible locations in and around Toronto, but none was adequate.[28] What they sought was an existing set of buildings that, with minimal renovation, could offer facilities for both teaching and housing as many as a few thousand students. This was no simple quest.

Then, with the war in Europe suddenly over in May, new possibilities arose. The most appealing was the huge Ajax munitions plant east of Toronto, scheduled to close in August. The plant, given its name to commemorate H.M.S. Ajax's participation in the remarkable British naval victory at the mouth of the River Platte early in the war, seems to have come to the attention of the university through the personal connections of Toronto business-man W.E. Phillips, then serving as chairman of the University of Toronto's board of governors. Phillips was also head of Research Enterprises Limited in Leaside, and quite likely personally associated with Canadian Industries Limited, the company operating the crown corporation, Defence Industries Limited, that had built and still owned the munitions plant.[29] Among Phillips's friends was C.D. Howe, whose Department of Reconstruction was responsible for decommissioning war properties. Through arrangements with Howe's department, a university delegation including Dean Young and university president-designate Sidney Smith inspected the site in early June 1945.[30] Having been built to accommodate many of the huge plant's employees, the complex included a residential area with dormitory accommodation for over 2,500, recreation facilities, cafeterias, a central heating plant, even a small hospital and a five-room school house. About one-half mile away were the shell-filling works – lines of separate, small buildings – that could be made suitable for lecture and laboratory rooms. It looked ideal. Howe and Phillips met on 14 June to discuss leasing arrangements, and this was followed by a formal agreement in which the university leased a large part of the site for $50,000 per year.[31] DIL vacated the premises in August, and the work of converting the place from a munitions plant to an engineering school began immediately.

Ajax, although created solely for the use of the Faculty of Applied Science and Engineering, was a University of Toronto project. Accordingly, two men were put in charge: J.R. Gilley, comptroller of Hart House since 1922 and acting warden there during the war, was named the director of Ajax by the university board of governors, and Prof. W.J.T. Wright of the Faculty of Applied Science and Engineering was named Director of Studies by Dean Young. Together they oversaw a remarkable four-month transformation of the site that was by all accounts a striking success.[32] Ajax was made into not just a place of instruction, but a university campus, as well – something which both Gilley, with his years at Hart House, and Wright, a great advocate of student life, went to lengths to achieve. Not only were the munitions buildings thoroughly converted into classrooms, but all the residences were renovated, the cafeteria was expanded to handle 1,050 students, and the central building transformed into 'Hart House Ajax,' complete with a tuck shop, barber shop, browsing library, music room, and chapel.[33]

Since work began only in August, there was no hope of the facilities being ready for the start of the fall term, so first-year classes had to be delayed until January. This suited circumstances, for the repatriation of military personnel from Europe was taking time and many were not yet back when the school year began in September. There was some room for first-year students on the Toronto campus, so 426 veterans, all with more than twenty-nine months' service, began their first year there in September. But the remaining first-year students, over 1,400 of them, of which about 80 per cent were veterans, began their classes at Ajax in January 1946.[34]

Ajax would run for three and a half years – four full academic sessions – from January 1946 to April 1949, during which, for several thousand students, it was the University of Toronto. Peak enrolment came in the 1946/47 session, when the original first year class, which finished its year in August and went directly into second year with scarcely a break, were augmented by another huge (and this time complete) first year of 1,794 students. Total student attendance at Ajax was thus 3,312 at the start of the session. This was as large as it would be; since the Ajax laboratories were not sufficient for third- or fourth-year work, instruction was limited to first and second year. As the original Ajax class moved to Toronto to start its third year in the fall of 1947 they were

A new classroom awaits students at Ajax, 1946. UTA, A74-0008P.011(01)

replaced by another first-year class, but the numbers were starting to subside. Total enrolment that year was 2,595. The following year it was just 1,500, and of the first-year students, only 31 per cent were veterans. The post-war phenomenon had ended; so, too, did the Ajax campus in the spring of 1949.[35]

The administrative effort required to make all this succeed can scarcely be imagined. Timetabling, transporting, and teaching such a huge group of students – not to mention feeding them – taxed the skills and perseverance of Gilley and Wright as nothing before or since. Ajax had a complete athletics program (inter-residence and inter-faculty), regular drama and music performances, an office for the *Varsity*, the Engineering Society's book-store, and many other amenities of student life. The Faculty sought to keep all classes in the core subjects of science and engineering under 100 students, so a huge expansion of staff was required. More than 170 instructors were needed in the 1946/47 session, many of whom were recruited just for that session – not an easy task when demand for engineers was high. Of these, 58 also taught on the Toronto campus, easing the need for recruitment but confounding the work of timetabling.[36]

That it all worked, academically and socially, can be seen in the fact that failure rates for students were no higher than they had been in the generation before the war, and that the Ajax experience is so fondly recalled to this day by many who lived through it. Failure rates for veterans were generally higher than for non-veterans, and higher than long-term averages, but not significantly. Perhaps instruction could have been better, but standards were evidently being maintained. As for student life, the spartan rooms – just twelve feet by ten feet, with two beds – the 'cattle cars' that carried students from dorms to classes, and the weeks upon weeks of overcooked parsnips all had to be endured, but such hardships were slight. How could these petty discomforts be taken seriously by students who knew, whether first or second hand, what had been endured chasing U-boats in the North Atlantic or storming the beaches of Normandy? If anything, these inconveniences only enliven the recollections, for it is the camaraderie of shared experience, above all, that Ajax students remember. It was 'reminiscent of some northern mining town or logging camp,' one former student recalled.[37] The move to the main campus in Toronto for third year was not always welcome; a comforting cohesion was lost when students were forced to find their own rooms in boarding houses on city streets. Ajax was close to what the Faculty had always wanted for its students, a shared educational and social experience, and in this it was a remarkable success.

Ajax might be the most remembered event in the Faculty's history, but its uniqueness and success should not overshadow every-

The Evans brothers in their dormitory room at Ajax, c.1947. UTA, A74/0008P.011(03)

thing else occurring in the Faculty in these post-war years. For one thing, Ajax was not the only place over-run with engineering students. The downtown Toronto campus was filled to capacity, as well. The Faculty had hoped to have at least one of its two new buildings completed before the great mass of third-year students from Ajax descended on the campus in the fall of 1947, but failed to achieve this. The grand new Wallberg Memorial Building running along College Street east from St George Street, which had been under construction for several years, was being delayed by post-war shortages of men and material and was still at least months from completion. The new west front of the Mechanical Building, a project with a long history, had finally been approved in 1946, but was just 'an enormous hole in the ground in which concrete pillars and steel girders are beginning to appear' when classes began in 1947.[38] So the great influx – the third-year class alone numbered 1,325, higher than any previous total enrolment – had to be accommodated in existing buildings. This necessitated, among other things, extending the teaching day to thirteen hours, from 8:00 a.m. to 9:00 p.m. each weekday.

Most of the increased teaching load was carried by temporary staff, hired as lecturers or instructors. Some were practising professionals, while others were recent graduates not yet embarked on careers. Scores of such instructors were engaged.[39] Most moved on to other work, but a few stayed. Heavy post-war teaching demands brought Gordon Slemon, Jim Ham, Frank Hooper, Boris Stoicheff (all later notable professors), and Jim Gow (later the school's secretary) into the Faculty as demonstrators. Few new permanent appointments were made. Several men had been hired during the war, however, and in these post-war years they began to move into roles of greater responsibility. G.F. Tracy and Robert Legget had been hired in 1939, while David Cass-Beggs (1940), Mark Huggins (1942), Ben Etkin (1943), L.E. Jones (1943), L.M. Pidgeon (1943), and W.F. Graydon (1944) all were on the academic staff by the end of the war. The last three named all had doctorates – no longer such a novelty among the academic staff. There was also something of a change in departmental leadership, as the old guard began to move on. L.M. Pidgeon had been named head of Metallurgical upon his appointment in 1943, replacing G.A. Guess. E.A. Allcut had replaced R.A. Angus as head of Mechanical in 1944, R.R. McLaughlin replaced J.W. Bain as head of Chemical in 1946, and G.F. Tracy replaced A.R. Zimmer, who had himself only recently replaced H.W. Price, as head of Electrical in 1947. This left only Civil, the halves of which were headed by W.M. Treadgold and T.R. Loudon, and the teaching department of Engineering Drawing (W.J.T. Wright) with heads dating back to the Galbraith days.

During these post-war years, through the very time that Ajax

was attracting so much attention, a new and entirely novel enterprise took shape within the Faculty: the Institute of Aerophysics.[40]
This research institute was not, and never would be, a conventional department, but in its ways of operating, its international
connections, and its commitment to advanced research, it was a
sign of things to come. The institute resulted from the efforts of
the remarkable Gordon N. Patterson. Patterson had been raised
in Edmonton, where he had remained to study Engineering Physics at the University of Alberta in the late 1920s. Having developed an interest in aerodynamics as an undergraduate, and
knowing about the wind tunnel operated by J.H. Parkin of
Mechanical Engineering at the University of Toronto, Patterson
applied to the Faculty to do graduate work. He was disappointed
to learn that Parkin had by this time left the Faculty and, further,
that his Engineering Physics degree was not sufficient qualifica-
tion for entry into the Faculty's graduate program. Physics, however, was quite prepared to accept him, and he enrolled there as
a graduate student in the fall of 1932 under the supervision of
E.F. Burton. He was further dismayed to learn that the head of
Mechanical Engineering, R.W. Angus, would not allow him to use
their wind tunnel, but Patterson was able to secure summer work
under Parkin at the NRC in Ottawa, where he began to conduct
the research that would eventually form the basis of his PhD,
awarded in 1935.

Patterson then set off on a remarkable globe-spanning career
that established him as among the best-informed and most
advanced aerodynamics researchers in the world. All the while,
however, he stayed in touch with colleagues in Toronto, Burton
and T.R. Loudon in particular, and harboured a wish to return.
In January 1946, while at the Guggenheim Aeronautical Laboratory at the California Institute of Techonolgy, the University of
Toronto offered Patterson a position in Civil Engineering, the
department that housed the Faculty's two aeronautics instructors
at the time, Loudon and Ben Etkin, but Patterson turned the

offer down. A devoted research scientist, he let it be known that only if placed in a Department of Aeronautics would he consider their offer. Almost certainly because of this, the Faculty created a department of Aeronautical Engineering later that year (there had been a course since 1944, but no department) into which Etkin and Loudon were then placed, with Loudon as head.[41] The offer was then revived and, this time, accepted. Patterson joined the staff as Professor of Aerodynamics in October 1946.

Some academics might have seen this as the culmination of their career, but not G.N. Patterson. His work was just beginning, for he was determined to establish a first-rate aeronautics research facility at the university and would do whatever it took to achieve this. What he needed, of course, was financial support. The university, although it had hired him knowing his wishes, was not prepared to spend the money needed for a sophisticated high-speed aeronautics laboratory and urged him to look elsewhere for funds. This he did, and immediately found success with a grant from the National Research Council that allowed him to construct a small apparatus for studying the fluid dynamics of shock waves. The following year Patterson succeeded in interesting O.M. Solandt and the newly created Defence Research Board, of which Solandt was the head, in his plans, and promptly secured a grant of $350,000 to establish a new research institute in the disused RCAF facility at the Downsview airport north of Toronto. With this grant as its seed, the University of Toronto Institute of Aerophysics (UTIA) came into existence in April 1949.

The Faculty had never seen anything like this before. A new staff member with a stellar international reputation had appeared, having set his own terms of employment, and in a little over two years had secured an enormous external grant for a new laboratory. On top of this, the new lab was to be a research facility, and Patterson's mission clearly research, not teaching. A Department of Aeronautical Engineering remained for the time

A view of the newly completed E.A. Wallberg Memorial Building from the south-east, c.1948. UTA, A78-0050/007(18)

being, to which Patterson nominally belonged, but Loudon and Etkin did most of the aeronautics teaching, not Patterson.[42] Could one be a professor in the Faculty of Applied Science and Engineering and teach but two hours a week? The reporting structure of this new facility was unusual, as well, for its director reported to the dean of the Faculty without being part of any department. Could such an anomalous thing survive? Indeed it could, as the years ahead would show.

When the academic term began in the fall of 1949, much more was new at the Faculty than this Institute of Aerophysics. The Ajax campus had been shut down that summer, and all students were now on the downtown Toronto campus. This was possible only because the Faculty's two new buildings were at last completed. The Wallberg Memorial Building, designed by Toronto architects

The front of the new Mechanical Building just prior to its opening in 1949. It is still one of the city of Toronto's finest examples of early modern architecture. UTA, B78-0001/010(05)

Page and Steele, with subtle Moderne details revealing its pre-war inspiration, would now house Chemical Engineering, leaving the Mining Building to Mining alone. As well, the new Mechanical Building, its striking design by architects Allward and Gouinlock being the first show of modernism on the university campus, had just opened that spring.[43] The Faculty had lost one of its original parts, however, as the School of Architecture had been made a separate faculty in 1948; already effectively independent, its formal separation was regretted by the Faculty but not opposed.

The Faculty also had a new dean. Having reached the age of 70, C.R. Young had retired and passed the deanship to K.F. Tupper. Young's deanship, from 1941 to 1949, had run through truly extraordinary times. These war and post-war years were probably the most difficult, administratively, in the Faculty's history. Nothing could be relied on from one session to the next; military policies, government regulations, staff availability – not to mention student enrolments – could all change drastically at any time. Young devoted himself to keeping the Faculty running smoothly through this instability, and he deserves credit for his effort and success. His two main academic initiatives – the expansion of humanistic studies and the introduction of the course in Engineering and Business – were not, however, destined to last long. The problems that elicited them were real and, as later deans could attest, long-lived, but the solutions Young provided, derived largely from Dugald Jackson's Report of 1939, would not endure. The humanistic program worked well during his deanship. Perhaps because of Young's stature in the university, he always arranged to have senior professors in the arts departments teach these subjects: George Brett taught Philosophy of Science, V.W. Bladen taught Economics, McGregor Dawson taught Political Science, and Edgar McGinnis taught Modern World History. Without Young, however, this university connection seems to have weakened; less experienced instructors were given the task and the classes steadily lost favour among the teachers and the

C.R. Young, Faculty dean through the Ajax years, on the steps of the temporary faculty club at Ajax, c.1947. Young devoted much of his life to the Faculty. He was a professor of structural engineering for many years before serving as dean from 1941 to 1949, and after his retirement he carried out valuable research on the history of both the Faculty itself and Canadian engineering education more generally. UTA, A74/0008P.11(03)

taught.[44] The Engineering and Business course succeeded at first, and attracted students, but it gradually lost support among the Faculty's own academic staff. It was a pre-war solution, and by the 1950s looked out of date.

Young's service to the Faculty did not end with his retirement. Knowing and admiring the Faculty's past, he soon took for himself the task of being its first historian. All those interested in the Faculty's history are in his debt, for much of what is now known about the Faculty's founding derives from his assiduous research in the years of his retirement. But in the early 1950s C.R. Young might have been the only man looking back. All other eyes were on the future.

The 1950s in the Faculty of Applied Science and Engineering look quite different from a distance of fifty years than they looked at the time.[45] Those who were there saw and felt strong connections with the past. Students, still overwhelmingly young men, still wore jackets and ties to lectures and comported themselves with due respect. The frosh still had their green ties aggressively clipped during orientation. St George Street still lay beyond the western edge of the university campus, and the street itself still formed a long graceful tunnel beneath a bower of trees. Many of the senior professors in the Faculty had been delivering lectures – sometimes the same ones – since before most of the students had been born. The curriculum and timetable still bore remarkable resemblance to what it had been early in the century. Yet despite this undeniable continuity with the past, what stands out to a historian of the decade is a pre-occupation with reform. Little actually changed in the 1950s, but by the middle of the decade the Faculty had grown nearly obsessed with preparing for and promoting change.

The dean who presided over the first few years of the decade was K.F. Tupper who, like C.H. Mitchell thirty years before, was a

K.F. Tupper, dean of the Faculty from 1949 to 1954. UTA, A78-0041/022(29)

Faculty outsider at the time of his appointment. Tupper had graduated from the school in Mechanical Engineering in 1929 and promptly found employment in aerodynamics research with the NRC's division of Physics and Engineering Physics. In 1937, he took an SM degree at the University of Michigan. During the war, he was one of a small team of researchers that travelled to Britain to investigate the development of jet engines, and was subsequently appointed chief engineer of Turbo Research, the Canadian Crown corporation formed to carry on Canada's jet research. After the war he headed the Engineering division of the

Atomic Energy Project at Chalk River, from which he was recruited to be dean.[46]

Tupper carried out a few small but important changes. Starting in 1950/51, admission requirements were raised to include minimum third-class honours in all Grade XIII subjects. This had actually been C.R. Young's initiative, a manifestation of his wish to lift the level of humanities in the Faculty, but it had taken several years to come into effect. The course in ceramics was dropped in 1951, having for some years attracted very few students; the year it was dropped, only seven of the Faculty's 1,600 students were taking it. Its failure was viewed as a sign that industry-based programs, rather than subject-based, were not desirable, and the Faculty never again established such a course. Tupper also ended the long-standing division of the Department of Civil Engineering in 1953, and put the entire department under the headship of T.R. Loudon, and then, the following year, of Carson Morrison.[47]

One might expect that Tupper, considering his background, would be the man to raise scientific standards and introduce more research into the Faculty. But this was not to be. Nor did Tupper take action on any other fundamental questions facing the Faculty. He saw them clearly enough. He wondered how student workload might be lessened, whether or not enrolment should be capped, how relations with the university should evolve, whether the province needed new engineering schools, and how young academic staff could be recruited when demand for engineers was so high. He also served on the American Society for Engineering Education's committee, chaired by L.E. Grinter, on engineering education in the United States, and was thus well aware of current issues.[48] But Tupper appears never to have been fully engaged by the job. He found the meetings endless and the wheels of academic democracy hopelessly slow. The Faculty, as a result, never warmed to him. After only five years in office he resigned, moving on to a private consulting firm to resume the practice of engineering.[49]

Tupper was replaced in 1954 by R.R. McLaughlin, a long-time professor and recently appointed head of Chemical Engineering. McLaughlin had been among the earliest members of the academic staff to hold a PhD, and had been a productive researcher since the 1930s, so, he too, came to the deanship with a background suggesting he would lead the Faculty towards science and research. As things turned out, McLaughlin's appointment brought no sweeping reforms either, for he proved to be a cautious dean who favoured consensus and gradual change. Nevertheless, it was in the early years of his deanship that the Faculty seriously began to question itself, and to consider what steps were needed to move into the rapidly expanding world of scientific engineering.

Underlying this fledgling movement for change was the belief that the Faculty would soon see huge increases in enrolment. The 1950s themselves were not a time of expansion. Enrolment was still over 2,000 in 1950/51, but by then the last large group of veterans, those who had begun their studies in the fall of 1947, were in their final year; the next year, once they had graduated, enrolment fell to about 1,600 and stayed below 2,000 for most of the decade.[50] There was, however, an assumption that enrolment would soon begin a steady rise, and that before long the student numbers would be comparable to those of the Ajax years. The Faculty was not alone in this. The whole university was expecting a flood of students. As university president Sidney Smith put it in 1955, 'the boys and girls who will knock on university doors are now in the schools of the province.' What a later generation would call the 'baby boom' was already clearly in view. To prepare, the university acquired land west of St George Street, with Ontario government assistance, and started development of the 'West Campus.' It also laid out a plan to double its academic staff in ten years.[51]

Apart from this expectation of rising student numbers, however, was a notion growing among many of the academic staff, and even some students, that aspects of the Faculty's educational program had fallen behind. This sense of obsolescence was not imaginary. Changes in engineering that were evident in the 1930s had now begun to overwhelm the profession, and although certain individuals within the Faculty were travelling the new roads, many were not.

Chief among the new tenets was that engineering had to be built upon advanced science and mathematics, a belief born in the interwar years, if not before, that was now widespread and inescapable.[52] Old engineering problems in thermodynamics, electric power distribution, hydraulics, and statics were increasingly being seen as complex theoretical problems calling for fundamental solutions in mathematical language, rather than as physical problems to be solved by observation and measurement. Furthermore, a whole new set of engineering subjects had emerged from scientific discoveries earlier in the century – aerodynamics, solid-state electronics, controlled nuclear energy, synthetic materials – that required fairly advanced knowledge of science and mathematics simply to work in. Yet with practical subjects like engineering drawing and surveying still filling a large part of the curriculum in all but Engineering Physics, there was just no room for more science and mathematics.

Closely connected to the increasing importance of science was the growth of research in the engineering profession. Not that engineering research was new; as one will recall, research of a sort had been common in the Faculty in the 1920s and 1930s. But no longer would trials or tests, or the development of workable equipment, be considered true research. The focus of research was increasingly on the scientific or mathematical fundamentals of the subject under study,[53] but there were few signs of this new approach at the Faculty. To the new academic staff with doctoral degrees from major research universities, such as G. Sinclair (Ohio), J.M. Ham (M.I.T.) and G.R. Slemon (Imperial College), all recently appointed in Electrical Engineering, or W.H. Rapson, recently brought back to Chemical Engineering after twelve highly productive years as a research chemist at Industrial Cellulose Research Limited, things were not how they should be.[54]

The Faculty's concern with its future took concrete form in January 1955 when council struck what it called a Committee on Development, 'to recommend the general course, with as much detail as possible, that this Faculty should follow for the next few years.'[55] It consisted of the dean and senior representatives (in some cases heads) from all departments. The committee named G.R. Lord as chairman and appointed four sub-committees to consider particular subjects – building accommodation, graduate study and research, industrial liaison, and curriculum. It then embarked on nearly two years of monthly meetings, reporting its views on various matters to council from time to time.

The most pressing problem was the predicted expansion; the Faculty could not wait long to take action on this. Based on figures obtained from the university, the committee calculated that the Faculty could face enrolments of 3,600 within ten years and over 4,000 a few years later. Thinking it would be wrong to restrict admission too severely, the committee concluded that the Faculty should 'admit and accept all qualified applicants who present themselves'; if this many engineers were needed, the necessary adjustments would just have to be made. As to what these adjustments would be, it considered holding year-round classes, expanding the days and hours of teaching, and introducing the semester system – all of which it rejected. It also considered moving the Faculty to a new site on the Langstaff farm property north of the city where it could freely expand, but rejected that, too, on the grounds that ties to the university science departments were too important to forsake. The committee's solution to the impending crisis in accommodation, which council accepted, was to join the university by expanding west to St George Street.[56]

Another recommendation from the committee was that the Faculty foster research among both students and staff. There were noticeable qualifications in the wording of its recommendation which make it clear such a view was not unanimous 'there is ... a feeling among some of the staff of our Faculty that we are not meeting the challege as we might ...' In the end, it recommended, 'that more thought should be given to this matter and a vigourous and determined effort made to ensure the future of this essential part of our academic function,' but gave no specific suggestions for how this might be done. It was something short of complete endorsement, although it did bring the matter into the open.[57]

If one examines the state of research in the Faculty when the committee was preparing its report in 1957, one can understand its qualified position. Although there was plenty of talk about research, and plenty of urging that it be done, the rhetoric seems to have exceeded the output. The number of published researches had risen quite quickly after the war, especially in Mechanical Engineering, but publications had levelled off in the later 1950s. Dean McLaughlin stated in 1955 that although the Faculty's research was of good quality, it was of inadequate quantity.[58]

There were several reasons for this. A good number of the academic staff of the Faculty simply had not adopted, and never would adopt, the 'gospel of research.' The idea that the Faculty's only true job was to prepare students to be professional engineers still held sway with many of the staff, especially in teaching departments like Engineering Drawing and Applied Physics. None of the men in these departments (and few in the others) had the advanced scientific training needed to prepare them for the sort of research now being undertaken. Furthermore, to many of the staff in Mining and Civil Engineering, maintaining a professional practice, and thus keeping up to date on work methods and trends, was a better use of time than conducting research.[59] The custom of maintaining a private practice had been growing since the days of C.H. Mitchell, and may have been given added impetus by the use of so many practising professionals as part-time instructors during and after the war. By the 1950s, some staff members were taking it to an extreme. Carson Morrison, head of Civil Engineering, operated a nearly full-time consulting business. G.R. Lord, head of Mechanical and a specialist in hydraulics, had commitments elsewhere, too; he served for many years as head of the Ontario Conservation Authority. Teaching had evolved into a part-time job for these men, and taking time away from their consulting work to do unpaid research would have interfered with their professional lives and their incomes. Another drag on the development of research was the heavy teaching load that all academic staff had been carrying since the post-war years. Twenty hours of lecturing per week was not uncommon, even in the mid-1950s after the heavy enrolments had subsided.[60]

At the heart of all these, however, was a shortage of money. The School of Engineering Research still provided grants to members of the staff, but the amounts had not kept up with the rising cost of research. Annual budgets of $25,000 to $30,000 were still the norm for the school in the late 1940s (years for which complete records exist), and that sum was spread widely around the Faculty. Chemical Engineering usually received the most, but staff in all departments other than Mining received some. This likely helped maintain good relations among the department heads, but with individual grants rarely exceeding $1,000, major research initiatives, especially any that required sophisticated equipment, were out of the question. These sums provided no teaching relief for academic staff, nor could they be used as summer income supplements. They quickly disappeared on either salaries for research assistants or on equipment – mostly on the former.[61]

The federal government's Defence Research Board (DRB), whose generous grant had founded the UTIA in 1949, had become the Faculty's largest source of research funds. Their support was officially limited to research with possible military appli-

A graduate student seminar at the Institute of Aerophysics in the later 1950s. Patterson, *Pathway to Excellence*, 67

cations, but the board interpreted its guidelines fairly liberally. It granted the Faculty $223,450 in 1957/58 (the first year that full details are readily available). By far the largest share of their funds went to the UTIA, which was flush with DRB funds – over $100,000 per year through the middle of the decade – but this was only about half of what was given to the Faculty. E.A. Allcut and F.C. Hooper in Mechanical Engineering both received DRB grants through the early 1950s, as did J.M. Ham in Electrical, L.M. Pidgeon in Metallurgy, and R.R. McLaughlin in Chemical. DRB funds also went towards development of a university computation centre in the early 1950s, in which the Faculty was involved.[62]

A third source, or at least possible source, of funds was the National Research Council. But its emphasis, now more than ever, was on what was deemed fundamental scientific research –

the Council's reaction, one historian has suggested, to having been forced into research on applied science during the war.[63] The Faculty of Applied Science and Engineering thus was not a common destination of their funds. While the University of Toronto overall received $454,076 from the NRC in 1957/58, for example, the Faculty only received $17,100 of that, most of which went to Metallurgy.[64]

This, then, was the state of research in the Faculty when the Committee on Development reported: a mixed commitment among the academic staff, very little institutional support within the Faculty itself, and a single, albeit fairly generous, public granting body for projects that fit its mandate. The Faculty was keen enough on developing research, however, that council acted on the suggestion to study the matter further, and it created a special committee to do just that. This committee in turn reported a little over a year later with its own recommendations, in which one theme stands out: what they needed, above all, was money. More research funds should be provided by both the federal government and the university, as well, if possible, by 'industrial and private sources.'[65]

Graduate studies, always considered an essential part of university research, were in much the same state – a general agreement that they should expand, but no sign of actual expansion. There had been a big jump in graduate enrolment in the immediate post-war years, but this growth was not being sustained. The Faculty had 132 graduate students enrolled in the fall of 1950 and 123 in the fall of 1957 (although with a rising proportion of PhD students).[66] The reason for this lack of progress was, once again, a lack of money – in this case, for graduate fellowships. Most top students in the Faculty were quite capable of finding good jobs when they graduated into the booming economy of the early 1950s. To choose instead the insecure and poorly paid life of a graduate student was not, for most, a sensible choice. Here was a critical problem, and the special committee on research recognized it as such. They recommended providing graduate students with secure monthly stipends, but were, of course, unable to suggest where these funds would come from.[67]

By the end of the 1950s, several of the Faculty's leaders had set their sights on expanding research among both students and staff, but how this goal was to be reached was not so clear; it was easier to say more money was needed than it was to find the money. The Faculty had also decided how to handle its expected growth: there would be a new building on the downtown university campus. As for the other two aspects of the Development Committee's mandate, industrial liaison and curriculum revision, little was done. The sub-committee on the former never reported, while that on the latter got bogged down in details over guidelines for class sizes and never addressed the matter of reforming the existing curriculum. One senses a reluctance to move too fast.

Now, many years later, the deliberations and recommendations of this development committee appear critically important, for in them lie the seeds of so many of the Faculty's future developments. Yet, at the time, this committee's affairs would not have stood out above everything else. The dean and academic staff had other matters to address, faculty council had other committees and sub-committees at work, and all the while students had their own lives to live. The routine business of the Faculty carried on.

In 1955, the Faculty introduced what it called a 'substantially common' first year. A common program for all first-year students had long been thought desirable, for it would allow students to hold off on their choice of specialty until they had experienced a little of everything, and it was also seen as something that might mitigate the fragmenting effects of specialization on the profession. But since the departments usually had their own ideas about what first-year students needed, standardizing the year had proved impossible. One long-standing impediment, the need to keep surveying in the first year, was at last partly removed. Chemical had dropped first-year surveying long ago, in 1919, as had Metallurgical in 1950; now, in 1955, Electrical and Mechanical did so as well. This left Civil, Mining, and Applied Geology with surveying in the first-year of their programs, but apart from this, all first-year programs were the same. With just two different first years for the regular engineering courses – one with surveying and one without – as well as a third for students in Engineering Physics, the Faculty declared that a 'substantially common' first year was now in place.

Other small changes in the courses on offer, and in their content, are worth noting. Questions had been raised as to whether the Engineering and Business course should continue, and, if so, whether it needed modifications; practical matters such as engineering accounting or contract law looked next to useless, and hopelessly outmoded, to the new guard of scientific engineers. But after assessing the status of recent graduates from the course, and consulting with the university placement officer, the committee came out in favour of retaining the course, unchanged.[68] It was, however, now given the number Department Four, unused since the departure of Architecture. The retirement of T.R. Loudon in 1954 had brought about the end, in 1955, of Aeronautical Engineering, both as an administrative department and a course. The aeronautics option in Engineering Physics was reinstated for undergraduates, and the academic staff who taught the subject were all attached to the Institute of Aerophysics. The amount of engineering drawing was slightly reduced over the decade for all courses, especially for Mechanical and for Engineering and Business, athough it remained significant in all courses.[69]

The Faculty added a small 'sub-critical' nuclear reactor to its research facilites in 1958. These were years of great enthusiasm for the peaceful use of nuclear power. The first commercial nuclear power stations were finally close to reality and Canadian

Professors Gordon Slemon (seated) and Doug Andrews (left) study the operation of a Honeywell Reactor Simulator with a Honeywell representative, c.1957. The simulator, an electronic system that behaved like a reactor, was purchased at about the same time as the Faculty's first research reactor; it was used for many years to introduce students to reactor start-up and control procedures. UTA, A78-0041/029(17)

scientists and engineers were near the leading edge in the field. Atomic Energy of Canada Limited had developed a prototype of a natural uranium, heavy water type of reactor, which they planned soon to put in commercial production under the name CANDU. Researchers at the university were anxious to take part. In late 1955, Dean McLaughlin was among a group of university scientists trying to procure a research reactor for the campus, but it was proving to be a complex and expensive proposition. At one point, a committee from the Faculty recommended a new institute, like that of Aerophysics, with involvement from several university departments. Nothing quite this grand ever took shape, but the university eventually agreed to have a nuclear facility installed. After exploring a number of possible equipment suppliers, Dean McLaughlin settled with Canadair Ltd. to design and construct an AECL-type reactor, on the assumption that this was the design of the future for the Canadian nuclear industry. The reactor was installed in the basement of the Wallberg Building, deemed the safest and most suitable space, through the winter of 1957/58 and officially opened in June 1958. It was the first working reactor in Canada outside of the AECL's Chalk River facility. Because of its location in the Wallberg Building, the reactor's management was placed in the hands of Chemical Engineering, and the Faculty's first professor of Nuclear Engineering, D.G. Andrews, was hired in 1957 as a member of that department. The second, R.E. Jervis, was hired the following year; Jervis had several years of experience with AECL. The Faculty introduced a new nuclear option for undergraduates in Engineering Physics, and began to offer opportunities for a limited amount of graduate research in the field.[70]

New academic staff for the Faculty, almost all with advanced education and research experience, were recruited at a rapid pace in these years. The number of staff in all professorial ranks rose from fifty to seventy-five between 1955 and 1960. Recruitment was aided by a rise in academic salaries throughout the university;[71] this made the Faculty's salaries competitive with those for research engineers at the National Research Council, with obvious benefits for the development of a research-inclined professoriate. Rising salaries, it was hoped, might also induce professors to spend less time on other outside remunerative work, as the problem of summer absences was increasingly being seen as an obstacle to the development of research. This problem was being remedied in other ways, too. G.N. Patterson at the UTIA had begun to use funds received from the U.S. government to pay summer supplements for his staff – the terms of his research grants demanded year-round work – and the NRC began to offer a supplement of $800 for engineers or scientists who would take on research tasks in the summer months.[72]

In the students' world the immediate post-war years, perhaps because of the large enrolments, were rich in activities. It was at Ajax, where social affairs were such a centrepiece, that students held the first Engineers' Ball, an event that, renamed the Cannon Ball in 1955, turned into an enduring annual tradition. In 1950, the Lady Godiva Memorial Band gave its debut performance on the back of a flat-bed truck in the annual homecoming parade. The band was following in the steps of the Toike Oikestra of two generations past, but the name was new, as was the association with the defiant lady whose populist challenge to authority had long been inspirational to engineers. The tradition of the school cannon became even more deeply fixed in the Faculty's student culture on Christmas Day 1949, when a fine new cannon, carefully machined from steel and bronze, was given to the Engineering Society, the handiwork once again of W.H. Kubbinga of the Civil Engineering shops. It would be cherished from that day forward, and brought into public view only with an inviolable guard of students close by.[73]

The rougher side of engineering student life had by no means disappeared, and the pranks and fights of initiation were as spirited as ever in the post-war years. In 1954, however, a seemingly benign orientation activity ran wildly out of control, bringing the Faculty's long-standing tradition of physical initiations into serious disrepute and, ultimately, to an end. The Engineering Society in these years customarily gave the Faculty's first-year students a campus tour as part of their initiation, and on 24 September 1954 such a tour was taking place with about 600 engineering freshmen. After being shown through Hart House, the first stop, this mass of students completely lost themselves and began 'touring' about the campus according to their own whims – storming through the halls and stairways of University, Trinity, and Victoria colleges, damaging walls and fixtures, harassing and molesting students and staff, and stealing furniture. The registrar at University College, Professor W.J. McAndrew, met them in the hall to make peace, and ended up with a gash on his right cheek that required a stitch to close, apparently the result of a tussle with a chair-wielding student. The day's activities were rounded out first by disrupting traffic on nearby streets, then by the feat of carrying a 'small English car parked on a laneway south of Hoskin Ave. into the main entrance of Hart House,' and finally by stealing the ball from a soccer game in progress on the main campus. 'ENGINEERS WREAK HAVOC,' declared the *Varsity* the next day.[74]

Indeed they did, for reasons that nobody ever adequately explained. Such actions were well beyond even the most exuberant student pranks. Drawing blood from Professor McAndrew put the affair into a class of its own. A week later, university President Bissell spoke of some people on campus who 'have technical qualifications but are moral morons.' U.C. Lit. President Martin Friedland, who years later would be dean of Law at the university, commented that 'we regret not so much the physical damage, but the moral damage to the University as a whole.'[75] Not surprisingly, the consequences were severe. The Engineering Society, which was held responsible, was fined $4,000 and had its constitution suspended for what turned out to be four months. So notorious was the incident that it was even commented on months later by Dean McLaughlin in his annual report to the university president.[76]

Talk of restricting or even banning destructive initiation activities had been heard for years. This episode, however, looks to have galvanized the move to rid the campus of them. The next September, engineering frosh were tidying up city parks for their initiation. By 1956, the term 'constructive initiation' had entered common speech at the university, and students of all faculties

Under the watchful eyes of their superiors, first-year engineering students clean a Toronto Island beach as part of a 'constructive initiation' in 1959. UTA, A78-0041/027(16)

were more often seen cleaning public property than damaging it during the first week of school. This was a university-wide trend in the 1950s, but one that engineering students seem to have followed with more enthusiasm than any others – their socially-conscious side, always present, now much more in evidence. Not everyone at the university liked this. A group of dissident St Michael's College students complained that such activities were 'wishy-washy' and 'too soft,' but the change stuck.[77] 'Destructive initiations' were now unquestionably improper.

The student body itself remained much the same as it had always been, with one important exception: graduate students were becoming increasingly international. The number of graduate students in the Faculty changed little over the decade, but the proportion who came from abroad was clearly rising. Academic staff involved in graduate supervision recall the change well enough, and lists of graduate students from the 1950s reveal many Arabic, Indian, Chinese, and eastern Europeans names. One incident that contributed to this was the sudden arrival, in January 1957, of some eighty Mining and Surveying students from the University of Sopron in Hungary. They were part of a large exodus of Hungarian students who fled their country after the failed anti-communist uprising, and who, in those Cold War times, were welcomed by an unusually hospitable Canadian public. After intensive English instruction, forty-eight registered in the Faculty and more than half of them successfully graduated some years later.[78] The university and the Faculty were proud of this growing international connection, although it probably resulted more from international circumstances than from anything done in Toronto.

One aspect of the Faculty's student body that remained unchanged was the near absence of women. Despite enrolments of some 2,000 students, the number of women remained in single digits year after year – a miniscule proportion. There appears to have been nothing in the school's reputation at this time that deterred women from enrolling, nor anything about the school's culture that the women who did enrol found unacceptable. Those who attended had fine experiences. Some professors were more accepting than others, and repeated comments about the novelty of their presence could become tiresome, but generally young women thought attending university in the midst of hundreds of 'brothers' was no harder than life itself. Finding employment after graduation was another matter. Professional engineering was indeed still a man's world, as most of the female graduates found to their dismay. This fact of the profession, rather than anything in the Faculty, probably explains the tiny female enrolment. Most young women simply did not consider engineering as a possible career, nor evidently did their high-school teachers or parents urge them to do so.[79] As for women on the academic staff, they were rarer still. Women had worked occasionally as temporary demonstrators, but the first woman on the permanent academic staff was Marion Currie (later Bassett), an illumination instructor in the Applied Physics department who was appointed in 1958; not until 1964, when Mary Jane Phillips was appointed in Chemical Engineering, would there be a second.

In 1959, R.B. Myers, a well-educated academic electrical engineer from the United States, came to Canada to join the staff of the new University of Waterloo. He found the experience so distasteful that he left as soon as he could, and was moved to write a book reflecting on his short stay in Canada. Among their many quirks, Myers observed, Canadians were overly fond of ice hockey and summer cottages. He was also appalled at the state of Canadian engineering education – the absence of advanced science in the curricula, the staff's indifference to research, the teaching of practical skills and professional deportment. 'Engineering education is still in a pre-World War Two rut,' he declared, by then safely back in the United States. Some at the Faculty might have agreed. Yet beneath the surface, where Myers had not had the time to explore, something fundamental had indeed begun to shift.[80]

Although we have no sign that anyone knew it at the time, the academic year 1959/60 marked the beginning of a rush of change in the Faculty. Over the next decade, old ways were swept out with what now looks like nearly reckless confidence. Values and traditions, many dating from Galbraith's day, were finally put to rest. In their place came the new: new programs, new research institutes, a different kind of academic staff, and a different kind of student. These changes would take several years. Not until the

1970s would the transformation be complete. But the first step, moving out the old in preparation for the new, began in the early 1960s.

The first of the line of changes came that summer when the teaching department of Engineering Drawing came to an end with the retirement of its head, W.J.T. Wright, and two of its senior professors, W.B. Dunbar and A. Wardell.[81] All three were Faculty graduates, with no other advanced education, who had devoted their entire careers to teaching engineering students. Wright, the son of the Faculty's first professor of Architecture, C.H.C. Wright, had joined the staff before the First World War, and thus carried the cachet of a personal connection with Galbraith himself. They were undoubtedly men of the old school, and their retirement marked a passing of the old ways. More important was the fate of their subject. Engineering drawing was not just any subject. It had long been the core of the school's curriculum, and the heart of formal engineering education since the start of the nineteenth century. Although a mix of several quite different subjects – draughting and lettering, descriptive geometry, graphical problem solving – all had the drafting board as their common element. Long hours spent there trained students to attack problems visually, and the common experience helped to establish a foundation of professional camaraderie. The end of the department did not immediately mean the end of the subject. Most students still took nine hours of drawing a week in first year, and many also took some drawing in their second and third years.[82] The teaching was done by a few younger instructors from the department, who were moved to Civil and to Mechanical Engineering. But the end of the department brought a loss of influence and profile for the subject.

That same summer saw the termination of Engineering and Business. This course had nothing like the pedigree or the central significance of Engineering Drawing, but it was similar in that its roots lay in an age when an engineering school was above all a place where young men were taught skills that prepared them for a professional career. The course's demise came not from a lack of students – the usual cause of a course's termination – but primarily from a recognition that a four-year program did not give adequate time for the thorough study of either engineering or business. As well, with business administration now developing into a university subject, post-graduate study in business was becoming increasingly popular among graduates of the other engineering specialties. The BASc followed by a MBA, in other words, was becoming the preferred route for students seeking a combined program. Being largely practical in emphasis, the course also suffered from not having a clearly defined body of knowledge to which research could contribute, an increasingly important part of any academic discipline.[83]

In its place appeared a new course in Industrial Engineering. This was by no means just Engineering and Business renamed, although it took the latter's place in the calendar and students in Engineering and Business with more than one year of study remaining were transferred into it.[84] Industrial engineering is not the simple joining of business skills with engineering; it is the application of engineering approaches and an engineering mindset to problems of industrial management. The principle on which it is based is that a complex operation involving a variety of human, technical, and economic factors can be optimized by using rational mathematical techniques; industrial management problems can thus be 'engineered' in much the same way as a water system or electrical grid.[85] Although it has roots in earlier notions of 'work study' and 'scientific management,' the field had taken its mature form only in the Second World War, during which the military had subjected some of its complex activities to scientific analysis. Unlike Engineering and Business, it was very much a specialty of its own, well suited to advanced research. The subject was not entirely new to the Faculty in 1959. E.A. Allcut, an early advocate, already employed some of its concepts in his

The Faculty's new Galbraith Building in March 1961, less than a year after its official opening. UTA, A78-0050/002(17)

teaching of industrial management.[86] Now, however, it was a full course, and designated Department Four.

One can only imagine what John Galbraith would have thought of Industrial Engineering and the diminishing importance of Engineering Drawing; the former would no doubt have per-plexed him – as it did most traditional engineers – and the latter dismayed him. Many aspects of the Faculty's curriculum were becoming distinctly non-Galbraithian, a tendency that would con-tinue in the years to come. Galbraith's name, however, would live on, for at the very time that his legacy was being supplanted, a new building bearing his name was being erected to handle the expected rush of students. Excavation began in the summer of 1959 on a site running west from the back of the old Physics Building to St George Street. The cornerstone was laid on 24 May 1960, and the building, designed by architects Page and Steele, was fully in use that fall, primarily for the Civil and Electrical Engineering departments and the Faculty's administrative offices.

The following year, 1961, saw the creation of a new Department of Industrial Engineering – it had previously been only a course taught by members of other departments – and the appointment of Arthur Porter as its head. Porter was an Englishman with a PhD in Physics who had served as a scientific officer with the British Admiralty during the war, in which capacity he took part in some of the earliest operations research programs. In his war work, Porter had encountered the Canadian scientist O.M. Solandt, also working for the British military at the time. It was Solandt, now chancellor of the University of Toronto, who had arranged to have a chair in Industrial Engineering established and for Porter to come and occupy it.[87] A non-engineer, with a PhD in Physics, was for the first time head of a Faculty department. What would John Galbraith have thought of this?

In 1962, the course in Engineering Physics was renamed Engineering Science. Although a change in name only, it should not be viewed as entirely insignificant. It was prompted by the fact that three years earlier, a chemical option had been added to the long list of specializations available to third-year students in the course. Using the word 'physics' in the name, already a little off the mark considering the range of options available, now seemed clearly unsuitable, and the more general name was introduced.[88] But with the addition of the chemical option, and the name change, the course took a further step towards becoming something of a separate division in the Faculty. Although technically just one of nine courses, students had always been able to specialize within the course, and now specialties analogous to most of the other engineering courses (except some aspects of civil) were available within Engineering Science. It had become, in other words, something of a parallel, academically more advanced, stream rather than a single course, and, as its large and rising portion of the Faculty's students made quite clear – it now had about

20 per cent of the Faculty's enrolment – an increasingly popular one.[89]

The retirement of faculty secretary Col. W.S. Wilson in 1962 broke another old tie with the past. Wilson had graduated from the Faculty in 1924, in Architecture, and taken the position of secretary in 1927. As the Faculty's sole full-time administrator he had carried a heavy burden indeed, yet judging by the recollections of all who worked with him, he did so with devotion and exceptionally good humour. More than once, Col. Wilson settled the waters after temperamental department heads had whipped them up, and he deserves much of the credit for holding the Faculty intact under the war and post-war strains. The loss at his departure was tempered, however, by the appointment of Jim Gow in his place. Gow, also a Faculty graduate, had worked in the office under Wilson since the Ajax years.[90]

At the end of the following academic year, in June 1963, the erosion of old ways went a step further with the end of the department of Applied Physics upon the retirement of its senior professor, K.B. Jackson. This department had had a rather eccentric history in the Faculty, but its roots went deep. Formed by Galbraith in 1904, renamed and reconstituted in 1934 when the Engineering Physics course began; it had gradually been shunted aside as the Faculty grew, but it had survived. Staff in the department had been teaching basic first-year applied physics to students in some courses, and giving specialized upper-level instruction in acoustics, photographic surveying, and illumination; but students in Mining, Mechanical, Chemical, Metallurgical, and in most Enginering Physics options made no use of the department. Its physics instruction was, in fact, rather elementary for the time. But K.B. Jackson, like his mentor G.R. Anderson, had been a valued staff member, and the Faculty had done its best to use his skills. C.R. Young had appointed him chairman of the committee running Engineering Physics in 1942 – curious, considering Jackson's role in the creation of the course – and Jackson continued to serve as something of a student counsellor in Engineering Physics until his retirement.[91] It was Jackson, not the department, that the Faculty had retained; when he retired, the department died. Its few staff who taught the specialized subjects were dispersed to other departments, where they continued to teach for several years.

So ended the last teaching department of the Faculty. The origins of this sort of department lie far in the past. The name had originally applied to all administrative units of staff, and had been used to distinguish 'department' in the administrative sense from 'department' as a synonym for 'course' or 'program.' But it had come to be used only for departments of staff who taught all students in the Faculty and whose field did not coincide with a particular course. Most of these teaching departments, and their subjects of instruction, had been subsumed by departments organized around courses; Applied Mechanics and Surveying (at one time both separate teaching departments) had become part of Civil Engineering, and Applied Chemistry part of Chemical Engineering and Applied Chemistry (its dual name revealing its dual origins). But Engineering Drawing and Applied Physics had had nothing to be attached to, and both had remained independent departments. Both were now gone. Perhaps the loss was not so great – nobody seems to have even noticed it at the time – but with historical perspective it does stand out. The name recalls a time when the allegiance of the academic staff was to the students collectively, not to those in a particular specialty, and, more importantly, a time when, since the purpose of the school was to teach, the natural way of organizing its staff was by the subject they taught.

Earlier that year, in February 1963, the Faculty had announced something which, perhaps more than any other single event, turned it towards the future. The Ford Foundation, a philanthropic organization in the United States that was custodian of much of the Ford family fortune, had just given the Faculty $2,325,000 to strengthen its graduate program.[92] Such a sum was unprecedented, far exceeding even the generous DRB grant that had founded the Institute of Aerophysics.

Oddly enough, this treasure came to the Faculty nearly unsolicited. The foundation had sold much of its Ford Motor Company stock holdings in the late 1950s, and having become embarrassingly flush with cash, had promptly set about giving money away to educational and cultural organizations, mostly in the United States, by the tens of millions of dollars. Included in this was $71.7 million to engineering education between 1959 and 1965, almost all of which went to major engineering schools in the United States.[93] Agents of the foundation had had Toronto in mind, for they had visited Dean McLaughlin and some of the academic staff in the fall of 1958, and again in the winter of 1960, but nothing had come of these visits.[94] In the fall of 1961, however, Dr Carl Borgmann of the Foundation called upon Dean McLaughlin and, over lunch at the York Club, asked how the Faculty would make use of a $1 million to $2 million dollar grant from the Ford Foundation. Quietly elated, no doubt, McLaughlin asked for time to consider such a matter, which Borgmann was quite willing to give, and the meeting ended with the understanding that McLaughlin would prepare a proposal in the months ahead and submit it to the Foundation. He invited a few senior staff to form an advisory committee, requested submissions from all department heads, and prepared and sent a proposal to Borgmann at the end of the following March. McLaughlin requested $2 million to be spent over a five-year period, half of which would go to people – graduate fellowships, research associateships, and visiting faculty – and half to equipment and materials. After some discussions and modifications, the Foundation formally approved a grant of $2.325 million in early January 1963.[95]

The funds caused a great stir in the Faculty, first administra-

Dean R.R. McLaughlin teaching a class in chemistry, c.1958. McLaughlin served as dean from 1954 to 1967, during which time he started a number of important transformations in the Faculty. UTA, A78-0041/029(16)

tively, as committees were formed to review applications for equipment purchases and fellowships, and then in scholarly activity, as the numbers of graduate students and the amount of research activity rose steeply. By the time the five years had run its course, hundreds of graduate students and post-doctoral research fellows had come through the Faculty, and a good many had gone on to notable careers. Consequences went far beyond this. The grant funded over $700,000 of new equipment, distributed almost equally among the Faculty's main departments; Chemical Engineering purchased an infrared spectrophotometer, Metallurgy and Materials Science an Instron testing machine, and Civil

Engineering some sophisticated photogrammetry equipment for aerial surveying.[96] Aerospace received funds to move research equipment from its original Downsview site to its new quarters on Dufferin Street (to which it had begun moving in 1959). Metallurgy and Materials Science received $325,000 towards the cost of new facilities, which took the form of an addition to the northeast corner of the Wallberg Building; this sum had been added to the original $2 million at the foundation's suggestion.[97]

The Ford Foundation grant, although a big boost at a critical time, was not the only stimulus to research in the Faculty. Funds from other sources were growing rapidly. The one missing piece of the research puzzle, money, was at last being put into place. In the academic year ending June 1960, the Faculty received a total of some $422,000 in research funding, about half of which came from the DRB (much of which went to Aerophysics). Ten years later, even without the Ford Foundation's money (by then all spent), total annual research funding for the Faculty exceeded $2.7 million, a nearly seven-fold increase. The source of this was almost entirely the National Research Council, whose annual contribution had risen from $71,000 to almost $2 million over those ten years. Other sources of research funds were also being tapped. The government of Canada was providing funds from several departments, and Atomic Energy of Canada was supporting two substantial research projects, while the U.S. government and U.S. Air Force were providing generous grants to Aerophysics – which caused some concern when it began. Private industry was also beginning to contribute small amounts; W.H. Rapson was by this time running a flourishing pulp and paper laboratory in Chemical Engineering, with generous support from industry. But the NRC was the prime source of funds.[98] The result of this increase was, not surprisingly, a substantial rise in research output. The number of publications per staff member of professorial rank nearly doubled over the decade.[99] Dean McLaughlin's concern about the amount of Faculty research was fast being remedied.

This plentiful supply of public research funds came about for two quite different reasons. One is that the government of Canada had resolved in 1961 to provide more government aid for industrial research, and the NRC's mandate had been expanded accordingly.[100] This was part of a general increase in government support for science and scientific education that had begun in the late 1950s and been spurred on by the western world's embarrassment at the Russians' successful launch of Sputnik.[101] But a second reason is that, as engineering grew more rooted in scientific fundamentals, engineering research became a more fitting recipient of public research funds. Engineering researchers in the Faculty were not engaged in product development, nor were they simply conducting tests to determine the best practical solution to an engineering problem. A distinct type of research had by now clearly evolved, in this faculty and elsewhere, which addressed fundamental scientific problems in man-made materials and processes.[102] Whether in wood chemistry, electronics, soil mechanics, or metallurgy, there were fundamental scientific facts to uncover that pure scientists were simply not going to seek. This sort of research, often rather misleadingly called 'applied science,' was now being recognized; it, as much as pure science, deserved public funds.

With growing support for research came rising numbers of graduate students. Some new funds went directly to the students – such as the Ford Foundation graduate fellowships – but nearly all research grants aided graduate studies in one way or another. The money allowed academic staff to undertake large research projects, often requiring specialized equipment, in which graduate students participated. Not surprisingly, graduate enrolment, already rising at the end of the 1950s, jumped from 178 students in 1959 to over 600 in 1969; of this latter number, 189 were PhD students.[103]

This sudden increase in graduate students, of course, put new pressures on the academic staff, but not by coincidence it was accompanied by a new provincial government funding scheme that permitted a corresponding increase of staff. The province's new system, introduced in 1967, based annual grants to universities on a formula in which graduate students counted five or six units and undergraduates only one or two.[104] So the Faculty's rising graduate enrolment was generously rewarded, and it permitted an increase in academic staff from 75 in 1960 to 152 in 1969, even though undergraduate enrolment rose by only about 30 per cent over that time. The anticipated great rise in enrolment had never occurred because the Ontario government had decided that the growing demand for engineering education could best be met by building more engineering schools.[105] Undergraduate teaching loads for the staff therefore fell quite noticeably, allowing more time for both research and graduate supervision.

With the emphasis on research and graduate study, the Faculty began to see more research institutes taking shape; this trend would show more clearly a few years later, but it began in the 1960s. The first, and until that time the only, such body had been the Institute of Aerophysics, renamed the Institute of Aerospace Studies in 1964, which continued to flourish under the leadership of G.N. Patterson. It was a compellingly successful model. With secure sources of funds in the DRB, the NRC, and several branches of the U.S. military, the institute attracted top-calibre graduate students and research associates who, together with its permanent staff – numbering ten by 1965 – conducted and published the results of copious researches every year. Situated miles north of the main university campus, its ties to the Faculty had always been tenuous, but it was, nominally at least, part of the Faculty and its success was impossible to overlook.

In 1962, the Institute of Biomedical Electronics was formed. There had been some interest in this field in Electrical Engineering for several years; I.R. Dalton, in association with department head G.F. Tracy, had recently conducted research in devices for monitoring heart-lung activity in premature infants.[106] But the

Professor N.F. Moody, first head of the Institute of Biomedical Electronics, in a
laboratory at the institute, mid-1960s. UTA, A78-0041/029(01)

institute proper started through the efforts of other men, among
them E. Llewellyn Thomas of the Department of Pharmacology
in the Faculty of Medicine, and Arthur Porter, the newly
appointed head of Industrial Engineering, who had overseen the
introduction a biomedical engineering program at the University
of Saskatchewan prior to his coming to Toronto. The man they
both wanted to head the institute was N.F. Moody, an Englishman

who had moved to Canada after the war to work for AECL at Chalk River. He had latterly been working under Porter as Chair of Electrical Engineering at the University of Saskatchewan, and had been responsible for establishing biomedical engineering research there. The university agreed in 1962 to create a position in Electrical Engineering for the Institute; Moody was then hired away from Saskatchewan – much to their dismay – to fill it and the new Institute formally created.[107] Unlike Aerospace, however, it had no generous public benefactor and survived on funds from a number of small sources, chiefly the Johnson's Wax fund brought in by the Faculty of Medicine.[108] Thomas was moved full-time to the Institute later in 1963, but additional staff were not hired until 1965/66. By this time, research funds from the NRC had put the Institute on a more secure basis, and with a graduate student enrolment in 1967 of twenty-three, it had clearly found a niche. The Institute moved into renovated quarters in the old Electrical Building in 1967, by which time it was a permanent part of the Faculty.[109]

Meanwhile, renewal continued. In one of Dean McLaughlin's final acts, the Department of Mining Engineering and its course were terminated. This was a change carried out against strong opposition; participants recall the debates on this being among the Faculty's most acrimonious in years. Mining went back to the earliest days of the school, and the rugged life of the mining engineer still epitomized traditional engineering. But too much had changed for it to fit into a modern engineering school. A mining engineer had always been a generalist, with no distinct scientific subject at the heart of his specialty. As a result, although there was plenty of consulting in the department, there was next to no research. Aspects of mining that lent themselves to engineering research – rock mechanics, mine ventilation, the chemistry of refining, the mechanics of pumping slurries – all belonged in other engineering specialties. Mining engineering had no ground on which to stand in a research-centred establishment.

Furthermore, the Faculty's new academic staff, who nearly all had PhDs and who were inspired much more by the future than the past, saw mining engineering as rather un-academic and backward. On top of these matters of principle, enrolment in the course had been falling for years, and by the mid-sixties was next to nothing. A committee of council was struck early in 1964 to review the matter, and after a year of meetings, which included interviews with representatives from the mining industry, it presented three unequivocal recommendations to council: that the course and the department be terminated, that other departments in the Faculty be urged to carry out research applicable to the industry, and that the course in Applied Geology be reworked into a course in Geological Engineering with closer ties to the Department of Geology in the Faculty of Arts and Science. The recommendations were accepted, and one more piece of the original school was gone by the fall of 1965.[110]

Other changes in the curriculum were not as fundamental. In 1963, engineering drawing was dropped from second and subsequent years in all but Civil Engineering, further reducing its importance. Metallurgical Engineering was renamed Metallurgy and Materials Science in 1964, reflecting the growing importance of non-metallic materials in industry.[111] A new graduate program leading to a Master of Engineering (MEng, not a MASc) was introduced in 1965; this was intended to permit working professionals to attain a graduate degree, on a part-time schedule, by solving a practical engineering problem in an academic setting rather than through conventional research.[112] Slight changes were made in the content, names, and numbers of the humanities courses introduced by C.R. Young in the 1940s, but English, economics, and politics remained the subjects taught, and they held on to their roughly 8 per cent of the curriculum. The first-year English course was changed in 1963 to include the study of literature – as opposed to the basics of writing that had been taught for years by W.J.T. Wright – and, in 1964, a fourth-year English course was added. Overall, the drift in these non-technical subjects was away from practical professional training towards more conventional scholarly humanities – something the better-educated new guard found more palatable. 'The Profession of Engineering' had been dropped in 1957, and Engineering Law in 1968.

In the fall of 1966, the Faculty at long last established a common first year for all but Engineering Science students. The actual change that allowed it was small – surveying was dropped from first-year Civil and Geological, replaced by an extra hour of mathematics – but it represented another break from the past.[113] To the traditionalists in the Faculty, the few who remained, this small change was a loss; first-year surveying had been, like engineering drawing, the essence of the engineering student's experience. But hardly anyone thought that way anymore, and few engineering graduates in the 1960s would ever be called upon to 'run a line.' Mathematics, not surveying, was now the profession's foundation.

That same year, in the summer of 1966, R.R. McLaughlin's twelve-year tenure as dean came to an end. Having reached the age of 65, and with failing health, he retired and passed the Faculty's leadership to a younger generation. For many of the new men of the academic staff, 'Rolly' McLaughlin had been the cause of much frustration. He had not been the progressive force they felt the Faculty needed, so slowly had he moved in clearing out the old ways. Nor had he seemed welcoming to the younger staff so eager for change; forty years later, many still remember the formidable group of old department heads with whom he had kept counsel through the early years of his deanship. His opposition to new trends among the students – some of whom by the late 1950s were daring to attend classes without proper jackets and ties – seemed absurd to many.[114] Yet the amount of change over his twelve years cannot be denied. Cautious he might have been, but act he did. The termination of several old programs,

The old Engineering Building being demolished, November 1966. UTA, A78-0041/027(14)

the successful handling of the Ford Foundation grant, the expansion of research and graduate studies, the establishment of a research-oriented professoriate, the rising proportion of students taking Engineering Science, and a modest increase of science and mathematics in the basic curriculum all happened in the first half of the 1960s. These were important, progressive steps, and for them McLaughlin deserves credit. He was the bridge from the old to the new.

Into the deanship now moved James M. Ham, an accomplished

and highly respected scholar and engineer who was very much a man of the new way. To him fell the task of carrying the Faculty further down the new road on which it had been irreversibly set. At this very time, by a curious stroke of coincidence, the old Engineering Building, the powerful symbol of the Faculty's past, was finally demolished.

chapter five

THE FACULTY TRANSFORMED

As the Faculty's history so far has shown, change has been a fact of its life. Circumstances and events of many kinds – provincial elections, new industries, great wars – have repeatedly borne upon on the Faculty of Applied Science and Engineering, causing numerous alterations in its offerings and organization. Changes were usually made cautiously, and in some cases almost reluctantly, but they were made. Nonetheless, the generation from the late 1960s to the 1990s stands out above all the others in this respect. The speed and extent of change in these years truly was remarkable. From the staff- and student-driven reforms of the later 1960s through to the creation of a vast research enterprise with close ties to private industry by the 1990s, the Faculty truly was transformed.

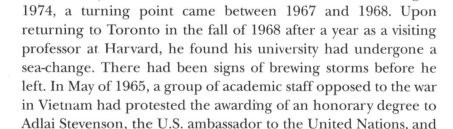

As University of Toronto President Claude Bissell saw it, writing in 1974, a turning point came between 1967 and 1968. Upon returning to Toronto in the fall of 1968 after a year as a visiting professor at Harvard, he found his university had undergone a sea-change. There had been signs of brewing storms before he left. In May of 1965, a group of academic staff opposed to the war in Vietnam had protested the awarding of an honorary degree to Adlai Stevenson, the U.S. ambassador to the United Nations, and that same year students and staff had organized large group gatherings, called 'teach-ins,' on radical themes. Bissell had also begun to sense disharmony between himself and the students.

But these were all within the limits of normal university life.[1] Back at his president's job in the fall of 1968, however, Bissell encountered something new. The student leaders bore a new, much less respectful attitude; 'it was as if a great dividing line separated them from their predecessors,' he observed.[2] The student revolt of the 1960s had arrived in Toronto. Although the Faculty of Applied Science and Engineering was far from the centre of this movement, the shock waves did ripple through. By the time this burst of radicalism had lost its force in the early 1970s, the Faculty was a different place.

What was not so clear at the time, but which Bissell did recognize six years later when he wrote, was that the academic staff had actually begun the movement for university reform some years earlier. It was staff concerns about closed-door university decision-making, expressed by a province-wide association, that had prompted the provincial Duff-Berdhal Commission of 1965–66. This in turn had led to a radical new process for appointing department chairs (and later deans) at the University of Toronto in which academic staff could participate, and to the setting of a five-year limited term for chairs. The latter abruptly ended the old system of life-long departmental fiefdoms, and had far-reaching effects in the Faculty. Lifelong headships were ill-suited to a dynamic, changing educational institution; they, perhaps more than anything else, had retarded the adoption of new ways. These new rules, generally referred to as the Haist Rules after Professor R.E. Haist of the Faculty of Medicine who chaired the committee that set them, took force in 1967.[3]

This spirit of reform lived within the Faculty's own academic staff, too, many of whom were new by the later years of the decade. They undertook two major changes: restructuring first the undergraduate curriculum and then the Faculty's governance; neither would have been imaginable in more traditional times.

The roots of the curriculum reform went back several years. The Development Committee of 1955–57 had had the mandate to consider changes to the school's curriculum, but in the end had sidestepped the issue. A group of younger professors – Ham, Hooper, Huber, and Slemon – had offered the committee some suggestions on the matter, but with little effect.[4] Dean McLaughlin, aware that unfinished business remained, had formed a Faculty Study Committee in 1961 with one of the earlier renegades, J.M. Ham of Electrical Engineering, as chair; this committee was to carry out 'a critical examination of our entire academic program, undergraduate and graduate alike.'[5] Consistent with its name, however, the committee reviewed many things but made no specific recommendations.

Two years later, in 1963, a Committee of the First Year was spun off to take over responsibility of all first-year matters – curriculum, recruitment, quality of instruction, student counselling, and anything else that arose.[6] This committee stood for several years, and towards the end of the decade was finally able to implement several important changes. First, in 1967, computer programming was introduced for all first-year students. Then the committee recommended, after long consideration, severe reductions in the amount of engineering drawing and descriptive geometry taught in first year, effectively ending engineering drawing as it had been known. In its place, in 1968, went engineering graphics, a one-hour lecture and a three-hour laboratory each week for all students, and a new course, engineering applications of mathematics.[7] The long-sought move away from the practical to the mathematical was finally taking place.

Radical though these changes might have been when compared with the static curriculum of generations past, they were not enough. In March 1967, at the suggestion of D.J.L. Kennedy, who had joined the permanent staff in 1960, a new Special Committee on Curriculum was formed to consider possible revisions to the structure (not the content) of the Faculty's curriculum.[8] When it reported a year later, it had concluded that, above all, the system was too rigid. Programs in each engineering field were too strict, as was the Faculty's requirement that all students take a full load every term. It recommended several fundamental changes, among them a greater number of elective subjects in all programs, a 'semester' system in which all courses ran for only one term, and a generally lighter student load. Council's response was to call into being a Curriculum Task Force to assess how, and with what consequences, these extensive changes could actually be implemented. Following this, a Composite Committee on Curriculum was struck to study the matter further still. The old guard must have been hoping this reform thrust would dissipate, but the young staff pressed on. Finally, after what must have seemed countless meetings and reports, an entirely new curriculum structure was approved by the Faculty council, to be put in place for the fall of 1971.[9]

Its flexibility was unprecedented. Students had an unheard-of choice of courses, both technical and non-technical. They would take all their subjects (now officially called 'courses') by semester, and these courses would be passed or failed as units. There was no passing or failing of a year based on average marks, and students could now fail a course without failing their year. They could even pursue studies at their own pace, taking more than four years to finish their degree. It was, all in all, a complete transformation of the school's curriculum structure in a remarkably short time, and although students had been consulted by one of the committees in November 1968, the initiative for the change came from the academic staff.[10]

Overlapping with this was a movement to restructure the Faculty's governance. The retirement of Dean McLaughlin and some of his older colleagues had opened up the Faculty's affairs somewhat, but many of the newer academic staff still felt that too much decision-making was being done inside a closed circle. True to the spirit of the times, they wanted greater democracy in Faculty affairs. This problem was compounded by the fact that, with so much business to transact, monthly council meetings had

Dean James Ham, second from left, is presented with a ceremonial chair to commemorate his stepping down from the chairmanship of Faculty council in 1972.
Professor Frank Hooper, far left, has been elected the first speaker of the newly
constituted council. Presenting the chair are Ted Gerson (right), retiring president of the Engineering Alumni Association, and John Cowan, the incoming
president. Ham served as dean from 1967 to 1973. UTA, A78-0041/027(16)

become too long. Attendance, therefore, was poor, since most of the staff could not give as much time to Faculty affairs as these meetings demanded. The democratic system in place was not working.

The main advocate of restructuring was T.C. Kenney, a recent appointee in Civil Engineering who had just been made chair of the department. He brought forward a motion in January 1969 that a committee be formed to review the matter. This was done, with Kenney as chair, and after a year of meetings it brought to council a set of recommendations calling for far-reaching reform.[11] Under their proposals, council would meet only three times a year, with an expanded membership that included students, but the routine business of the Faculty would be handled by a new executive committee consisting of the normal inner circle of dean and chairs plus a number of members elected from the academic staff at large. An elected chair, not the dean, would preside over council meetings. These were major changes, and since they did not meet with complete consensus council decided, as they had with the proposed curriculum reforms, to strike another committee to study them further and plan their implementation. Professor Olev Trass was appointed chair of the new committee. Carrying this through was no simple job – the committee held twenty meetings in its first eight months – and the task was complicated by the creation of the university's Committee on University Governance, which was at this very time working to re-define the governing structure of the whole university. Eventually disagreements were settled and in 1972 a new council and committee system, much like that proposed by the Kenney committee, was approved, except that meetings were to be held four times a year and the reporting process for the committees was altered. The academic staff, probably half of whom were fairly new at their jobs, had once again initiated and carried through a fundamental reform.

What of the students? When one thinks of Canadian university

campuses in the late 1960s it is not endless staff meetings on curriculum or governance that come to mind. It is student protests.
These were years of student power, of sit-ins and demonstrations,
and of the crumbling of professors' authority and students' deference – the very thing that President Bissell began to witness in the
fall of 1968. Where does this fit in the history of the Faculty?

By and large, such student activities bypassed the Faculty. Engineering students rarely took part in protests, and felt no common
cause with the student radical movement. Why this should have
been so has been asked many times, and never answered with
complete satisfaction, but the students of the Faculty were, quite
clearly, not animated by a spirit of rebellion. Many of the causes
of curriculum dissatisfaction among arts students, such as insuffi-
cient 'relevance' and the absence of Canadian content, just did
not arise. Nor did engineering students feel that the absence of
contemporary perspectives, such as Marxist sociology or ethnic
history, lessened the value of their studies.[12] The heart of the matter might be that a different kind of student was attracted into
engineering in the first place, a student who was prepared to
accept and work within the industrial world as it was and whose
flights of fancy, one might say, were constrained by the laws of
aerodynamics.

That is not to suggest the spirit of the 1960s was entirely absent.
Although not politically radical, engineering students, like most
others at the time, wanted a greater voice in institutional affairs,
and they moved to achieve it. There had always been something
of a bond between the Faculty's students and its academic staff, a
connection that rested on their common profession. The Engineering Society's involvement in governance went back to repre-
sentation on the Faculty's council and discipline committees early
in the century. Calls for greater participation therefore found
success without much fuss. Staff student committees were formed
in some departments in the mid-1960s. When the Engineering
Society proposed student membership on faculty council in 1968,

Dean Ham replied that it was 'an eminently sensible idea.' The Society was divided at first on how many representatives it wanted to demand. A conservative faction thought that five was reasonable, but the majority favoured more and in the end won out. The Society called for twenty seats on council, but were granted twenty-four.[13] Perhaps the ease with which such demands were met weakened what radical spirit did exist among the Faculty's students.

Another manifestation of the spirit of the age, a much more visible one at the time, was the engineering students setting themselves up as opponents of the university student left, a group always dismissively referred to as the 'artsies.' The Faculty's students took on the role of campus counter-revolutionaries. They protested the protests.[14]

One of the earliest conflicts between the two sides, an episode that might well have set a mould that shaped later events, occurred in November 1967. Dow Chemical, through an arrangement with the University Placement Service, had agreed to come to the university campus to interview engineering students seeking summer jobs. Dow was at the time viewed by the student left as complicit in the Vietnam conflict because of its supposed manufacture of napalm, the nasty incendiary agent that was to play such a powerful role in turning public opinion against the war. Dow's presence on campus was thus an affront to the radical students and staff who opposed the war, and since the place and time of their visit was well known, campus police anticipated a lively protest. As expected, early morning brought protesters – about thirty of them, with placards – to the front of the building where the Dow interviewer was set up. Interviews nonetheless took place as planned. Then, in the afternoon, the protestors blocked the building by sitting and lying on the building's steps and porch, making it necessary for the engineering students attending interviews to clamber over and upon the bodies of protestors to enter the building. There was scuffling and shouting, but no damamge done. The climax came when the

Dow recruiter, with the interviews over, had to struggle through the crowd to get to his waiting car.[15]

To the engineering students, the offence was not the university's complicity with the war, but the protestors' denying them their freedoms. 'It's my building too,' called out one engineering student as he fought his way to the door. 'Do you deny me the right to an interview?'[16] The episode took a new form a few days later when the Students Administrative Council (SAC) passed a resolution that called for barring 'companies supplying war materials for Viet Nam' from recruiting on campus. This incensed SAC's opponents, and prompted several engineering students to form the 'Ad Hoc Committee for Representative Government' to lead a campaign to force the SAC president to resign.[17] The battle lines were clearly drawn.

Many other such episodes took place – at least one of which involved a snowball barrage upon some protestors that broke a student's glasses[18] – but the highest profile event of all occurred two years later in Convocation Hall. A working paper on student discipline prepared by a provincial committee of university presidents, of which President Bissell was a member, had circulated around the campus in late September 1969. The paper called for harsh punishments for transgressing students. Bissell, who was by this time under constant attack from the student left, was urged to renounce its contents. Several tense days followed, during which the 'New Left Caucus' of students called a large public meeting at Convocation Hall where the president would be given an opportunity to state his position. A group of engineering students, with the full complicity of Professor W.F. Graydon of Chemical Engineering, slipped into the hall early, prior to the appointed meeting time, and occupied the first five rows of seats before any of the more radical students had arrived. Come they did, however, and when the time came to convene the meeting the hall was overflowing and intimidating. Yet, much to everyone's surprise, when Bissell took the stage the front rows of the

Engineering students in the front rows rise to greet President Bissell at Convocation Hall, 3 October 1969. UTA, B98-0033/691261/ #75

great crowd rose to greet the president with a raucous standing ovation. The hostile mood was shattered. The unexpectedly friendly front rows also led a chorus of 'For He's a Jolly Good Fellow' when Bissell left the stage after his speech.[19]

Their point in all of this was that SAC and the student left were not speaking for all students and thus had to be opposed. As Professor Graydon said later that day, 'The issue was whether a small splinter group of people was going to run this place.'[20] Perhaps the oppositional antics of the Faculty's students were not all quite so principled, and one must look hard to find any lasting effects from these counter-revolutionary tactics, but the engineering students of the day played an important role and no doubt enriched and enlivened this period of student ferment.

Another related but quite separate change in university life in these years was a weakening of the divide between students and staff, part of a widespread social trend away from traditional formality and deference. Professorial authority might never have been as deeply entrenched in the professional schools as in the rest of the university, but it was there. The professors undoubtedly ruled, and they inhabited a social sphere entirely separate from that of the students they taught. There was thus ample room for change, and amid these 'organizationally turbulent times,' as Dean Ham labelled them, new attitudes did indeed begin to emerge. Ham's own views make this perfectly clear. 'Nothing short of a reaffirmation of the central role of interpersonal staff-student relationships will generate a renewed binding myth for the community,' he wrote in 1968.[21] It is hard to imagine any previous dean making such a declaration.

Students were motivated young adults now, not just educational underlings, and their welfare was a growing concern. In 1967, the Faculty introduced first-year seminars in which small groups of students met weekly with a member of the permanent academic staff to discuss academic and professional problems. These were an attempt to mitigate the impersonality of the first-year experience. But classes were no bigger than they had ever been. The novelty was not the impersonality, but the concern about it. In 1968, Dean Ham re-established a permanent Committee on First Year Studies, named a chair of First Year Studies, and organized a large conference on first-year teaching; he also appointed a secondary school liaison officer to improve communication with high-school students. This concern for students, when combined with the spirit of innovation so pervasive in those years, prompted the exploration of new teaching methods. In 1967 the Faculty formed an 'Experimental Teaching Unit' to develop effective ways of using television and other audio-visual materials in classrooms.[22] This turned out to be not as wonderful as expected, and after a few years was disbanded, but considerable money and effort went into the experiment. It did, however, leave an enduring legacy, for it was the seed from which the university's audio-visual services grew.

There was one single event that, for the staff of Mechanical Engineering at least, brought relations with the students to an all-time high – the Faculty's participation in the Intercollegiate Clean Car Race in the fall of 1970.[23] The project began when a fourth-year student in Mechanical Engineering, Doug Venn, heard of the race at a Detroit auto show early in 1970 and decided that his school of engineering should be among the competitors. The race was to run from one side of the United States to the other, from the Massachusetts Institute of Technology in Boston to the California Institute of Technology in Pasedena, and was scheduled for the following fall. Any school that could design and build a vehicle could enter, but to be eligible a vehicle would have to meet a strict emission test, and since the entries had to survive the very real rigours of a cross-country trip, vehicles would have to be fully roadworthy. Venn's professors were dubious. It seemed inconceivable that such a car could be produced in only about seven months.

Soon, however, Professors Frank Hooper and I.W. Smith of Mechanical Engineering were won over, and along with a few other students they set to work. They settled on an electric/propane hybrid engine as the best means of keeping emissions down, and on the use of existing parts and systems as the only way to have a vehicle finished in time for the race. It took numerous donations of equipment, some financial support from the Faculty, and a number of nearly sleepless, work-filled nights in the final days before their departure for Boston, but the Faculty's entry was there at the starting line on 24 August 1970, tested, admitted, and ready to go. The trip was long, and snags frequent, but their perseverance was rewarded. They crossed the finish line after six days on the road, first in their class and sixth overall.

It was a remarkable example of what a combination of student enthusiasm and faculty experience could yield, and the message

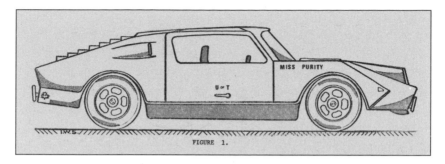

Professor I.W. Smith's drawing (reduced from original size) of Miss Purity, the Faculty's entry into the Clean Car Race, 1970. UTA, A85-0033/006

was not lost on the academic staff. Shared research projects would be much more common from this point on. It was also a welcome antidote to the falling image of the engineer in these anti-technology times. The car and the race received wide press coverage, with the unmistakable message that these student engineers were learning how to remedy, not add to, the world's environmental crisis.

By the early 1970s, a transformation had undoubtedly occurred. Those who taught through these years find it hard to specify what happened, but they know that something did. When the years of turmoil were over, the Faculty was a different place. The professor was not the authority he had once been. Students now participated, questioned, and challenged. A social gap between students and staff had been bridged. It was not just students who were different; the professors had changed, too – many of them had abandoned their ties, as well. Some staff did not like what they saw. They found the new students disrespectful and undisciplined, more likely to spend an hour playing cards in an empty classroom than practising their penmanship at a drafting board. But there was no going back.

Yet compared to the arts students, engineers had changed very little. In the spring of 1971, in his final months in office, President Bissell went to graduation banquets at University College, his *alma mater*, and at the Faculty of Applied Science and Engineering. At the former he saw nothing but sloppy, laughing, disrespectful students who were 'determined not to be impressed.' At Engineering he saw white ties and proper dresses, heard toasts formally prepared and delivered, and wondered if he might not be seeing 'one of the last survivals of the old, genteel, self-confident university.'[24] The Faculty had moved forward but, as usual, it had done so with appropriate caution.

Through these years of protest and reform another important trend was showing itself in the Faculty, one that was less visible but probably just as important: the proliferation of interdisciplinary research institutes.[25] This trend first appeared in the early 1960s with the founding of the Institute for Biomedical Electronics, but now was spreading through all the departments of the Faculty.

The first step toward establishing such a centre in the increasingly important and popular field of environmental studies occurred in 1967 with the founding of the Great Lakes Institute, in which the Faculty played a small part. Then, in 1968, Civil Engineering took a lead role in creating an interfaculty graduate program in Environmental Sciences and Engineering; although a university-wide program, it was closely tied to the Faculty, and, in 1970, its permanent offices were established in the newly renovated Mill Building (with the aid of a development grant from the federal department of Energy, Mines and Resources and a donation from the Ford Motor Company). The group acquired Institute status in 1971, at which time it absorbed the existing Great Lakes Institute, and then, in 1973, it was formally given the name Institute of Environmental Studies. P.H. Jones of Civil Engineering was chair of the Institute's graduate program, but the Faculty was still just one of several participants.[26] The Faculty's own graduate environmental program came a few years later.

Eleanor Lewicki, Nancy Ireland, and Edita Petrik, three of the roughly thirty young women enrolled at the Faculty in 1970/71, attend a reception hosted by Dean Ham for the Faculty's female students. A steady rise in the number of female students was about to begin; by the late 1970s, women would no longer be a novelty at the Faculty.

A new Institute for the History and Philosophy of Science and Technology was founded in 1968, after a few years of unsuccessful discussions with the Department of History concerning a possible joint chair in the History of Science and Technology. Several senior members of the academic staff, notably Jim Ham, then chair of Electrical Engineering, had developed an interest in this new and intriguing cross-disciplinary field, but exactly how to fit it into the university or the Faculty was not clear. The Institute arose when university president Claude Bissell, who also had an interest in the subject, and in cross-disciplinary approaches generally, agreed to let John Abrams of Industrial Engineering devote half his time to establishing it. Abrams had recently been brought to the Faculty by department head Arthur Porter to work in the field of operations research, but Abrams had a background and an interest in the history of science and welcomed the new task. He immediately introduced a course in the History of Technology and Engineering in the fall of 1968 as a humanities option for the Faculty's undergraduates. Soon, however, the institute went its own way; after a small staff of historians was engaged, all with their own research interests, it became administratively and academically separate from the Faculty. Its staff, however, continued to teach the undergraduate course started by Abrams, as well as other similar courses, to the Faculty's students as non-technical electives.[27]

Electrical Engineering and the new Department of Computer Science in the Faculty of Arts and Science together established a Computer Systems Research Group in 1969 to conduct research on computer software. This group, founded on the strength of a $1.25 million 'negotiated development grant' from the NRC, set a solid foundation of cooperation between the two departments. The Materials Research Centre, involving several of the Faculty's departments, was established in 1970 by an advisory group on the subject that had been in place for several years. It was founded on a similar NRC grant, this one for $350,000. Among the new staff brought in with the grant was Ursula Franklin, an expert in corrosion research and the third woman on the Faculty's academic staff; she would later gain renown as a social activist.[28] A Joint Program in Transportation Studies also began in 1970, with participation from the departments of Civil and Industrial Engineering, the Institute of Aerospace Studies, several departments outside the Faculty, and the Transportation Centre at York University. It was supported initially by the Canadian Transport Commission (in fact, J.W. Pickersgill of the CTC had solicited a proposal from the university to set it up) and then by the federal Department of Transport.[29] An interdepartmental Systems Building Centre was formed by M.W. Huggins of Civil Engineering in 1969 to 'investigate methods of improving and industrializing the total building process' by using prefabricated construction units; it was subsequently awarded a grant of $300,000 from the Department of Industry, Trade and Commerce.[30]

The Faculty also played a central part in expanding nuclear research on campus.[31] Throughout the 1960s, researchers using the small sub-critical reactor in the Wallberg Building had grown increasingly aware of that facility's limitations. By 1967, Dean Ham was in touch with representatives from the Faculties of Medicine and Arts and Science about how to improve matters. For a few years, nothing happened. Then, in 1969, R.E. Jervis of Chemical Engineering began discussions with Atomic Energy Canada Ltd. regarding a new 'Safe Low-Power Kritical Experiment' reactor (SLOWPOKE) that AECL had developed for use in hospitals and research laboratories, and within a year the university agreed to lease one such reactor on a two-year trial. Space was prepared in the basement of the Mill Building, and the new reactor was shipped and installed in the summer of 1971. Jervis was named director of the facility, and although no formal research institute was formed, the SLOWPOKE facility in the Mill Building served as the centre for neutron activation analysis in the three faculties of Medicine, Arts and Science, and Applied Science and Engineering from that point on.

Some of these initiatives lasted, often in altered forms, while others did not. But their creation shows the increasing focus on research among the academic staff in the Faculty, just as it does the federal government's generous commitment to building up university research in these confident, expansive times.

It was in the early 1970s that the Cockburn Centre for Engineering Design also came to be.[32] Unlike most of the other entities created with the word 'centre' in their name, it was dedicated to teaching, not research. The centre owed its existence to the generous bequest of the late J. Roy Cockburn, a revered professor of Engineering Drawing who had retired in 1950 from nearly fifty years of teaching. Cockburn died in 1967 and left the bulk of his family's estate to the Faculty. A committee was formed to consider how the funds – nearly $500,000 – might be utilized, and it proposed creating a body to improve the teaching of design in the Faculty. This was an element of engineering education that many felt was being overlooked with the new stress on science and research. After a few years of uncertainty, the Faculty created the Cockburn Centre for Engineering Design in 1972, and the funds were arranged so that they would sustain one professor of Engineering Design. I.W. Smith of Mechanical Engineering was appointed to the position, and he immediately introduced elective courses in design that proved very popular, especially among Mechanical Engineering students. It was pedagogically somewhat against the current, for students were being asked to solve real-world design problems at a very early stage in their studies, without yet having mastered the requisite advanced science and mathematics, but the students were keen and the course did maintain a link with the practical world that other parts of the curriculum were foresaking.

It was at this time that L.E. Jones of Mechanical Engineering was appointed to the honourary position of Faculty archivist.[33] Jones had joined the academic staff in 1943, one of the first staff members to have a PhD. But unlike the other early doctorates on the staff – McLaughlin, Graydon, and Pidgeon – Jones never developed into a researcher or an important graduate supervisor. His unique contribution to the Faculty lay in its life, not its scholarship. Students remember Jones fondly and vividly for his instruction in slide rule technique, his tutoring in the proper etiquette of formal dress, and his many contributions to the Engineering Society. Jones loved the Faculty, especially its past, and he became the unofficial custodian of the Faculty's history even before he retired. By naming him Faculty archivist in 1970, Dean Ham was formalizing what already was.

Professor L.E. Jones (right), in a group with his mother (far left) and his wife, admires the BASc degree just awarded to his son William at convocation, May 1968. UTA, A78-0041/030(15)

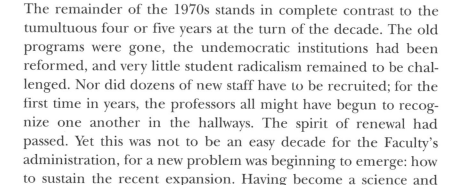

The remainder of the 1970s stands in complete contrast to the tumultuous four or five years at the turn of the decade. The old programs were gone, the undemocratic institutions had been reformed, and very little student radicalism remained to be challenged. Nor did dozens of new staff have to be recruited; for the first time in years, the professors all might have begun to recognize one another in the hallways. The spirit of renewal had passed. Yet this was not to be an easy decade for the Faculty's administration, for a new problem was beginning to emerge: how to sustain the recent expansion. Having become a science and technology research centre as well as an undergraduate engineering school, ensuring the Faculty's financial future was no simple job. Only gradually did this new problem come into sharp focus, and not until the end of the decade was its magnitude clear enough that the basic solutions required could be envisioned.

The dean for most of the 1970s was Bernard (Ben) Etkin, an outstanding professor of aerodynamics at the Institute of Aerophysics (now Aerospace) who had been on the staff of the Faculty since the 1940s. Etkin had been drawn into wider university affairs during the 1950s in the early organization of university teaching staff, and more recently as a member of the university's Committee on University Governance during the days of student unrest. He replaced Jim Ham in the summer of 1973.

Ham had been universally admired in the Faculty, and the end of his tenure was met with some regret. Most viewed him as having been the ideal leader for this time of turmoil. He had a deep commitment to the Faculty, having attended himself in the 1940s, and a sincere concern for its students. He was also a tireless advocate of higher levels of education and more research. His reputation carried him from dean of the Faculty into the deanship of the School of Graduate Studies in 1976 and then to the presidency of the University of Toronto in 1978. But when Ham stepped down as dean, the difficult job of following such a highly regarded leader and of settling the Faculty down after a period of rapid change passed to Etkin.

Curriculum alterations were, not surprisingly, low on most people's list. Learning to work with the changes just implemented was troublesome enough. Nevertheless, a few important developments did occur. One of the decade's few formal curriculum changes was done at the start of Etkin's first year, largely the product of work in the final stages of Ham's deanship. The program in Geological Engineering was terminated, and a new program in Geological Engineering and Applied Earth Science was introduced. It was to be administered not by a department, but a division, like Engineering Science, that would offer a program using staff from various departments both inside and outside the Fac-

Dean Ben Etkin explains the instrumentation of the LINK trainer to some young visitors at the Institute of Aerospace's open house, 1973. Etkin served as dean from 1973 to 1979. UTA, A78-0041/027(17)

ulty. Among three options available was a specialization in Mineral Engineering, so it did, to a degree, bring back a program to serve the mining industry.[34]

There was also, after years of negotiation, a graduate program in Environmental Engineering established within the Faculty.[35] P.H. Jones of Civil Engineering had proposed such a program in December 1972, while serving as the chair of the university's graduate program in Environmental Science and Engineering, but it had found little support. Environmental studies involved so many faculties and departments that consensus was extremely difficult to attain, and opportunities for discord were innumerable. Then late in 1975, after the Institute of Environmental Studies had been formed and its university-wide Master's program in

Environmental Studies established, Jones reproposed his engineering program to the Faculty, and this time it met with approval. A committee reviewed the scheme in the summer of 1976, recommended its implementation, and by January 1977 four departments – Chemical, Mechanical, Civil, and Industrial – had agreed to participate in a collaborative graduate program to begin that September.[36]

The social and environmental effects of technological change were drawing an increasingly critical public eye in the 1970s, and as a result the Canadian Engineering Accreditation Board was urging engineering schools to introduce instruction in the subject to their undergraduate curricula. In response to this, several staff members, primarily Jim Ham, Morris Wayman of Chemical Engineering, and Ursula Franklin of Metallurgy and Materials Science introduced a course on the social impact of technology in the fall of 1976 as a non-technical elective for fourth-year students. The course was team taught, with a number of senior academic staff contributing lectures in their areas of expertise. Ham had to withdraw from the initiative upon being appointed dean of Graduate Studies, but Wayman carried it on.[37] The development and management of energy resources was another public issue in the 1970s. International oil prices had risen sharply, with severe consequences throughout the country. To help the Faculty develop research in the field the university provided a good sum from its recent fundraising campaign for a new chair in Energy Studies and a new energy conversion laboratory in Mechanical Engineering. O.J.C. Runnalls of the federal Department of Energy, Mines and Resources was appointed to this chair in 1979.[38] The Cockburn Centre for Engineering Design suffered a loss when I.W. Smith, the director and heart of the centre, retired in 1978. D.W. Hoeppner was appointed the new director of the centre, but Smith's popular courses could never really be replaced.

Underlying these developments in courses and programs was a new and worrisome problem: a growing concern about the Faculty's finances. The shortage of money, in fact, became one of the main themes of the decade. During the 1960s, the governments of Canada's provinces, and apparently the people who elected them, had been enthusiastic supporters of post-secondary education. Why this should have been so is an intriguing question, with several answers, but the support itself is beyond doubt. Working from the premise that public investment in advanced education benefitted everyone, the province of Ontario had poured money into its universities, increasing its contributions far faster than enrolment rose. The number of students attending the province's universities roughly doubled from 1965 to 1969, but provincial government expenditures on universities rose by a factor of about five. The portion of university expenses paid by student fees fell from 28.8 per cent to 17.3 per cent over those same years.[39] This, of course, was the policy that had underlain the doubling of the Faculty's academic staff in the 1960s. Such generosity had come with a price, for this great government investment lifted the university high up on the political stage for all to see and criticize. And when public opinion shifted, as it did in the early 1970s after a few years of student protests, countless oft-repeated stories of unemployed PhDs, and a sharp recession, governments began setting strict limits on their contributions.[40] By the mid-1970s, the university found itself in trouble, as provincial grants were no longer sufficient to cover its expenses. This shortfall was, in turn, passed on to various divisions of the university, including the Faculty of Applied Science and Engineering.

Making troubles more acute, the Faculty was becoming a more expensive place to run. The large number of academic staff hired in the 1960s were moving up through the ranks, and drawing bigger salaries. In 1972/73, just 33 per cent of the academic staff held the rank of full professor; by 1980/81, the proportion was 49 per cent.[41] As a result, expenditures on salaries for academic staff nearly doubled over those years, even though the number of positions remained nearly constant.[42] The university did manage to fund these increases, but just barely. Most departments had to relinquish one or two positions over the decade, and to cut their departmental supplies budgets severely. All was not well with research funds, either. To sustain research programs, equipment had to be maintained and, in many cases, replaced, but most research grants did not allow for the cost of ongoing equipment maintenance. And with departmental budgets for equipment and supplies squeezed to almost nothing, researchers were left on their own. New research was hampered, too, since the Faculty's research funding – most of it from the federal government – remained steady at about $4 million per year through to 1976.[43] This was a disturbing change to those who were anxious to expand their programs and who were accustomed to rising research budgets year after year. In a time of inflation, it effectively meant a reduction.

The financial predicament began to ease somewhat after about 1976. The problem of government funds to the university did not disappear, so the Faculty's basic operating budget remained tight. The university would remain short of money for years, and eventually would have to recognize that the anomaly was the government's generosity of the late 1960s, not the distrust and frugality that followed. Research money, however, did begin to return. From 1976 on, funds rose steadily, and at times quite quickly; over the final half of the decade, the Faculty's research income doubled to $9.5 million. The main source of this growth was the National Research Council, whose grants began to grow as they had in years past. But within these rising figures something new, and important, was beginning to appear: a rising proportion of research funds from contract research.[44]

Research contracts had been a feature of the Faculty for years, even back before the Second World War, although in those earlier years contracts were small and often with an individual on a consulting basis rather than with the Faculty. But certainly since the 1950s most departments had been engaged in a little contract research. The word 'contract' might suggest a connection with private industry, but the Faculty's research contracts, at least the large ones in this period, were almost all with public agencies. Electrical Engineering, in collaboration with several other institutions, held a large contract with the federal Transportation Development Centre to develop high-speed, magnetic-levitation train technology; the Institute of Aerospace continued to hold contracts with the U.S. Air Force. Other departments held contracts with Energy, Mines and Resources Canada, the Ontario Ministries of Labour and of Environment, and with Ontario Hydro. Some departments held contracts with private industry, as well – with Esso Resources and Trans Canada Pipelines, for example – but these tended to be of shorter duration and for smaller sums of money.[45] What distinguishes a research contract from a research grant is simply that the contracting agent expects certain specified products as a result of the research, whereas a research grantor usually does not.

Researchers in the Faculty rarely found that research contracts put constraints upon their work. In most cases, researchers were simply linking up with a large public agency interested in some aspect of their existing research program, rather than undertaking research at the demand of the supporting agency. To those researchers anxious to expand their work, this sort of relationship was harmless. After all, although engineering research had become scientifically advanced, it was still connected to real-world problems, so connecting with the beneficiaries or utilizers of one's research did not in any way debase one's work. Contract research also had advantages. Terms could be set so that overhead costs connected with the research, such as space, utilities, or administration, were covered in the contract. Many research grants, especially those from federal agencies, did not permit this, and the heavy overhead costs associated with generous grants were becoming a problem of their own. Further still, contracts usually allowed supplementary stipends to the principal staff member doing the work, allowing a professor with a full commitment to research to do as well financially as one who did part-time consulting. Not surprisingly, by the final years of the decade, many individual researchers were actively seeking contract work, and the proportion of research money from contracts rose from about 20 per cent to 30 per cent in a few years.[46]

Students throughout the university were different in the 1970s, and those at the Faculty were no exception. The unrest of the late 1960s had broken down not only the old deference of student to staff, but many of the traditions of student life, as well. What remained of the old initiation competitions had vanished by the 1970s, as had the passion, among the general student body, for interfaculty athletics. Students now tended to participate more in the city life beyond the campus – unlike students of the past, they had the money to do so – and commitment to one's college or school seemed embarrassingly out-dated. Such long-standing activities as Skule Nite (the deliberate misspelling gradually came into use from the 1930s to the 1960s), School Dinners, and election-night hi-jinx died from indifference or irrelevance (although Skule Nite would be revived). What had been fun ten years earlier was just not fun anymore, leading one senior staff member to describe the students of the 1970s as being marked by 'a general lack of student joyfulness.'[47] Everthing was not lost. A new sort of student activity, more rational and useful than the old, began to appear in the 1970s. 'Shinerama,' where students shined shoes to raise money for charity, became a popular initiation activity. Engineering students still probably felt a stronger identity with their school than did other students on campus, and were correspondingly more involved. But even so, the turnout at Faculty social events was unpredictable.[48] School spirit lived on, but not as the dominant, deep-felt force it once had been.

What did flourish in these years was a highly visible ribaldry which, although practised by only a minority of the students, would have far-reaching and long-lasting effects on the Faculty's,

An unidentified engineering student performs his duty for Shinerama at
Toronto Union Station, September 1978. UTA, B83-0037/001P(21)

and to some extent the profession's, public image. Among the many widespread social changes of the 1960s had been a profound revolution in sexual mores. Most North Americans in the 1970s were far more open about sexual matters than they had ever been, and sexual practices among young people had been quite drastically transformed. A number of engineering students seem to have taken this as a licence for sexual explicitness and lewdness, and the *Toike Oike* newspaper became their medium of expression. The paper had been nothing more than a bearer of news and clever humour before the 1960s, with an occasional reference to kissing to keep it lively, but through the 1960s the paper's sexual content grew to such a degree that, by the 1970s, it contained explicit nudity and endless references to sex. In some issues, the only humour was sexual, and most of it quite profane.[49] Lady Godiva took on more and more significance as a symbol of the Faculty, but the fact that her ride had been a protest against arbitrary authority was entirely overlooked, as was the fact that although undressed she had cleverly devised a way of not revealing herself. It was her nudity, not her politics or her wits, that students now played up. The 'Slave Auction,' an old tradition in which female student volunteers were auctioned off for charity, had by 1973 evolved into a striptease show with receipts going to charity.[50]

It was for many an unwelcome development in the Faculty's student culture. It seems to have had a complex mix of causes, being animated partly by the vestiges of 1960s rebellion – engineering students showing that they could break rules, too – together with the engineering students' long tradition of spirited prankstership and troublemaking, and at times also by a wish to parody themselves as the 'party-animals' of campus (excessive beer-drinking was played up in the new student culture too). Some have suggested it was a symbolic resistance to women, whose numbers at the Faculty were beginning to increase. In any case, it did not last much beyond the decade; by the 1980s, such antics, although still present, were being carried on by a smaller

The Lady Godiva Memorial Band on the field of the CNE Stadium at the 1974/ 75 College Bowl, where the University of Toronto Blues played the University of Western Ontario Mustangs. The band is led by Jim Burpee on tuba. UTA, B85-0023P

minority and showing signs of passing. In the minds of students elsewhere on campus, however, and even among the public, it had made a lasting impression.

In the early-morning hours of 11 February 1977, a terrible catastrophe struck. A fire broke out in the east corner lecture room of the Sandford Fleming Building and spread for eight hours through the walls and ceilings before being brought under control. Nobody was injured, but the central rotunda and the entire north wing were completely destroyed, while the south wing and the adjoined Galbraith Building suffered substantial smoke and water damage. Fortunately, quick thinking by the emergency crews saved much of the computer centre in the south wing, and a large library rescue operation that began the follow-

Firefighters try to control the spread of fire through the roof of the Sandford Fleming Building in the early-morning hours of 11 February 1977. *Toronto Star* photo. UTA, B2000-0014/001P(05)

ing morning brought most of the books to safety. But about 50,000 square feet of usable space was lost, among it classrooms, laboratories, and offices of the Faculty's staff and graduate students. The disruption to the Faculty, in the middle of the winter term, was enormous.[51]

As often happens in events such as this, countless people worked long hours and suffered great inconveniences, but in the end everyone pulled through. Two strokes of good fortune made the disruption manageable. The following week was Reading Week for Arts & Science students, so vacant classrooms were available for one week while the Faculty made alternative arrangements. And soon it became known that the Toronto Reference Library, across St George Street from the Faculty offices, planned to vacate its building that coming summer, and the university was able to obtain a four-year lease of those premises for the Faculty's use while the Sandford Fleming Building was rebuilt. Although the countless meetings on the building's reconstruction sapped the Faculty's administrative energy for years, when the job was finally finished in 1982, an old building badly in need of renovation had been splendidly revived.[52] Aided by a special Ontario government grant of $12.8 million procured with the help of university President John Evans, the new Sandford Fleming Building provided fine new facilities for the Electrical Engineering and Computer Science (in the Faculty of Arts and Science) departments, a new structures laboratory for Civil Engineering equipped with the aid of $754,000 from NSERC, and a much improved Faculty library.[53]

One innovation that would in time develop into an integral part of the Faculty, the Professional Experience Year, quietly slipped into place in the late 1970s. The idea that engineering students should have professional experience as part of their education had long been an article of faith to which the Faculty had fully subscribed. Work experience of varying amounts had been required for the BASc degree in all departments until the 1970s (and even later for some). But a newer idea that had begun to appear in U.S. schools in the interwar years, that work experience would be organized by the school and somehow mixed in or alternated with formal classroom and laboratory studies, the Faculty had never favoured. Such a scheme had been brought to the attention of university President Sidney Smith in 1949 by J.R. Nicholson, executive vice-president of Polymer Corporation in Sarnia and Smith's former student. Nicholson told Smith that his company had just been asked by the University of Detroit if they would take some engineering students for a work placement, and asked for Smith's thoughts on such an arrangement. Smith than asked Dean C.R. Young for his views. Young consulted the department heads, who generally expressed negative opinions on such a scheme because of the disruption it caused the students.[54]

When the University of Waterloo began its engineering 'co-op' program at its inception in 1957, in which students alternated four-month terms of work and study, questions arose again. The minister of Education, W.J. Dunlop, asked university President Woodside why the University of Toronto did not use such a plan. Woodside passed on the query to Dean McLaughlin, who replied to the minister with a long list of reasons why it was a bad idea: it would break up the academic year, it would overtax the staff and disturb their research work, it would be too hard to administer; and students should find their own jobs. He also pointed out that the co-op scheme had not yet passed the test of time. The Faculty, McLaughlin concluded, had no intention of abandoning its 'well-tried evolutionary methods for revolutionary ones.'[55] Waterloo's subsequent success was difficult to overlook, and in the years that followed the subject often came up for consideration. The conclusion was always the same: the Faculty's system of allowing students to find their own jobs on their own time was superior.[56]

In 1976, however, Professor Peter Stangeby of the Institute of Aerospace Studies proposed to a Faculty Review Committee of which he was a member that the Faculty consider an optional full-year work placement for students after either second or third year. Stangeby had learned of this approach from the calendars of various U.S. engineering schools, and it seemed like a promising idea. The work placement would occur only once, so the disruption would be minimal, and the period of work – up to sixteen months – would allow for fuller integration into the workplace and thus a more beneficial experience for employee and employer. The committee gave it enough support to warrant preparing a proposal for circulation to department chairs, but there it met opposition. Some chairs gave mild support, but none were prepared to take on the heavy responsibility of finding the employers and organizing the placements. The idea fell dormant.[57]

Dean Etkin, however, persisted. Having learned much while working at the de Havilland aircraft plant in the summers after

Dean Ben Etkin assisting in the installation of Jim Ham as president of the University of Toronto, July 1978. Ham is the only Faculty dean to have been made university president. UTA, B99-0012/001P(06)

the war, Etkin was a great advocate of professional experience for aspiring engineers. Eventually David Scott, chair of Mechanical Engineering, began to support the idea, and late in 1978 Etkin and Scott agreed to try a pilot program the following fall. The challenge was to find employers, but by February 1979 Scott had received commitments from Ontario Hydro, de Havilland, and General Motors to hire two or three students each for a fourteen- to sixteen-month placement. The program went ahead that fall as planned, under the name Professional Experience Sandwich Term, or PEST for short, with eight student placements.[58] It was successful enough that the entire Faculty tried it the next year, now with the name Professional Experience Year (PEY). This proved a success, as well, and the Faculty adopted it permanently the following year.[59] It grew slowly. Building up a roster of employers and establishing the administrative procedures took time, and some departments remained aloof. Only a few students were placed each year through the early 1980s, but the program had found a place. An optional year of work placement was now a permanent part of engineering education at the Faculty.

When Gordon Slemon took over as dean in the summer of 1979, it was clear to him, and no doubt to many others, that the Faculty had to take its own steps to ensure its survival. As chair of Electrical Engineering for most of the 1970s, he as much as anyone had witnessed the effects of shrinking funds. Despite a fairly healthy research budget, the purchasing power of the Faculty's operational budget had declined, by most counts, about 10 per cent over the previous five years. In the process, the Faculty had lost some seven staff positions. All of this took place against a slightly rising enrolment. This, quite simply, could not be allowed to continue. In an annual report written near the end of his second year in office, Slemon stated bluntly that 'the time has passed when we can reliably count on public funding only for the support of the Engineering Faculty.' Instead, he went on, the Faculty would seek support from those whom the Faculty's work benefits the most. 'Among the resources on which we must increasingly call,' he wrote, 'are industries which employ our graduates and incorporate the results of our research, alumni who have benefited in their careers from their engineering education, and engineering students who contribute through their tuition fees.'[60] Here was the agenda for the next generation.

Among the first of Dean Slemon's initiatives was founding an official Faculty Alumni Office. The alumni had been involved in

Faculty affairs for years. They had provided advice – formal and informal – to the academic staff and the school's deans since the earliest days, and had donated money for several student scholarships.[61] All of this involvement, however, depended on the initiative of the graduates themselves, which in turn usually depended on a committed class president. There was no mistaking the attachment that most alumni felt to the school long after graduation, for alumni organizations often sprang up where groups of alumni resided. The task was to focus that sentiment. In 1982, after consulting with the Alumni Council, Dean Slemon established the Alumni Office and created the position of 'Assistant to the Dean, Alumni Liaison' to manage it. Staff in the office went to work immediately, setting up a financial appeal to alumni – the first to be run from the Faculty itself – that succeeded far beyond expectations. Within a few years, they had re-established the Faculty's Open House (some departments had held open houses in the 1960s) and introduced the Leaving Class Pledge in which graduating students make a commitment to continue financial support of the Faculty. Both of these were later adopted by the entire university; the former as U of T Day and the latter as 'Graditude.' Along similar lines, Slemon appealed to the students. One of the most damaging consequences of declining funds upon undergraduate teaching was the inadequate budget for supplies and equipment. The dean proposed to the Engineering Society that students be asked to contribute an additional $100, above their fees, for equipment and services for undergraduate teaching. The Society agreed to hold a student vote on the proposal, and with a good-sized majority the extra charge was accepted for a three-year period. This student contribution amounted to some $250,000, a significant sum that raised the supplies budget by about 20%.[62] It was subsequently retained, with the name voluntary special levy.

One of Slemon's other priorities was to enhance, in his words, 'the linkage between this engineering faculty and the industry of our community.'[63] This offered possible financial benefits, of course, since private industry was a possible source of research funds and a potential donor of equipment. But such linkages would also bring more opportunities for student work placements under the PEY program, and they might permit the Faculty to do a better job of providing extension teaching to practising engineers, something it was doing increasingly in the 1970s. Individual staff members might also gain knowledge about current industrial activity in their field. The Faculty, in other words, stood to gain in many ways from improving its connections with industry.

Signs of steps in this direction are unmistakable. The Faculty organized and took part in a conference sponsored by the Ontario Department of Industry and Tourism in March 1980, at which participants explored ways of enhancing collaboration between Ontario's univerities and its industries. Slemon spurred the university to create the Innovations Foundation, an autonomous body connected to the university, whose mandate was to promote the inventions of university researchers to private industry, and whose costs were expected to be covered by the royalties these inventions generated. Donations from industry to the Faculty began to come in, the largest being $5 million worth of computer equipment from IBM in 1982 that provided a badly needed expansion; a new Engineering Computer Facility, with fifty remote terminals, was subsequently set up in the Mechanical Building and the renovated Sandford Fleming building, and undergraduate access to the Faculty's computer system was vastly improved. The Faculty also created a new Centre for Nuclear Engineering in 1983 with financial support from several parties in the nuclear industry. O.J.C. Runnalls, whose chair of Energy Studies was losing its financial support, was moved into the position of director of the new centre.[64]

The Faculty's involvement with professional development also grew amid this push toward greater connection with the outside world. Academic staff had been providing evening courses for working engineers for years through the university's School of

Continuing Studies. Professor I.G. Currie of Mechanical Engineering was the Faculty's coordinator of this instruction in the 1970s, and was, in fact, appointed part-time with the SCS. In 1978, at Currie's urging, the Faculty took full control of these courses and created its own secretariat to administer them. Through an arrangement with the Association of Professional Engineers of Ontario, the Faculty's Continuing Education Program, as it was known, offered courses designed to prepare aspiring working engineers for their P.Eng. certification, and courses for established professional engineers to improve their knowledge and skills in certain areas. These courses proved very popular; enrolment rose steadily through the early 1980s.[65]

In 1986, the Faculty took the unusual step of creating a Centre for Technology and Social Development – a move quite unconnected to outside partnerships, but important nonetheless – and appointed W.H. Vanderburg to a position as its director. Vanderburg held a PhD in Mechanical Engineering from the University of Waterloo, but he had moved on from engineering to study the social aspects of technological change. He came to the Faculty in the late 1970s and began co-teaching Morris Wayman's course on the social impact of technology, which he took over himself when Wayman retired. In 1985, the Canadian Engineering Accreditation Board made it a requirement that all undergraduate engineering programs include instruction in this field, so Dean Slemon, with the support of university President Jim Ham, secured for Vanderburg a position that enabled him to continue working in the Faculty permanently. This was the Faculty's first appointment of an academic staff member whose research and teaching was not in the scientific or technical aspects of engineering.

The Faculty's research endeavours continued to be strong and well supported throughout the 1980s. Academic staff still drew ample funds from the main federal government granting agency, now the Natural Science and Engineering Research Council (NSERC) since the NRC's break up in 1979; amounts of $6 million or $7 million per year came into the Faculty in the early

Gordon Slemon, dean of the Faculty from 1979 to 1986, in his office in the final year of his deanship. UTA, B98-0033/861051 (#51)

1980s. Research contracts with government departments and public agencies continued as well; the federal Departments of Energy Mines and Resources, Supply and Services, and Industry Trade and Commerce all held large contracts with the Faculty.[66]

Beginning to appear among the long list of Faculty research supporters, however, was a new agent: the government of Ontario. The provincial government had been the main source of funding for the Faculty since it had breathed its first breath in 1873 as the Ontario School of Practical Science, and in the subsequent century, the province had sustained the Faculty through grants to the University of Toronto. Research support, however, had never been its main contribution. But new circumstances now called for new actions. Frustrated with its lack of control over federal distribution of research grants, and feeling the need for an industrial policy of its own to help restructure the provincial economy out of traditional manufacturing, the Ontario government resolved to try something new.[67] In the early 1980s, the Ontario Conservative government of William Davis introduced something it called BILD, the Board of Industrial Leadership and Development, to assist Ontario industry in restructuring to a high-technology, global economy. This board, comprised entirely of government cabinet ministers, made funds readily available to a myriad of programs, several of which pertained to advanced scientific research and product development. Amounts were small, but several researchers in Mechanical Engineering received money from BILD-supported programs, and the entire Faculty benefitted from an increase in provincial funds for university research equipment that came through BILD.[68]

Then, in 1984, another new twist appeared in provincial policy. The Ontario government had grown concerned about the provincial university system, especially with how it could be sustained in times of slow economic growth. To explore the matter it created the Commission on the Future Development of the Universities of Ontario, in January 1984. This commission, chaired by Edmund C. Bovey but including the influential educator and medical researcher J. Fraser Mustard, concluded among other things that for Ontario universities to maintain their excellence they were going to need much greater private-sector support, noting that the private sector was 'one of the major beneficiaries of the university system in terms of the graduates employed and the application of research results.' It suggested that to encourage this, the government should establish 'university-industry linkages and research relationships.'[69] Linkages of this sort were, of course, just what the Faculty had been working toward on its own. It was a remarkable conjunction of interests. Provincial government policies in both industrial development and advanced education were about to play directly into the Faculty's hands.

The Conservative government lost the provincial election in

1985, but this did not end the new direction in provincial affairs. The following April, the new Liberal premier, David Peterson, introduced what he called his 'Premier's Council' to, in words from his government's throne speech, 'steer Ontario into the forefront of economic leadership and technological innovation.' The new government's program was to be similar to the Conservative's BILD, but more generously endowed.[70] One of the council's first projects was the Ontario Centres of Excellence program, under which it proposed to create several 'Centres of Excellence' to serve as conduits for substantial government investment in university industrial research.[71] Each of these centres was to be an incorporated body, with its own board of directors drawn from universities and industry, and each would provide funds for research in a particular technological field. But the money available from these centres was not going to be in the form of simple grants. Research funds would be provided as part of a contract, with a specified expected output, and furthermore, research proposals to the centres were expected to show close connections with an industrial partner interested in commercial applications of the research being proposed. The Premier's Council had been created to 'involve the private sector more effectively in university and government research and insure that industrial priorities play a much more important role in guiding such research,'[72] and the Centres of Excellence were clearly being created right in line with this mandate.

When it came time to establish the centres in late 1986, the government called for proposals. These were to state the field in which research would be carried out, the team that would conduct the research (it had to involve researchers from more than one university), and the initial research program. Twenty-eight proposals were submitted, and of the seven centres selected by the government in the spring of 1987, five had substantial involvement from researchers in the Faculty. Suddenly, a large portion of a generous new program would be coming to the

Premier David Peterson comments on new centres as Dr. Fraser Mustard, evaluation panel chairman, waits at lectern.

'Centres of excellence' to get research funds

BY STANLEY OZIEWICZ
The Globe and Mail

Ontario Premier David Peterson named seven so-called centres of excellence yesterday to be part of a five-year $200-million program to spin off more university research into industrial technology.

"We believe that tomorrow's technology represents economic growth and jobs in our province," he told a news conference that was well-orchestrated but low-key.

The announcement, made at Ontario Place to an audience of about 200 academics, businessmen, labor representatives and members of the Premier' Council, is a key part of the minority Liberal Government's $1-billion technology fund.

Mr. Peterson said the aim of the centres of excellence is to help reverse Canada's dependence on imported high technology by getting universities and industry to collaborate more effectively.

"We don't want research sitting on the lab table and nothing happening," he said.

Twenty-eight applicants, involving post-secondary institutions and industry, had applied to be named centres of excellence. Seven, bringing together eight universities and 100 companies, were chosen. They include:
● Centre for Advanced Laser and Lightwave Research, the University of Toronto ($22.6-million).
● Centre in Space and Terrestrial Science, York, Toronto, Waterloo and Western Ontario ($39.3-million).
● Centre for Integrated Manufacturing, McMaster, Toronto, Waterloo, Western Ontario,

Carleton and Queen's ($31.2).
● Centre for Groundwater Research, Waterloo ($8.2-million).
● Centre in Information Technology, Waterloo, Toronto, Western Ontario and Queen's ($35.1-million).
● Centre for Materials Research, Queen's, McMaster, Toronto, Waterloo and Western Ontario ($39.5-million).
● Telecommunications Research Institute of Ontario, Ottawa, Carleton, Queen's and McMaster ($20.5-million).

The figures refer to the amounts the centres have asked the Government to provide over the next five years. Each centre is designed to be a joint venture of at least one university and one company, and Mr. Peterson said they will now have 90 days to draw up the legal documents for their projects.

Dr. Fraser Mustard, who was chairman of the Premier's Council panel that evaluated the applicants, said the announcement was historic because a political leader was involved in decisions based strictly on merit.

"I suspect that this is actually a very historic occasion. And I hope all of you respect the significance of that," he said, noting that the projects were assessed by a team of independent experts.

Dr. Mustard, president of the Canadian Institute for Advanced Research, scoffed when a reporter attempted to draw a comparison between the centres of excellence concept and the $57-million Exploracom high-technology computer project that was trumpeted and then abruptly aborted by Mr. Peterson.

"To put this in the same context as Exploracom is in my judgement irresponsible," he said.

"What you're dealing with are a group of highly credible institutions which have a hell of a lot at stake."

He said the centres will have to undergo a rigorous review after 2½ years and will be cut off if they do not meet performance standards. He said the centres will be judged on how well industry makes use of the research undertaken.

"It is our expectation that the centres will contribute to advanced technology, economic growth and our capacity to maintain the strength of the social fabric of our society," he said, repeatedly pointing to the Japanese model of economic development.

Mr. Peterson was equally unhappy when a comparison was made with former premier William Davis's multi-million-dollar Board of Industrial Leadership and Development Plan introduced just five days before the 1981 election call and with former premier Frank Miller's $1.3-billion Enterprise Ontario scheme announced just before he called the 1985 election.

"If you're looking at BILD, Enterprise, Exploracom, get that idea out of your head," said Mr. Peterson, who is expected to call an election within several months.

A senior official of the Premier's Council said that Mr. Peterson insisted that the announcement be staged in a non-partisan way and without the elaborate fanfare and hype used by the Tories in the BILD and Enterprise Ontario schemes.

New Democratic Party House leader Ross McClellan questioned the need for centres of excellence at a time when 40 per cent of students entering high school fail to graduate.

Not since the announcement of the Ford Foundation grant in 1962 had the Faculty's affairs received such high-profile newspaper coverage. The *Globe and Mail*, 19 June 1987

Faculty's researchers – some $8 million annually for five years. It was an unprecedented jump in research support.[73]

This preoccupation with industry/university partnerships was everywhere by the mid-1980s, not just in the Ontario government. NSERC had begun funding 'industrial research chairs,' in which it contributed towards the support of a research professor in a specific field, provided that private industry gave equal support; the Faculty had five such funded chairs by 1987, in steel-making, welding metallurgy, rock engineering, and two in microelectronics design. NSERC also now had 'cooperative R&D grants' available to researchers seeking funds for projects with clear practical applications and a designated industrial partner. How things had changed! Public support of research had for so long been granted in areas where minimal commercial potential existed, and where private industry could not be counted on venturing. Money had thus been more freely given to pure science than to engineering. Now the reverse was true. The political climate favoured spending public funds to help develop industries, especially high-technology industries, and the research most likely to gain public financial support was that with the most direct commercial application.

Managing the Faculty now had a whole new dimension: liaison with private industry. When Dean Slemon's seven-year term had ended in 1986 (while the Centres of Excellence were still taking shape), and Gary Heinke, the former chair of Civil Engineering, was appointed to replace him, Heinke took an unusual step. He named Michael Charles, the former chair of Chemical Engineering, to the new position of vice-dean in charge of industrial collaboration. This new dimension was now formalized in the Faculty's governance.

Over the next few years, under Dean Heinke's leadership, most new developments related in one way or another to extending industrial partnership. New programs were introduced by the Ontario Premier's Council; one of particular value to the Faculty was the University Research Initiatives Fund (URIF), which, like the NSERC Research and De-velopment grants, provided funds for problems related to commercially viable projects. Two new research centres were established in the Faculty, one in pulp and paper in 1987 and the other in chemical process metallurgy in 1988, both with close ties to industry. The federal government began a program in 1988 called the National Network of Centres of Excellence, rather like the similarly-named provincial program, and several Faculty researchers began to draw funds from this. NSERC industrial chairs proliferated – there were eleven by 1991 – all with their requisite industrial partners.[74] The Professional Experience Year had begun to expand, with the Faculty now able to make use of its many new industrial partners as employers; in 1989, 106 students were placed in jobs, almost a four-fold increase over four years.

Something new had clearly taken hold. The Faculty was growing in an unusual way by the early 1990s. The number of students attending remained fairly steady; graduate enrolment did rise somewhat over the 1980s, from 570 to 769, but undergraduate enrolment stayed at about 2,600 students. As an education institution, the Faculty was expanding only slightly. Yet the Faculty's annual expenditures nearly tripled over the same period, the cause of which was, of course, the great rise in research activity. While the Faculty's basic operating budget from the university increased slightly over the decade, external research funds rose by a factor of more than four, and external funds were now roughly equal to the basic internal budget.[75] The Faculty had become much more than an engineering school; it was now an important, and expanding, engineering research institute. Furthermore, the great expansion in research was being accomplished almost entirely in partnership with others. Slemon's wished-for linkages were firmly in place.

Walking the halls of the Faculty in the later 1980s, something even looked different; so many of the students' faces were not light-skinned. This change had begun earlier, in the 1950s for graduate students and probably in the 1970s among undergraduates, but by the 1980s the student body, in appearance at least, had been thoroughly transformed.[76]

Citizenship data for students are not available until the 1980s, but by 1983 already only 68 per cent of the Faculty's graduate students were Canadian citizens. Five years later that had fallen slightly to 66 per cent, and the portion would fall further to just over 50 per cent in the 1990s. Among undergraduates, the number of Canadian citizens was higher, but it, too, was falling – from 83 per cent (1983) to 74 per cent (1988) – and the number of non-Canadians rising correspondingly. More than half of the non-citizen students were permanent residents who probably intended to acquire Canadian citizenship, but most had likely come from abroad to study. Thus, by the end of the 1980s, nearly half of the Faculty's graduate students and one-quarter of its undergraduates were from outside Canada.

Non-Canadians, of course, do not necessarily look like non-Canadians, nor do they have to have particular racial characteristics; but in this case, because most of the new arrivals came from countries whose populations are almost entirely non-caucasian, the high number of foreigners did indeed affect the overall look of the student body. Among graduate students studying at the Faculty on student visas, the most common home countries were Hong Kong, China, and India; they alone accounted for half the visa graduate students. Among undergraduates, the citizenship of foreign students followed roughly the same pattern, but was more widely distributed to include fair numbers from North and South Vietnam, Sri Lanka, Iran, and Malaysia, as well as the United Kingdom.

But foreign citizenships and corresponding racial qualities made up only part of the new phenomenon, for the majority of the Faculty's students were Canadian citizens. The other part is

The Mechanical Club for 1999/2000. Courtesy of the Engineering Society

that so many of the Canadians were also 'non-white.' This is probably the greatest reason for the changing look of the student
body, and it was due to the ethnic diversification of the greater
Toronto area, from which the Faculty still drew most of its students. Ethnicity is a vague concept – some would say an artificial
one – but a survey of the ethnicity (self-attributed) of students at
the university in the early 1990s revealed more than thirty different ethnicities among the Faculty's students. British ethnic origin,
or British in combination with something else, was claimed by
18 per cent, European origins (a wide variety of nationalities) by
22 per cent, Chinese origins (of all types) by 28 per cent, and
other Asian (mostly east and south Asia) by 13 per cent. Quite
apart from citizenship or country of origin, the student body at
the Faculty was diverse indeed, and ethnically quite different

from what it had been for the school's first 100 years. Yet the different appearance of the new student body should not distract from a basic continuity with the past – most students in the 1980s were still, as the Faculty's Canadian students had nearly always been, the children or grandchildren of immigrants to Canada who saw an engineering education as a means to a useful and satisfying career.

Another novelty one might have observed was the surprising number of young women students in the Faculty's halls. Beginning in the 1970s, the long-standing absence of women had finally begun to change. Slowly but steadily the proportion of women rose until in 1980 it reached 9 per cent, by which time women were participating in nearly all aspects of social and academic life at the Faculty. This was still a small minority, and far below what most in the Faculty wanted, but an upward trend had at least begun. It continued through the 1980s, the proportion passing 15 per cent in mid-decade and approaching 20 per cent by the early 1990s. Nearly 400 of the Faculty's 2,600 students were female by this time, something that would have been hard to miss.

Yet despite these changes, the low number of women in the engineering profession became a greater concern in the 1980s than it had ever been, for engineering still lagged behind most other professions in this regard. A critical eye was cast on engineering schools to see what might be deterring women from entering. It was not hard to find aspects of Faculty life that looked unwelcoming to women; the school had for so long been a men's preserve that many aspects of its culture were decidedly male.

In its student culture, a rather puerile preoccupation with sex still lingered in many of the so-called traditions of the school. The more offensive activities – the charity stripteases and the Slave Auctions, the vulgar *Toike Oikes*, and the ride of the apparently nude Lady Godiva – already seemed to be passing by mid-1980s. They had always been the work of a small number of students, and such people were simply not as common as they had been, perhaps because of the Faculty's changing ethnic composition. But women's groups and reformers in the Faculty targeted what remained, and worked to sweep the vestiges away. When an offensive *Toike Oike* issue appeared, something that still occasionally happened, condemnation was swift from concerned students and the dean's office. Such aggressive cleansing prompted a spirited defence from those who valued traditions for tradition's sake or who thought the problem was being exaggerated, and this in turn caused some disagreements within the Faculty, but in the end the reformers began to win out.

Whether such activities were in fact the deterrent to women that they were assumed to be can be questioned. Most of the women who attended the school, even at the height of sexual explicitness in the 1970s, paid little attention to these matters, and found the school a very accommodating place. Many of them suggest that the deterrent to women entering the profession was still an ignorance of it, not an informed dislike.[77] Nevertheless, standards of tolerance had changed, and if the Faculty was to succeed in attracting a larger number and greater variety of female students – women, for example, who were not comfortable amid such activities – it had to change, too. For public relations purposes alone, the Faculty had good reason to be vigilant, for the 'gender wars' at engineering schools were attracting close media attention, some of it not very sympathetic or well informed.

There were aspects of the Faculty other than its ribald student culture that some thought might have been keeping women away. The idea of a pregnant student or academic staff member was something that a good many senior academic staff found hard to accept. In a few laboratories and some departmental common rooms, a 'men's club' atmosphere persisted. Authority in the Faculty still resided almost entirely in the hands of men, and students rarely encountered a female professor. There was still a long way to go to achieve equal participation of women.

There the matter sat, unresolved and a little troublesome, when the great tragedy of December 1989 at the École Polytechnique de Montréal, in which fourteen female engineering students were massacred, brought it front and centre. This cataclysm sent shock waves through the entire Canadian profession, and led to several new efforts to understand the problem. Dean Heinke responded by forming a Task Force on Professional Image and Women in Engineering. He also served on the new Canadian Committee on Women in Engineering, a reform group advocating fundamental changes in the profession to accommodate women.[78] Heinke became fully committed to seeking out and hiring qualified female academic staff for the Faculty. This, however, proved hard to accomplish, and just how difficult it was raised further questions about what was keeping women out of the engineering professoriate. Addressing these questions would be a task of the next decade.

The early 1990s saw the first major addition to the Faculty's buildings in many years: the Pratt Building. This came about through the generosity of Lorne Pratt and his wife Lucille. Pratt had graduated from the Faculty in Civil Engineering in 1922, and on his death in the 1960s had left the bulk of his estate to the Faculty, with the proviso that it sustain his wife for as long as she should survive. The situation remained unchanged for two decades until 1987 when Dean Heinke, in serious need of more space now that the Centres of Excellence were being established, resolved to approach Mrs Pratt to see if the Faculty might be able to take over both the capital in the estate (now some $6 million) and the obligation to support her. To this she agreed, and plans took shape for a substantial addition atop the single-storey Metallurgy Wing of the Wallberg Building. The wing was increased to a full three storeys, suitably renamed, and officially opened in January 1991. At the same time, and for much the same reason, the university carried out a major renovation to the old Mining Building. It took a year longer than expected to secure the

The Pratt Building, October 2000. The ground floor was built in the 1960s, a part of the large program of expansion made possible by the Ford Foundation grant. The full building was completed in 1991. Steve Frost photo.

money from the provincial government, but the work was completed in 1992.

One cannot help but notice that it was a demand for research space, not rising student enrolments, that caused the need for new buildings. This was the new way. Research was king. Most new academic appointments, especially those to NSERC industrial chairs, were made on the basis of research excellence, and the senior staff gave more time than ever to research. Graduate students were increasing as a proportion of the student body, from 18 per cent in 1980 to 23 per cent in 1990. Nevertheless, the Faculty remained a large undergraduate school. Undergraduate studies were by no means overlooked. The dean and staff continued their efforts to improve both its services to students and the content and structure of its curriculum.

In 1987, a study of the first-year program had recommended a slight relaxation in the common first year. Since the 1960s, first-year students, apart from those in Engineering Science, had been undifferentiated by department and had taken a common curriculum. This was proving unsatisfactory to those who felt that students intent on following certain programs needed specialized grounding in first year, so students were once again admitted to a department in their first year and took two technical electives prescibed by their department.[79] In 1991 Dean Heinke set up a Task Force on First Year to study the undergraduate program once again, and several important new ideas emerged, one being the 'T-program' to assist students having trouble making the transition from high school to university, and the other being an appointment of an associate dean in charge of just first-year studies.[80]

In 1990, a separate undergraduate program in Computer Engineering was established within Electrical Engineering. Relations between Electrical Engineering and the Department of Computer Science (in the Faculty of Arts and Science) had always been harmonious – many of the staff in the two departments were cross-appointed – and engineering students had for years been taking computer courses from both their own department and from Computer Science. When Computer Science moved into the renovated Sandford Fleming Building in 1982 alongside Electrical Engineering, this close relationship was further strengthened.[81] But a separate program in computer engineering had been slow to take shape. The Faculty was cautious about this, because highly developed computer skills were considered essential in all engineering fields.[82] Nevertheless, by the late 1980s it seemed like a logical development, since student demand for such a program was high and the Faculty now had so much expertise. Engineering Science introduced a computer option in 1987, helped along by a gift of computer equipment from IBM, and a formal undergraduate program in computer engineering was established for the fall of 1990. No new department was created;

the program was administered by Electric Engineering, chaired at the time by A.S. Sedra. In 1992, the department changed its name to Electrical and Computer Engineering. The program was popular right from the start, with enrolment exceeding 100 in just two years.[83]

From the 1980s to the early 1990s, through the deanships of Slemon and Heinke, the Faculty had, in a quiet, consensual way, gone through a remarkable period of change. If one notes matters of prime concern to the Faculty's dean and senior staff in the early 1990s – centres of excellence, industrial partnerships, active promotion of women, research chairs, a widely used Professional Experience Year, a burgeoning Computer Engineering program – one finds not a single topic that would have appeared on a comparable list before 1980.

When the deanship passed from Gary Heinke to Michael Charles in 1993, few would have expected much change in the Faculty's successful overall direction.[84] It had been Michael Charles, after all, who as vice-dean had overseen many of the new developments. But there was still some distance to travel along this new course. Under Dean Charles's leadership, the Faculty built upon many of the initiatives from the 1980s, added several important new ones, and remained a flourishing institution. It also raised its sights. Dean Charles had the Faculty, for probably the first time, compare itself with the top engineering schools of North America. This allowed him to identify what the Faculty had to do to place itself in those top ranks, and then to develop and implement a five-year plan to do just that.

The Faculty's research enterprise, not surprisingly, continued to prosper throughout the 1990s. With the guidance of Ron Venter from Mechanical Engineering, now in the vice-dean position formerly occupied by Dean Charles, the Faculty kept up and even expanded its external research income. The Centres of Excel-

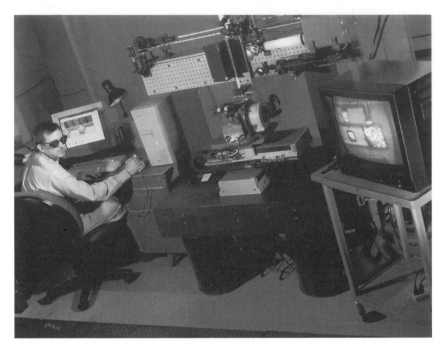

Dr Marc Nantel, senior staff scientist at the Laser Micromachining Facility of Photonics Research Ontario, one of four centres of excellence reconstituted by the Ontario government in 1996. Equipment used for research in this era dwarfs that used in the past – in its complexity and in its cost. Courtesy of PRO

lence program was reviewed by the Ontario government in 1996, by this time a Conservative government led by Mike Harris, and renewed in a slightly altered form the following year; the seven centres were consolidated into four, but the Faculty remained a major recipient of their funds. The province introduced the Ontario Research and Development Challenge Fund (ORDCF) in 1997, another university/industry collaborative program, which Faculty researchers quickly began to utilize. The Canadian government kept up its support of industrial research with grants from NSERC and the National Networks of Centres of Excellence. Since these were all matching-fund programs requiring industrial partners, linkages continued to grow, with both small and large firms, local and international. The many industrial partnerships formed under these programs yielded secondary benefits as well, for they helped the PEY expand to over 200 placements by 1996.

Linkages and partnerships were everywhere, and to help sustain these connections, as well as to guide the Faculty's fundraising campaigns and assist in setting academic priorities, Dean Charles formed a Dean's Advisory Board in 1995. This new body consisted of some two dozen leaders in engineering and industry, many of them Faculty alumni. John Bahen, a successful civil engineering alumnus and exceptionally generous Faculty benefactor, took on the job of chairing the board for an initial five-year term. The creation of this board was an unprecedented step in reaching out to the industrial sector with which the Faculty was becoming increasingly connected.

The Faculty's well-funded research was yielding some very real, and very successful, applications. Researchers were making valuable contributions in such diverse fields as computer modelling of urban transportation patterns, wireless communication technologies, robotic inspection of tires and casings for the tire-retreading industry, laser-based systems for molecular analysis of solid materials in the pharmaceutical and biomedical industries, quality control of paper production through beta-radiography, three-dimensional computer modelling of underground rock stresses for the mining industry, and software for the emerging computer technology of parallel processing. In many cases, research led to spin-off companies formed on the basis of technology developed in the Faculty, and since business and job creation had been the purposes of these public programs in the first place, the spin-offs pleased the government granting agencies and made continuation of the programs that much more likely.

Governments also introduced programs that provided funds for expanding the physical infrastructure needed for this growing industrial research. The Canadian government created the Canada Foundation for Innovation (CFI) for this purpose, which in turn prompted the Ontario government to create the Ontario Innovation Trust (OIT) to provide money to match CFI contributions. These programs went far beyond anything that existing government granting programs could have provided. The Faculty quickly began to develop plans for much-needed new buildings and laboratories that would make use of their funds.

There was, however, one important aspect of the Faculty not being quite so generously nourished: undergraduate education. Not that research was entirely separate from classroom teaching; equipment purchased for research often found its way into student laboratories, and professors at the forefront of knowledge frequently were the most stimulating instructors. Yet the fact remained that most of the new funds coming into the Faculty were for research, so the staff supported by these funds naturally gave research much of their time and effort. Under the NSERC industrial research chairs program, for example, the Faculty had added eighteen new academic staff. These appointees were among the Faculty's most prolific researchers, and their work was moving the Faculty into important new fields. But NSERC funding for the chair lasted for five or, if renewed, ten years, and while in the position the chairholder was limited to a half teaching load. As a means of adding permanent staff to fulfill the Faculty's teaching responsibilities the NSERC program came up short.

Instead, in the mid-1990s, the Faculty turned toward expanding its academic staff through 'endowed chairs,' a scheme developed in recent fundraising campaigns that was proving to be one of the best solutions to shortfalls in public financial support. Under this program, the university, which had managed to set aside funds in an 'endowment pool,' agreed to match any outside donation – be it from an individual, a corporation, or an association – to create an endowment sufficient for the ongoing support of a full-time academic position (the 'chair') in a specified field.

Such a position would be endowed in perpetuity (although hold-ers would usually be limited to fixed terms) and the chairholder would work like any other academic staff member, carrying full teaching and administrative responsibilities. The scheme had obvious appeal to the Faculty as a way of employing external funds for something other than research.

All of these partnerships were just what the provincial commis-sioners and former Dean Gordon Slemon had recommended in the early 1980s – reaching out to the 'beneficiaries' of its endeav-ours for financial support – but they were being done now on a scale much greater than ever before. Establishing and maintaining these connections was now a central part of the Faculty's affairs; as well, efforts in this direction were increasingly independent from those of the university. In 1997, when the Faculty embarked on a major fundraising campaign, it created its own Development Office with several staff members to manage the campaign; the original Alumni Office, formed in 1982, was just not large enough to handle the growing workload. The campaign was also given guidance by a new 'Campaign Cabinet' co-chaired by John Bahen and William Daniel, a spin-off from the Dean's Advisory Board, that acted as the campaign's board of directors. The purpose of fundraising was now much broader than ever before; the object was to bring in funds to enhance all aspects of the Faculty – schol-arships and bursaries, laboratory facilities, general infrastructure – not just research. And the campaign's goals – $65 million and thirty new endowed chairs – were far beyond those of any past cam-paign. With industrial partnerships so well established, alumni liai-son being expanded, and the dean's new board in place, the Faculty was well-positioned to meet its goals. In fact, by late 1999, it had already exceeded its financial goal and founded seventeen endowed chairs. Such names as the Pierre Lassonde Chair in Mining Engineering, the Bahen-Tannenbaum Chairs in Civil Engineering, or the Nortel Chairs in Electrical and Computer Engineering were now part of the Faculty's everyday vocabulary.

A dance number performed in Skule Nite 1999. These humourous musical revues had become more popular than ever by the 1990s. Talented students and alumni put on a multi-night run of original skits every year at Hart House Theatre. Courtesy of Alex Kung

New staff was certainly needed because the Faculty was expanding once again. Student enrolment began a steady rise in the mid-1990s, exceeding 3,000 students for the first time in the fall of 1997. Much of this was due to the rapid growth of the Computer Engineering program, which, although begun just in 1990, had become by 1997 the Faculty's most popular program, with 513 students. The appeal of computer engineering seemed limitless in the 'information age.' The Ontario government aided the program's ongoing expansion with funds from its new Access to Opportunities Program, a scheme aimed at expanding facilities and academic staff in fields with growing employment opportunities. Rising student enrolment was also due to more active recruiting, especially for Engineering Science, which began promoting its challenging program to students in more distant parts of the

country. Graduate registrations reached new heights in the early
1990s, peaking at over 1,200 in 1993, but an expanding economy,
in which industrial jobs were plentiful, reduced graduate enrolment slightly in the later years of the decade.

Programs and departments were altered somewhat, partly in
response to a set of peer reviews of the Faculty that Dean Charles
had commissioned in 1994 as the first stage of his planning process. While generally quite favourable, these reviews had noted
several areas of possible improvement, and the Dean's subsequent
five-year plan stated his intention to take action on them all. The
Department of Industrial Engineering was amalgamated with
Mechanical Engineering to create a new Department of Mechanical and Industrial Engineering in May 1996. The program in
Industrial Engineering, however, remained distinct, so the one
department now administered two programs. Metallurgy and
Materials Science, after a thorough review, was kept independent,
but its undergraduate program was renamed Materials Engineering; the department had always been rich in research, but short
on students, so new efforts were put into recruitment. The Institute of Biomedical Engineering and the existing Centre for Biomaterials in the Faculty of Dentistry (which already had links to
the Faculty through the Departments of Chemical Engineering
and Applied Chemistry and Metallurgy and Materials Science)
were joined together to create a newly named and much higher
profile Institute of Biomaterials and Biomedical Engineering.

Another important development was the inauguration of a
Division of Environmental Engineering in 1996 to administer a
new collaborative undergraduate program. A graduate program
in environmental engineering had been in place since the 1970s,
and undergraduate students in several programs had for years
been able to take courses with environmental content, but until
now no formal undergraduate program had existed. Students
wishing to enrol registered in either Civil, Mechanical, or Chemical Engineering, but they followed a course of study set by the

division. The program was popular right from the start, with enrolment exceeding expectations.

One entirely new initiative in the Faculty's teaching came with the introduction of the Language Across the Curriculum program in 1996. The Faculty's concern about improving written and oral skills among its students went back many years, and several different approaches to the task had been tried. The most recent effort, a technical writing course taught by the Department of English, was serving reasonably well, but the course suffered from having little connection to the rest of the Faculty's curricula. The need for language enhancement had also become more acute, and of a rather different nature, with more than half of the Faculty's students not having learned English as their first language. The idea then began to take hold that students might best learn their writing and speaking skills not in separate courses but within their own discipline. It was engineering reports, after all, that the Faculty's students were going to have to write in their professional work. With this premise as its foundation, the LAC program was introduced. Staff in the program worked with professors of selected engineering courses to incorporate writing assignments in those courses, which the LAC staff then critiqued. It was a novel approach to an old problem, and after a few years was having good effect.

All told, the successes of the recent years were unmistakable and quite extraordinary. As Michael Charles prepared to leave the deanship in the summer of 2001, he could feel confident that the Faculty was in as secure a position as ever. Student enrolment, both graduate and undergraduate, had reached new heights. Students were participating enthusiastically in a great variety of extra-curricular activities. Research, generously supported by public and private funds, was of an exceptional quality and quantity in all departments. New endowed chairs were being established at the rate of almost one a month. The university was now contributing to the Faculty's rise in excellence through a new

Gary Heinke (second from right), dean of the Faculty from 1986 to 1993, and Michael Charles (far left), dean from 1993 to 2001, are joined by the two previous deans, Ben Etkin (far right) and Gordon Slemon, at an informal gathering around John Galbraith's bronze bust in the lobby of the Galbraith Building, January 2000. Steve Frost photo

Academic Priorities Fund introduced by university Provost A.S. Sedra, former chair of Electrical and Computer Engineering. The number of female academic staff had risen to thirteen, and the Faculty was working to increase that further still; women now made up over 25 per cent of the undergraduate body (over 50 per cent in chemical engineering). A grand new building was fully approved and under construction: the Bahen Centre for Information Technology, a large complex financed through an assemblage of government grants, corporate support, and alumni donations. A new combined program, the Jeffrey Skoll BASc/ MBA, had been just approved that offered students an opportunity to extend their education into another part of the university.

Then, in June 2000, the Faculty received the largest benefaction in its history – $25 million from Edward S. ('Ted') and Loretta Anne Rogers in honour of Mr Rogers's late father, the radio pioneer Edward S. Rogers, Sr., a student at the Faculty in the early 1920s; these funds will support two research chairs and over a hundred student scholarships, graduate and undergraduate. The terms of this generous donation included the Faculty taking an unprecedented step, renaming its electrical and computer engineering department, in perpetuity, the Edward S. Rogers Sr. Department of Electrical and Computer Engineering.

When a new set of peer reviews was conducted in 1999 as the basis for another five-year plan – this time by engineering educators from leading schools outside Canada – it revealed that the few weaknesses noted five years earlier had been remedied, and that the Faculty had indeed moved into the ranks of the very best. Yet it had also unquestionably been transformed. The Faculty was no longer the public institution it had been for most of its history. A whole new system of financing had taken shape employing a complex combination of university funds, two levels of government support for both research and infrastructure (much of it targeted towards industrial growth), partnerships with private industry, and donations from supportive alumni and private corporations. There could be no denying that the new ways were working. These were good times. There were, nevertheless, people with a long history in the Faculty who found these new ways unsettling, and who were inclined to ask where this new direction might lead. What will become of engineering fields where industrial partnerships are not feasible? Will the reliance on external funding cause restrictions on research? How long will political consensus remain around the belief that university-based research brings economic growth that benefits all? Are there no limits to the growth in computer engineering? But if the past is any guide to the future, these questions will in time be met and successfully answered by a new generation of leaders in ways not yet imaginable, and the Faculty, through its distinctive blend of caution and progress, will flourish for many years to come.

If, through the magic of time travel, John Galbraith could be brought back to the Faculty in the year 2000, and set free to explore what has evolved at the school he so devotedly wrought some one hundred years before, he would of course be bewildered and amazed. He might blush at first at the sight of his name on the Faculty's principal building, and on entering and noticing his bronze bust in the building's lobby he might demand, in embarrassment, that it be removed from public display. But once reconciled to the impotence of the time traveller to change what he observes, he would begin simply to gaze about in wonder. The size of everything would astonish him, for he would recall that the original little red schoolhouse had been not much bigger than the wide-open public lobby of the building now bearing his name. If the term were in session, and the hallways and classrooms in use, the number of students might not surprise him much, for he had seen halls and classes more crowded than this. The students themselves, however, would astound him – their dress, their demeanour, and their general lack of formality – and he would be tempted to speak sharply to them as they slouched on benches and jostled along. The young women he might not recognize at first, dressed so much like the young men with whom they freely fraternized; once he did, however, he would be speechless. So it would continue, hallway after hallway, building after building; the laboratory equipment would puzzle him, and the lectures confound him. The world had indeed changed beyond his recognition.

Yet if he should find his way into a meeting of the department chairs or higher level administrators, Professor Galbraith might not feel so out of place. At first he would not recognize the sort of meeting it was, since informal dress and the presence of women would indicate a casual gathering. Soon he would see it for what it was, and would immediately begin to hear subjects he well recognized: how much the Ontario government will be contributing to the Faculty's new building, how little it would be granting to the rest of the university, the value of the school's instruction to the province's economy, the importance of students gaining professional experience, how best to teach mathematics to first-year students, and the proper content and amount of non-technical instruction. Galbraith could then turn and leave, comforted a little by the thought that, for all the changes his old school had undergone, so much had stayed the same. He might also be secretly pleased that nobody had yet put to rest the problems that had bedevilled him for so many years, so long ago.

APPENDIX

A recognition of excellence among
the Faculty's staff and alumni

The University of Toronto, in 1966, began to honour its outstanding academic staff with the rank 'University Professor'. Since that time, seven members of the Faculty's academic staff have been so honoured:

Howard Rapson,
Chemical Engineering and Applied Chemistry

Jui-Lin (Allan) Yen,
Electrical Engineering

Ben Etkin,
Institute of Aerospace Studies

Ursula Franklin,
Metallurgy and Materials Science

Andre Salama,
Electrical and Computer Engineering

Murray Wonham,
Electrical and Computer Engineering

Michael Collins,
Civil Engineering

THE SKULE STORY

In 1939, the University of Toronto Engineering Alumni Association, in association with faculty council, began to award the Engineering Alumni Medal to graduates of the Faculty who had distinguished themselves through extraordinary professional achievement. At first, medals were awarded every few years. More recently, the medal has come to be awarded annually, to a single recipient. Medal recipients are as follows:

Year	Name	S.P.S. Dip.	BASc	Discipline
1939	Young, C.R.	1903	1905	Civil
	Runciman, A.S.	1911		Mech
1942	Dobson, W.P.	1910	1915	Elec
	Phillips, W.E.		1914	Chem
1946	Swan, W.G.	1905	1906	Civil
	Thompson, H.G.		1922	Mech
1948	Banks, H.R.		1914	Mining
	Boyd, W.		1939	Mech
1951	Parkin, J.H.	1911	1912	Mech
	White, J.R.		1931	Mech
1954	Brown, E.L.		1922	Mining
	Sauer, M.V.	1901	1902	Mech
1957	Langford, G.B.		1923	Mining
1960	Holden, O.		1913	Civil
	West, C.W.		1915	Civil
1963	Challies, J.B.	1903		Arch
	Forward, F.A.		1924	Chem
1966	Chamberlin, J.A.		1936	Mech
	Shenstone, B.S.		1928	Mech
1969	Bruce, F.C.W.		1927	Mech
	Dyment, J.T.		1929	Mech
	Kirkpatrick, W.S.		1926	Met
1973	Berry, A.E.		1917	Civil
	Gooderham, R.M.		1926	Elec
	Ham, J.M.		1943	Elec
1976	Lord, G.R.		1929	Mech
	Daniel, C.W.		1947	Mining
1979	MacLaren, J.W.		1946	Civil
	Rapson, W.H.		1934	Chem
1984	Hooper, F.C.		1946	Eng Phys
	Lapp, P.A.		1950	Eng Phys
1986	Gordon, J.P.		1943	Mech
	Slemon, G.R.		1946	Elec

270

Year	Name	S.P.S. Dip.	BASc	Discipline
1988	Redfern, D.B.		1948	Civil
	Winegard, W.C.		1949	Met
1989	Heffernan, G.R.		1943	Met
1990	Dudgeon, E.H		1948	Mech
1991	Ellis, M.E. Dormer		1948	Eng Phys
1992	Thomson, R.M.		1955	Eng Bus
1993	Bartnikas, R.		1958	Elec
1994	Wright, G.D.T.		1949	Civil
1995	Morgenstern, N.R.		1956	Civil
1996	Brzuskowski, T.A.		1958	Eng Phys
1997	Maynard, O.E.		1951	Acro
1998	Bahen, John E.H.		1954	Civil
1999	Blundell, William R.C.		1949	Eng Phys
2000	Turner, William I.M.Jr.		1951	Eng Bus

The Alumni Association and faculty council have also, since 1977, named illustrious graduates to a Hall of Distinction. Membership in this hall recognizes both outstanding professional achievement and exemplary professional values.

Elect Year	Candidate	S.P.S. Dip.	BASc	Discipline
1977	Acres, H.G.	1903		Mech
	Baldwin, F.W.	1906		Mech
	Berry, A.E.		1917	Civil
	Black, W.D.	1909	1910	Mech
	Haultain, H.E.T.	1889		Mining
	Hogg, T.H.	1907	1908	Civil
	Iler, R.K.		1930	Chem
	Loudon, T.R.	1905	1906	Civil
	Thomson, T.K.	1886		Civil
	Young, C.R.	1903	1905	Civil
1978	Armstrong, W.M.		1937	Chem
	Chamberlin, J.A.		1936	Mech
	Corman, W.E.		1909	Mech
	Forward, F.A.		1924	Chem
	Hearn, R.L.		1913	Civil
	Langford, G.B.		1923	Mining
	Proctor, E.M.	1908	1909	Civil
	Tracy, G.R.		1921	Elec
	Young, S.	1911	1912	Civil
1979	Breen, J.M.		1921	Civil
	Hamilton, C.B.	1906	1908	Mech
	Harvey, D.W.	1909	1910	Civil
	Lord, G.R.		1929	Mech
	McLaughlin, R.R.		1922	Chem
	Mitchell, G.		1915	Civil
	Rapson, W.H.		1934	Chem
	Smith, I.W.		1938	Mech
	Smith, V.G.		1924	Elec
	Traill, J.J.	1905	1906	Civil

Elect Year	Candidate	S.P.S. Dip.	BASc	Discipline
1980	Carruthers, C.D.		1927	Civil
	Dobson, W.P.	1910	1915	Elec
	Emery, R.W.		1932	Civil
	Frost, J.G.G.		1914	Chem
	MacGill, E.G.		1927	Elec
	McCurdy, J.A.D.	1907		Mech
	Morrison, R.G.K.		1923	Mining
	Parkin, J.H.	1911	1912	Mech
	Powlesland, J.W.		1935	Civil
	Sankey, C.A.		1927	Chem
1981	Boyd, W.		1939	Mech
	Brown, E.L.		1922	Mining
	Challies, J.B.	1903		Civil
	Dyment, J.T.		1929	Mech
	Marshall, O.J.		1926	Civil
	Palm, W.H.		1933	Chem
	Phillips, W.E.		1914	Mech
	Presgrave, R.		1921	Chem
	Sauer, M.V.	1901	1902	Civil
	Swan, W.G.	1905	1906	Civil
1982	Barber, F.	1906		Elec
	Bruce, F.W.		1927	Mech
	Chadwick, R.E.	1906		Mech
	Gooderham, R.M.		1926	Elec
	Keys, C.R.		1915	Elec
	Kirkpatrick, W.S.		1926	Mining
	McDonald, N.G.		1919	Civil
	Runciman, A.S.		1911	Mech
	Shenstone, B.S.		1928	Mech
	White, J.R.		1931	Mech

Elect Year	Candidate	S.P.S. Dip.	BASc	Discipline
1983	Angus, R.W.	1894	1897	Mech
	Bain, J.W.	1896	1897	Mining
	Haldenby, E.W.		1921	Arch
	Hiscocks, R.D.		1938	Eng Phys
	Holden, O.		1913	Civil
	James, E.A.	1904	1905	Civil
	Keith, J.C.	1910		Civil
	Mathers, A.S.		1917	Arch
	McQueen, A.W.F.		1923	Mech
	Wright, C.H.C.	1888	1893	Civil
1984	Ardagh, E.G.R.	1900	1901	Mining
	Clarke, K.H.J.		1936	Met
	Cockburn, J.R.	1901	1902	Mech
	Cousins, E.L.	1906	1907	Civil
	Page, F.P.	1906		Arch
	Price, H.W.	1901	1902	Elec
	Reid, W.		1924	Mech
	Steele, H.		1925	Arch
	Tate, H.W.	1909	1910	Civil
	Titus, O.W.		1917	Elec
1985	Banks, H.R.		1914	Mining
	Breckenridge, J.G.		1927	Chem
	Heller, E.D.		1935	Mech
	Keefler, R.H.		1924	Mech
	Le Pan, A.D.	1907	1908	Mech
	Leworthy, J.V.		1937	Elec
	Osbourne, W.A.		1924	Mech
1986	Argo, J.W.		1929	Civil
	Daniel, C.W.		1947	Mining
	Ham, J.M.		1943	Elec
	Huggins, M.W.		1932	Civil
	Lloyd, D.S.		1925	Elec

Elect Year	Candidate	S.P.S. Dip.	BASc	Discipline
1987	Bryce, J.B.		1935	Civil
	Hawrylyshyn, B.		1952	Mech
	MacLaren, J.W.		1946	Civil
	McIntyre, R.B.		1936	Mech
	Young, R.B.		1913	Civil
1988	Chisholm, D.A.		1949	Eng Phys
	Macklin, H.L.		1943	Civil
	Morris, J.L.	1881		Civil
	Richardson, R.J.		1950	Chem
	Stoicheff, B.P.		1947	Eng Phys
1989	Bailey, E.T.W.		1926	Chem
	Bayly, B.D.		1930	Elec
	Duggan, G.H.	1883		Civil
	MacDonald, D.H.		1945	Civil
	Winegard, W.C.		1949	Met
1990	Pounsett, F.H.R.		1928	Elec
	Redfern, D.B.		1948	Civil
	Ross, R.A.		1890	Elec
	Thall, B.M.		1945	Met
	Uffen, R.J.		1949	Eng Phys
1991	Fox, J.H.		1927	Civil
	Gordon, J.P.		1943	Mech
	Hooper, F.C.		1946	Eng Phys
	Self, R.H.		1938	Civil
	White, H.B.		1944	Civil
1992	Curlook, W.		1950	Met
	Glass, I.I.		1947	Eng Phys
	Heffernan, G.R.		1943	Met
	Rubin, L.J.		1938	Chem
	Slemon, G.R.		1946	Elec

Elect Year	Candidate	S.P.S. Dip.	BASc	Discipline
1993	Allen, D.L.		1950	Chem
	Cawley, J.T.		1943	Mining
	Etkin, B.		1941	Eng Phys
	Moore, R.F.		1945	Mining
	Shemilt, L.W.		1941	Chem
1994	Blundell, W.R.C.		1949	Eng Phys
	Craig, G.B.		1949	Met
	Crawford, G.B.		1944	Civil
	Dudgeon, E.H.		1948	Mech
	Monsaroff, A.		1934	Chem
1995	Booth, R.L.		1945	Civil
	Gerson, F.T.		1947	Met
	Graydon, W.F.		1942	Chem
	Hendrick, K.C.		1947	Mech
	Toguri, J.M.		1955	Met
1996	Cooper, M.A.		1935	Civil
	Dainty, E.D.		1953	Mech
	O'Neil, W.A.		1949	Civil
	Shore, L.E.		1928	Arch
	Tamblyn, W.G.		1945	Civil
1997	Avery, B.A.		1946	Mech
	Cockshutt, E.P.		1950	Mech
	Howard, A.W.		1935	Elec
	Oakley, K.A.		1949	Civil
1998	Burton, H.R.		1921	Civil
	Kappele, J.L.		1948	Elec
	Keary, G.D.		1945	Civil
	Munk, P.		1952	Elec
	Sakus, G.A.		1962	Elec

Elect Year	Candidate	S.P.S. Dip.	BASc	Discipline
1999	Alloway, D.M.		1945	Mech
	Bergman, R.A.		1955	Met
	Blundell, W.R.C.		1949	Eng Phys
	Bowman, C.W.		1952	Chem
	Davenport, A.G.		1957	Civil
	Molozzi, A.R.		1953	Eng Phys
2000	Bruneau, A.A.		1958	Eng Phys
	French, J.B.		1955	Chem
	Geller, L.B.		1958	Mech
	Laidlaw, W.R.		1950	Aero
	Urry, L.F.		1950	Chem

NOTES

Abbreviations

AR   Annual Report
FASE   Faculty of Applied Science and Engineering
OSP   Ontario Sessional Papers
PUH   Papers of the University Historian
SPS   School of Practical Science
UT   University of Toronto
UTA   University of Toronto Archives
UTM   University of Toronto Monthly
UTIAS   University of Toronto Institute of Aerospace Studies
UTPR   University of Toronto President's Report

Chapter 1

1 Gidney and Millar, *Inventing Secondary Education*, 287
2 Ross, *The College on the Hill*; Evans, *Sir Oliver Mowat*, 206; 'Special Report of the Minister of Education on the Mechanics Institutes (Ontario),' Report No. 46, *OSP*, 1881, 6–13
3 Annual Reports of the Chief Superintendent, in Hodgins, ed., *Documentary History*, e.g., Vol. 14 (1859), 268, Vol. 22 (1869), 92, and Vol. 23 (1871), 212–13
4 Mouré, 'Outline of the Financial History of the University,' 71–7
5 McKillop, *Matters of Mind*, 32
6 UTA, UC Calendar 1866/67; Loudon, *Studies of Student Life*, Vol. 1, 6 for the bells
7 Burwash, 'The Development of the University, 1853–1887,' 41–2
8 Veysey, *The Emergence of the American University*, 57–68

9 Hilken, *Engineering at Cambridge University*, 26–9

10 Veysey, *The Emergence of the American University*, 95, 67

11 UTA, UC Calendars, 1857/58 and 1866/67; Young, *Early Engineering Education*, 9–21

12 'Report of an Enquiry in Regard to Schools of Technical Science in Certain Portions of the United States, 1871,' Hodgins, ed., *Documentary History*, Vol. 23, 1

13 Ibid., 5, 9

14 'Circular Issued by the Government on the Establishment of a College of Technology to the Manufacturers of Ontario,' Hodgins, ed., *Documentary History*, Vol. 23, 32

15 UTA, James Loudon, 'Memoirs' (unpublished, unpaginated)

16 Reports of the School of Technology/SPS, in Hodgins, ed., *Documentary History*, Vol. 24, 232, Vol. 25, 233, Vol. 27, 85; UTA, A74-0008/013, Biographies and Obituaries file, 'William Hodgson Ellis: A Family Record by his Daughter'

17 'Blake, Edward,' *Dictionary of Canadian Biography*, Vol. 14, 74–85; 'Crooks, Adam,' *Dictionary of Canadian Biography*, Vol. 11, 220–3

18 'An Act to Establish a School of Practical Science,' Hodgins, ed., *Documentary History*, Vol. 25, 68–9

19 Young, *Early Engineering Education*, 43–4

20 Hilken, *Engineering at Cambridge University*, 28–9

21 Langton, *James Loudon and the University of Toronto*

22 UTA, James Loudon, 'Memoirs'; 'Report of the School of Practical Science,' Hodgins, ed., *Documentary History*, Vol. 27, 85

23 'Report of the School of Practical Science,' Hodgins, ed., *Documentary History*, Vol. 27, 88–9

24 UTA, James Loudon, 'Memoirs'

25 Galbraith to Thompson, 1906, cited in Young, *Early Engineering Education*, 58–9

26 'Banquet to Principal Galbraith' (text of speech by John Galbraith), 157

27 Young, *Early Engineering Education*, 62–5; Averill and Keith, 'Daniel Wilson and the University of Toronto,' 156; 'Banquet to Principal Galbraith' (text of speech by Loudon), 148

28 Moriarty, *John Galbraith*, 7

29 Wright and Alexander, 'The Arts Faculty,' 91–2

30 UTA, A74-0008/008, typescript copy of letter, 29 July 1878, Galbraith to Minister of Education (noted on typescript as letter no. 12439 in files of Ontario Department of Education for 1878)

31 Wright, 'History of the Applied Science Buildings,' 159–62; Young, *Early*

Engineering Education, 59–60; 'Annual Report of the School of Practical Science, Toronto, 1885,' *OSP*, Vol. 18, No. 5, 229–30

32 Mouré, 'Outline of the Financial History of the University,' 73; Loudon, 'Buildings and Equipment,' 207

33 UTA, *Prospectus of the School of Practical Science, Province of Ontario*, Second Session, 1979–80, 5–9

34 ARs of the SPS, *OSP*, Vol. 11, No. 67, 4; Vol. 12, No. 13, 3

35 Averill and Keith, 'Daniel Wilson and the University of Toronto,' 161–2

36 *OSP*, Vol. 11, No. 67, 3

37 UTA, A71-0008, SPS Board Minutes, 7 Nov. 1878, 7 Jan. 1879

38 UTA, A71-0008, SPS Board Minutes, 6 Mar. 1880, 29 Mar. 1880, 19 Nov. 1880, 14 Jan. 1881, 8 Apr. 1881, 11 Nov. 1881, 16 Dec. 1881, 10 Mar. 1882, 8 Dec. 1882, 12 Jan. 1883

39 'Annual Report of the SPS for the Year 1882–83,' *OSP*, Vol. 16, No. 28, 2

40 UTA, *School of Practical Science, Province of Ontario, Prospectus for the Session 1886–7*, 19

41 UTA, *Prospectus of the School of Practical Science*, various years, title varies; 'Annual Report of the School of Practical Science, Toronto, 1886,' *OSP*, Vol. 19, 167

42 UTA, SPS Syllabuses of 1879–80 and 1885–86

43 'An Act to Establish a School of Practical Science,' Hodgins, ed., *Documentary History*, Vol. 25, 68–9, Rule No. 8

44 *OSP*, Vol. 11, No. 67, 2

45 UTA, B65-0014/004, Wilson Diaries, 14 Nov. 1881

46 *OSP*, Vol. 16, No. 28, 5

47 UTA, A71-0008, SPS Board Minutes, 19 Nov. 1880, 21 Oct. 1888, 8 Feb. 1984, 14 Mar. 1884, 13 Mar. 1885; *OSP*, Vol. 15, No. 15, 4; 'Banquet to Principal Galbraith' (text of speech by Loudon), 149

48 *OSP*, Vol. 18, No. 5, 226; Vol. 19, No. 7, 168

49 *OSP*, Vol. 17, No. 5, 197–8; Young, *Early Engineering Education*, 19

50 UTA, A71-0008, SPS Board Minutes, 14 Oct. 1887; also 10 Feb. 1882, 29 Apr. 1882, 20 Oct. 1882

51 *OSP*, Vol. 15, No. 19, 7

52 *OSP*, Vol. 20, No. 7, 244

53 *OSP*, Vol. 18, No. 5, 230; Vol. 19, No. 7, 168–70

54 *OSP*, Vol. 19, No. 7, 167

55 *OSP*, Vol. 20, No. 7, 247; UTA, SPS Syllabus, 1886–87, 9

56 Averill and Keith, 'Daniel Wilson and the University of Toronto,' 166, 181

57 *OSP*, Vol. 20, No. 7, 249 (emphasis added)

58 Wallace, *A History of The University of Toronto*, 114–32

Chapter 2

1 UTA, A71-0008, Council Minutes, 13 Dec. 1889
2 Loudon, 'Buildings and Equipment,' 209–10; Wallace, *History of the University of Toronto*, 144; Annual Report of the SPS, 1889, *OSP*, Vol. 22, No. 6, 308; UTA, A71-0008, Council Minutes, 14 May 1889
3 Annual Report of the SPS, 1889, *OSP*, Vol. 22, No. 6, 310–11
4 Young, *Early Engineering Education*, photograph facing page 86; Loudon, 'Buildings and Equipment,' 209, 213–14; C.H.C. Wright, 'History of the Applied Science Buildings'
5 UTA, B65-0014/004, Wilson Diaries, 12 Mar. 1889; UTA, Prospectus of the SPS, 1889/90
6 UTA, Prospectus of the SPS, 1891/92
7 AR of the SPS, 1890, *OSP*, Vol. 23, No. 4, 364
8 Simmins, *History of the Ontario Association of Architects*, 28–32; *Canadian Architect and Builder*, Vol. 1(8), Aug. 1888, 5; AR of the SPS, 1889, *OSP*, Vol. 22, No. 6, 310; AR of the SPS, 1890, *OSP*, Vol. 23, No. 4, 367–8; UTA, SPS Calendars
9 AR of the SPS, 1890, *OSP*, Vol. 23, No. 4, 367; UTA, SPS Calendar 1893/94, 46
10 Loudon, 'Buildings and Equipment,' 214; Galbraith, 'Technical Education: Address Delivered by Professor Galbraith'
11 Haultain, 'The Univertsity of Toronto and the Mineral Industry'
12 UTA, SPS Calendars, various years
13 'Arthur Philemon Coleman, 1852–1939'
14 UTA, SPS Calendars, various years; ARs of the SPS, *OSP*, various years
15 AR of the SPS, 1895, *OSP*, Vol. 28, No. 2, 285
16 Loudon, 'Buildings and Equipment,' 212–13
17 Langton, *James Loudon and the University of Toronto*, 16–17; McKillop, *Matters of Mind*, 164
18 ARs of the SPS, various years, *OSP*
19 McKillop, *Matters of Mind*, 171–2
20 Both quotations from UTA, James Loudon, 'Memoirs'
21 AR of the SPS, 1899, in Report of the Education Department, *OSP*, Vol. 32, 223
22 UTA, University Senate Minutes, 8 Dec. 1900; 'Banquet to Principal Galbraith,' 156–7
23 Ellis, 'The Faculty of Applied Science,' 183
24 *The Globe*, 7 Mar. 1901; UTA, A74-0008/008 (05), 'Petition of the Undergraduates of the Ontario School of Practical Science presented to the Lieut.-Governor-in-Council'

25 *The Globe*, 14 Mar. 1901; UTA, James Loudon, 'Memoirs'
26 'An Act Respecting the University of Toronto and University College,' 192;
ARs of the SPS, 1900, 1901, 1902, in Report of the Education Department,
OSP, Vol. 33, 202–3, Vol. 34, 209, and Vol. 35, 201; Haultain, 'The University
of Toronto and the Mineral Industry'
27 'An Act Respecting the University of Toronto and University College,' 192;
UTA, James Loudon, 'Memoirs'
28 Receipts by the University of Toronto from the Province of Ontario, *OSP*,
Vol. 40, No. 78, 2
29 AR of the SPS, 1904, in Report of the Education Department, *OSP*, Vol. 37,
263; Loudon, 'Buildings and Equipment,' 213
30 'Receipts by the University of Toronto from the Province of Ontario,' *OSP*,
Vol. 40, No. 78, 2–3
31 McKillop, *Matters of Mind*, 164–5; UTA, James Loudon, 'Memoirs';
Humphries, *'Honest Enough to Be Bold,'* 60–1, 109, 128–9; 'Report of the Royal
Commission on the University of Toronto,' *OSP*, Vol. 38, No. 42
32 Report of the Education Department, *OSP*, Vol. 38, No. 12, Appendix S,
Report of the President of the University of Toronto, 315
33 UTA, A74-0008-010, Young files, 'Memorandum from the University Council
to the University Commission ...'
34 Veysey, *The Emergence of the American University*, 1–18; McKillop, *Matters of
Mind*, 147–292
35 Loudon, 'Presidential Address'; Ross, 'The Establishment of the Ph.D.
at Toronto,' 204–5; Harris, *A History of Higher Education in Canada*, 312;
McKillop, *Matters of Mind*, 156–63
36 Harris, *Higher Education in Canada*, 311–12
37 Ross, 'The Establishment of the Ph.D. at Toronto,' 203; McKillop, *Matters of
Mind*, 149–51, is, in my opinion, mistaken in making this connection.
38 Galbraith, 'On the Conservation of Energy and the Nature of Force'
39 Ellis, 'Chemical Notes on the so-called Sudbury Coal,' 'Tannin in Cloves,'
and 'The Analysis of Milk'
40 Entries for L.B. Stewart, J.W. Bain, A.T. Laing, and A.G. Ardagh in Richardson and MacDonald, *Science and Technology in Canadian History*
41 Royal Society of London, *Catalogue of Scientific Papers*, entries for Chapman,
Coleman, Wright, and Loudon
42 Gingras, *Physics and the Rise of Scientific Research*, 17–21, 26–35
43 Eg. Rosebrugh and Miller, 'Mathematical Theory of the Changes of Concentration at the Electrode Brought About by Diffusion and Chemical Reaction'; McBride, Unpublished History of the Chemistry Dept, Ch 5, 20
44 Jarrell, *The Cold Light of Dawn*, 127–9

45 Entry for P. Gillespie in Richardson and MacDonald, *Science and Technology in Canadian History*

46 Burton, 'Scientific Work' in Langton, ed., *Sir John Cunningham McLennan*, 101–3; Gingras, *Physics and the Rise of Scientific Research*, 30–1; UTA, A74-0008/008, McLennan, 'Roentgen Radiation,' University of Toronto Publication; and Letter, 16 Mar. 1905, Wright to W.E. Meredith

47 UTA, A73-0025/003(6), Letter, FASE Council to Mrs. G.R. Anderson, 7 Nov. 1952; UTA, James Loudon, 'Memoirs'

48 UTA, James Loudon 'Memoirs,' together with transcribed correspondence entered into volume, especially 4 June 1904, Galbraith to Harcourt and 28 June 1904, Loudon to Harcourt; B72-0031/006, printed letter, 13 Sept. 1904, Loudon to Harcourt; /003, file 36, 'Memorandum of the President Respecting ... Department of Physics'

49 UTA, James Loudon, 'Memoirs,' transcribed letter, 23 Sept. 1904, Harcourt to Loudon, and transcribed memorandum, J.C. McLennan, 'Memorandum Re Controversy ...'

50 Ibid., transcribed letter, 4 June 1904, Galbraith to Harcourt

51 UTA, A68-0006/25, Engineering Physics file, 20 Nov. 1935, Burton to Cody

52 UTA, A71-0008, Council Minutes, 1 Nov. 1901, 26 Sept. 1906

53 Ibid., 16 Mar. 1904, 25 Sept. 1905; UTA, FASE Calendar, 1904/05

54 Gidney and Millar, *Inventing Secondary Education*, 274

55 *UTPR*s, various years

56 Angus, 'The New Laboratories of the University of Toronto for Steam, Gas and Hydraulic Work'

57 UTA, A74-0008/007, Letters, 21 Apr. 1901, Haultain to Galbraith; 19 Aug. 1908, Haultain to Falconer, with attached personal resume

58 UTA, Falconer Papers, Letter, 9 Nov. 1909, Haultain to Falconer and reply, 24 Nov. 1909, Falconer to Haultain

59 UTA, FASE Calendar, 1909/10

60 UTA, A71-0008, Council Minutes, 6 Mar., 2 Dec. 1908

61 UTA, FASE Calendar, 1909/10

62 UTA, FASE Calendar, 1911/12; UTA, A71-0008, Council Minutes, 7 Feb., 4 Apr. 1913

63 Haultain, 'The University of Toronto and the Mineral Industry'; UTA, A71-0008, Council Minutes, 6 Feb. 1914; *UTPR*, 1913, 22

64 McKillop, *Matters of Mind*, 232–52

65 UTA, A71-0008, Council Minutes, 9 Dec. 1908

66 Christie, *What Does an Engineer Do?*, 17–28

67 UTA, FASE Calendar, 1909/10

68 Gidney and Millar, *Inventing Secondary Education*, 282–3
69 FASE Calendars for these years list names and homes for all students in attendance.
70 UTA, A71-0008, Council Minutes, 11 Oct. 1895, 10, 17 Jan. 1896; 17 Feb. 1896; also 2 May 1892
71 FASE, Personal file of M.J. Phillips, 26 Apr. 1990, handwritten memo from L.E. Jones
72 Harris, *Higher Eucation in Canada*, 628–9; McKillop, *Matters of Mind*, 124–46
73 Young, *Early Engineering Education*, 82; Levi, 'Where the Famous People Were?,' 201
74 UTA, A74-0008/010, Young files, printed pamphlet, 'Constitution of the Engineering Society of the School of Practical Science'; Levine, *A Century of Skill and Vigour,* 4–5; *Papers Read Before the Engineering Society/Applied Science* (title changes), various years
75 Worthington, 'Engineering Alumni Association,' 129
76 UTA, FASE Calendar, 1890/91
77 UTA, FASE Calendar, 1913/14; McKillop, 'Marching as to War,' 75
78 UTA, A71-0008, Council Minutes, 7 Nov. 1895; Levine, *A Century of Skill and Vigour,* 22–3
79 'Is Toike Oike Irish?' *UTM*, Nov. 1945, 48; Walden, 'Respectable Hooligans'; Levine, *A Century of Skill and Vigour,* 12; MacElhinney, 'The Engineering Society,' 27
80 Walden, 'Hazes, Hustles, Scraps, and Stunts,' 101–2
81 *The Varsity*, 6 Oct. 1911; Benson, 'SPS 77 Years Young,' 23–6; 'Old School 1891–1901,' recollections of Charlesworth, 88
82 Levine, *A Century of Skill and Vigour,* 20; UTA, B94-0001, 13 Mar. 1915, Kent Duff to Mother; Levine, *A Century of Skill and Vigour,* 19; 'Old School 1891–1901,' 113–14
83 UTA, A71-0008, Council Minutes, 29 Mar. 1897; 29 Nov. 1905 and *The Varsity*, 30 Nov. 1905
84 Walden, 'Respectable Hooligans'
85 *The Varsity*, 6 Oct. 1911; Levi, 'Where the Famous People Were?,' 143–5
86 Friedland, work in progress, 'History of the University of Toronto,' part 15; McKillop, *Matters of Mind*, 238–9
87 *The Globe*, 19 Feb. 1895; *The Mail and Empire*, 19 Feb. 1895; thanks to Sara Burke of Laurentian University for providing me with these references.
88 UTA, A71-0008, Council Minutes, 29, 30 Nov., 4, 5, 6 Dec. 1905
89 UTA, A71-0008, Council Minutes, 11 Mar. 1892; 14 Nov. 1902; 13, 25 Nov. 1903; 3 Mar. 1911; 10 Jan. 1908; 16 May 1910; 5 Nov. 1909 and 9 Apr. 1914
90 'Old School 1891–1901,' 91

91 Young, *Early Engineering Education*, 136

92 *UTPR*, 1914/15, 19

93 Lockett, 'The Lesson of the Quebec Bridge'

94 UTA, A74-0008/010 (02), Young files, letter, 26 Nov. 1941, H.P. Elliott to Young, and 14 Mar. 1945, letter attachment, 'T.R.T.' to Young; 'Old School 1891–1901,' recollections of Laing, 79–82, Darling, 90, and Thorold, 90–2

95 Ellis, 'John Galbraith'; Galbraith, 'Technical Education'

96 UTA, A74-0008/009, Galbraith file, printed pamphlet, Galbraith, 'The Function of the School of Applied Science'

97 Millard, *Master Spirit of the Age*, 129, Figure 7

98 Galbraith, 'Address – Dean Galbraith,' 176; 'Banquet to Principal Galbraith,' 154

99 Sinclair, 'Inventing a Genteel Tradition'

100 UTA, A74-0008-010, Young files, 'Memorandum from the University Council to the University Commission ...'

101 UTA, B65-0014/004, Wilson Diaries, 179–80

102 UTA, A74-0008/009, Galbraith file, letter, 14 Nov. 1902, Galbraith to Harcourt

Chapter 3

1 *University of Toronto Roll of Service 1914–19*, xi

2 Ibid., xxxvii

3 UTA, B94-0001, 28 Oct. 1914, Kent Duff to Mother

4 UTA, A71-0008, Council Minutes, 15 Oct. 1914; B94-0001, Nov. 1914 (undated), Kent Duff to Mother

5 *UTPR*, various years, statements of salaries

6 *University of Toronto Roll of Service*, xxxvii

7 UTA, A71-0008, Council Minutes, 6 Feb. and 1 Oct. 1915

8 *UTPR*, 1914/15, 19

9 UTA, B94-0001, 11 Feb. 1916, Kent Duff to Mother

10 *UTPR*, 1915/16, 21

11 *UTPR*, 1916/17, 19; UTA, B94-0001, letters, 11 and 21 Feb. 1917; clipping, n.d., 'Fifteen Questions Asked on Registration Cards'

12 *University of Toronto Roll of Service*, xxiii; UTA, A67-0007/052(a), Correspondence files, Haultain to Falconer, 14 June 1919; UTA, *Varsity Magazine Supplement*, 1918

13 UTA, A83-0036/017 (PUH), 11 Mar. 1918, Falconer to The Comptroller, Munitions Inventions Department

14 UTA, A83-0036/003 (PUH), 13 Sept. 1917, Chairman to Board of Governors; Parkin, 'The Toronto Aerodynamic Laboratory'

15 UTA, A83-0036/017 (PUH), 11 Mar. 1918, Falconer to The Comptroller, Munitions Inventions Department

16 *University of Toronto Roll of Service*, xxii

17 Enros, 'The University of Toronto and Industrial Research,' 163; and 'The Bureau of Scientific and Industrial Research'

18 Thistle, *The Inner Ring*, 3–5

19 Ibid., 8–10; McKillop, *Matters of Mind*, 285–8; Gingras, *Physics and the Rise of Scientific Research*, 54

20 Ellis, 'The University and Industrial Research'; UTA, A83-0036/018 (PUH), 24 Mar. 1917, Ellis to Falconer; *UTPR*, 1916/17, 21

21 UTA, A71-0008/014, Minutes of the SER, 1 Aug. 1917

22 UTA, *Varsity Magazine Supplement*, 1918

23 UTA, A83-0036/003 (PUH), 28 Sept. 1915, Falconer to Wiers; A67-0007/036, 12 Sept. 1914, Falconer to Schurman

24 UTA, A74-0008/015, Mitchell Tributes file, clipping, 'Charles Hamilton Mitchell,' American Society of Civil Engineers, *Memoirs*, Memoir 1158; 'Resolution of the Senate Respecting the Late Brigadier-General C.H. Mitchell ...,' 14 Nov. 1941; B65-0020, Young, unpublished MS, 'Beating to Windward,' 197; A67-0007, correspondence files, 30 Apr. 1908, Falconer to Mitchell; 14 Apr. 1909, Mitchell to Falconer; 7 May 1909, Falconer to Mitchell; 8 Feb. 1913, Falconer to Mitchell; 30 Dec. 1913, Falconer to Mitchell; Brock and Silversides, *Gateway to the North*, 14

25 UTA, A67-0007, 12 Sept. 1914, Falconer to Mitchell

26 UTA, A67-0007, Good Friday, 1915, Mitchell to Falconer; A67-0007/053, 'Particulars of Service – Lieutenant-Colonel C.H. Mitchell ...'

27 UTA, A83-0036/003 (PUH), 6 Dec. 1916, Mitchell to Falconer (two letters); 13 Jan. 1917, Falconer to Mitchell

28 UTA, A67-0007/053, 8 Mar. 1919, confidential, Mitchell to Falconer

29 McKillop, *Matters of Mind*, 295

30 Reid, 'The Twenties,' 61

31 UTA, A74-0008/001, 1919–1940 file, internal memo, Nov. 1943, 'Special Session for Students Returned from Active Service ...'

32 UTA, A71-0008, Council Minutes, 3 Oct. 1919

33 UTA, B65-0020, Young, unpublished MS, 'Beating to Windward,' 190–215

34 *UTPR*, 1919/20, 1920/21, 1921/22 'Report of the Dean of the Faculty of Applied Science and Engineering'; UTA, A67-0007/053, 10 Feb. 1919, Falconer to Mitchell; Mitchell, 'Situation and Requirements of the FASE'; *The Varsity*, 17 Feb. 1919; *The Globe*, 20 Sept. 1919

35 UTA, A71-0008, Committee Reports, Report no.7, 6 Jan. 1920, 'Report of the Committee on Committees'
36 Weatherhead, 'The History of Collegiate Education in Architecture,' 5-35; Oliver, *The Making of an Architect*, 38
37 Entry for C.H.C. Wright in Richardson and MacDonald, *Science and Technology in Canadian History*
38 UTA, A67-0007/053, 4 Mar. 1919, Falconer to Mitchell
39 Ibid. 26 Mar. 1919, Mitchell to Falconer
40 UTA, A71-0008, Council Minutes, 5 Dec. 1919; A67-0007/059, 26 Jan. 1920, Mitchell to Falconer; /073, Department of Architecture, handwritten 'Report for Session 1921–1922'; 'Town Planning Course in February,' 158–9; FASE Calendar, 1922/23; *UTPR*, 1928/9, 18; *UTPR*, 1929/30, 21
41 UTA, A71-0008, Council Minutes, 4 Dec. 1918; Westman, 'The Department of Chemistry'
42 UTA, A68-0006/034, Applied Science — Chemistry file, confidential memos, 1 Oct. 1931, Bain to Council and 2 Nov. 1931, Miller to Council (copies of both to Cody); FASE Calendar, 1931/32
43 A74-0008/008(6), printed booklet, n.d., 'University Survey Camp'
44 Noble, *America By Design*, 32, 170
45 UTA, A71-0008, Council Minutes, 2 Nov. 1917, 5 Dec. 1919, 27 Jan. 1922, 7 Dec. 1922; *UTPR*, 1921/22; A74-0008/001, 1940 file, 5 Mar. 1922; A67-0007/053, 26 Mar. 1919, Mitchell to Falconer
46 FASE Calendar, 1922/23; A74-0008/001, 1919–40 file, 'Report of the Committee on Teaching Business'; Mitchell, 'The Future of Applied Science'
47 *UTPR*, various years, Reports of the School of Engineering Research; UTA, A67-0007/079, 3 May 1923, Falconer to Mitchell; UTA, A77-0005/020, 'Report of the Committee of Management Presented to Doctor Dugald C. Jackson,' 12 Dec. 1939
48 *UTPR*, various years, Publications and Reports of the SER; Haultain and Dyer, 'Ball Paths in Tube Mills'; 'Thousand Experts to Hear Haultain,' *The Globe*, 19 Feb. 1924; UTA, A74-0008/001, Randolph Bruce Gold Medal file, press release, 'Professor Haultain Awarded the Randolph Bruce Gold Medal,' 18 Mar. 1937; clipping, 'New Apparatus Invented Here Aid to Mining,' *The Globe and Mail*, 6 Jan. 1941
49 UTA, A77-0036/002(03), various papers
50 Haultain and Dyer, 'Ball Paths in Tube Mills'
51 Seely, 'Research, Engineering, and Science,' 346–58; Servos, 'Engineers, Businessmen, and the Academy,' shows the much greater involvement of private industry in early research at the University of Michigan.
52 *UTPR*, 1921/22, 40–3; see also Hull and Enros, 'Demythologizing Canadian Science and Technology'

53 *UTPR*, 1920/21, 4

54 *UTPR*, 1914/15, 9; 1915/16, 8; and various years

55 *UTPR*, 1922/23, 41; 1924/25, 21

56 UTA, A71-0008, Council Minutes, 5 Dec. 1919; 9 Jan. 1920; 6 May 1921; 7 Oct. 1921; 21 Dec. 1921; 8 Jan, 1926; Report Nos. 309 (5 Feb. 1926), 316 (5 Mar. 1926), 340 (3 Dec. 1926)

57 *UTPR*, 1929/30, 52

58 Mills and Dombra, *University of Toronto Doctoral Theses, 1897–1967*, 43–57; this reference work states R.R. McLaughlin's PhD (1926) was the first, but it was in Chemistry, not Chemical Engineering – McLaughlin, 'Some New Rubber Derivatives ...' PhD Thesis, U of T, 1926

59 *The Varsity*, 2 Nov. 1921

60 *UTPR*, various years, appointments listed in introductory section

61 UTA, A67-0007/059, 21 Oct. 1919, 'Memo Re Physical Training'; FASE Calendar, 1919/20, 18

62 UTA, A71-0008, Council Minutes, 3 Oct. 1919

63 MacIlhenney, 'The Engineering Society,' 32

64 'Brilliant Production Staged by "School" at Massey Hall,' *The Varsity*, 4 Mar. 1921

65 Ibid.; Levine, *A Century of Skill and Vigour*, 26, 33

66 'School Freshmen are Stimulated by Slats,' *The Varsity*, 15 Oct. 1920

67 Walden, 'Hazes, Hustles, Scraps, and Stunts,' 108; Levine, *A Century of Skill and Vigour*, 56

68 *The Varsity*, 21 Nov. 1928, editorial, 'Demolishing the Varsity' (written in response to a letter from K.F. Tupper, later the Faculty's dean; see 'School-man Makes Numerous Charges Against Varsity,' 1)

69 UTA, FASE Calendars, 1920/21 and 1923/24

70 UTA, A74-0008/015, Lectures file; FASE Calendar, 1930/31

71 UTA, FASE Calendars, 1923/24 and 1928/29

72 *The Varsity*, 30 Oct. 1922; Reid, 'The Twenties,' 60–1, mistakenly dates this as 1920.

73 *The Varsity*, 30 Oct. 1922, 26 Jan. 1923, and 9 Mar. 1923; Walden, 'Hazes, Hustles, Scraps, and Stunts,' 110; 'Initiations,' 107

74 Walden, 'Hazes, Hustles, Scraps, and Stunts,' 110; *The Varsity*, 19 Nov. 1925, 1; and 1 Oct. 1926, 2; for caput, 6 Oct. 1924; UTA, A83-0036/022 (PUH), Caput 1906–32, 9 Oct. 1924, Falconer to Hastings

75 Walden, 'Hazes, Hustles, Scraps, and Stunts,' 110; *The Varsity*, 30 Sept. 1929

76 McKillop, *Matters of Mind*, 439–40; Axelrod, *Making a Middle Class*, 101–5; *The Varsity*, 26 Oct. 1932

77 'Cat-Calls Resound, Panic Reigns as Engineers Crash into Shea's,' and 'The Civil Engineers,' *The Varsity*, 19 Nov. 1928; also 21, 22, and 23 Nov. 1928

78 UTA, A74-0008/001, 1919–40 file, various clippings
79 'Initiation Parade Takes Schoolmen By Tortuous Route to Downtown,' *The Varsity*, 16 Oct. 1931
80 'School Initiation Forbidden By Dean,' *The Varsity*, 29 Sept. 1932
81 'Initiations Earn Campus Support' *The Varsity*, 1 Oct. 1935
82 *UTPR*, 1928/29, 95; McKillop, *Matters of Mind*, 420–37
83 Ball, *Mind, Heart, and Vision*, 97; informal interviews by author with surviving female graduates
84 *The Varsity*, 30 Oct. 1922, and frequent references in the 'SPS News' column of other issues
85 Pedder, 'School Night at Hart House,' 104–7
86 UTA, B65-0020, Young, unpublished MS, 'Beating to Windward,' 200; *UTPR*, 1923/24, 21
87 UTA, A74-0008/010, Young files, *Applied Science*, Jan. 1910, 2
88 UTA, A71-0008, Council Minutes, 8 Feb. 1907 and 5 Apr. 1907; 6 Feb. 1925; *UTPR*, 1924/25, 21–2; *The Varsity*, 8 Oct. 1925; 'Ceramics – A New Course for School Men'; A67-0007/095, 6 July 1925, Mitchell to Falconer; Enros, 'The University of Toronto and Industrial Research,' 161–3
89 Parkin, 'The Toronto Aerodynamic Laboratory'; UTA, A67-0007/079, 5 Dec. 1922, Mitchell to Falconer; A71-0008, Council Minutes, 27 Feb. 1928; A83-0036/003 (PUH), 7 Mar. 1928, Mitchell to Falconer; FASE Calendar, 1928/29
90 UTA, A67-0007/128a, 29 Jan. 1931, Mitchell to Falconer; A83-0036/003 (PUH), 24 Apr. 1928, Mitchell to Falconer
91 *UTPR*, 1931/32, 18; UTA, A71-0008, Council Minutes, Mar. 1932, Report of the Committee on Accommodation
92 Axelrod, *Making a Middle Class*, 20–1; McKillop, *Matters of Mind*, 438
93 *UTPR*, 1931/32, 19; 1932/33, 22
94 UTA, B65-0020, Young, unpublished MS, 'Beating to Windward,' 205; Stewart, 'The Role of the Provincial Government,' 357–9, 559
95 *UTPR*, 1933/34, 28; Young, 'Emil Andrew Wallberg Contructor and Adventurer'; UTA, A74-0008/013, Wallberg file, Typescript, n.d. (c. 1948), 'Emil Andrew Wallberg as I Knew Him,' and various clippings; A85-0033/008, Wallberg Historical file, internal memo, 16 Dec. 1975
96 Hughes, 'The Faculty,' 7
97 UTA, A71-0008, Council Minutes, 16 Mar. 1916; 1 Feb. 1918, 5 Apr. 1918
98 UTA, A67-0007/066, Mitchell file, 19 Jan. 1921, Mitchell to Falconer and Mitchell to McLennan; clipping from *The Globe*, 19 Jan. 1921, attached to McLennan letter

99 UTA, A83-0036/003 (PUH), 6 May 1919, Rosebrugh to Falconer

100 UTA, FASE Calendars, various years

101 UTA, A68-0006/013, Engineering file, 24 Apr. 1934, Burton to Cody

102 Ford and Thompson, *Sons of Martha*, 42; McGill Calendar, 1920/21, 120; see also Richardson, *Queen's Engineers*, 60–1 for Engineering Physics of a different type.

103 UTA, A68-0006/013, Engineering file, 21 Dec. 1934, Burton to Cody; 6 Apr. 1934, Mitchell to Cody; UTA, A71-0008, Council Minutes, 3 Apr. 1934, Faculty Council Report No. 689, 'Committee on Teaching Engineering Physics and Photography'

104 UTA, A68-0006/034 (02), copies of memos to Faculty council, 5 Dec. 1932 and 29 Nov. 1932; A71-0008, Council Minutes, Committee Report No. 636, 22 Feb. 1933, 'Committee on Advanced Teaching of Mathematics and Physics'

105 UTA, A68-0006/013, Engineering file, 24 Apr. 1934, Burton to Cody

106 UTA, A68-0006/025, Engineering Physics file, 1 June 1934, Burton to McLennan, and copy of Burton's undated memo to Cody, 'Memorandum Re the New Course in Engineering Physics'

107 UTA, A68-0006/025, Engineering Physics file, 25 June 1934, Burton to Cody, with attached memo on course contents; FASE Calendar 1934/35, 40; UTA, A71-0008, Council Minutes, 1 Nov. 1934, Report No. 710, 'Committee Administering the Course in Engineering Physics'

108 Hughes, 'The Faculty,' 7

109 UTA, B65-0020, Young, unpublished MS, 'Beating to Windward,' 205

110 *UTPR*, various years

111 UTA, A74-0008/015, Mitchell, 'Recent Progress and the Present Situation in the Faculty'

112 UTA, FASE Calendars, 1930/31, 1936/37; A74-0008/001, 1919–1940 file, 3 Mar. 1936, Young to Angus, and 'Draft of Minutes of Meeting of Wind Tunnel Committee,' 31 Oct. 1936; A73-0026/122 (Graduate Records), T.R. Loudon file

113 *UTPR*, 1936/37, 30; A74-0008/001, 1919–1940 file, 20 Jan. 1937, 'Report of the Committee on Expansion of the Ceramics Option'

114 *UTPR*, 1934/5, 73; A71-0008/014, Minutes of SER, 8 Mar. 1937

115 UTA, A74-0008/007, Randolph Bruce Gold Medal file, 'Professor Haultain Awarded the Randolph Bruce Gold Medal'; 'New Apparatus Invented Here Aid to Mining,' *The Globe and Mail*, 6 Jan. 1941; *UTPR*, 1932/33, 67–8; Haultain would bequeath the royalties from these devices to the university in his will.

116 *UTPR*, various years, SER Reports

117 Seely, 'The Diffusion of Science into Engineering'; Seely, 'Research, Engineering, and Science,' 358, 361–66

118 Allcut, 'Heat Insulation for Buildings'; Angus, 'Kreitner's Diagram for Water-Hammer Problems'

119 Rosebrugh, 'The Analytics of Transmission Calculations'; V.G. Smith, 'Reactive and Fictitious Power'

120 Vincenti, *What Engineers Know,* 134; Seely, 'Research, Engineering, and Science,' 359

121 Mills and Dombra, *University of Toronto Doctoral Theses, 1897–1967,* 43–57

122 Noble, *America By Design,* 240–3; Grayson, *The Making of an Engineer,* 119–66; Carlson, 'Academic Entrepreneurship and Engineering Education'; McKillop, *Matters of Mind,* 338–42; Axelrod, *Making a Middle Class,* 76–83

123 UTA, A74-0008/015, Mitchell, 'Policies for Engineering Education,' 15 Dec. 1927, with attached 'Report of Committee on Engineering Education'

124 UTA, A68-0006/036, correspondence files, 12 June 1939, Cody to Compton; also /044, Applied Science file, 27 June 1939, Compton to Cody, and same date, Jackson to Cody

125 Grayson, *The Making of an Engineer,* 122–3; Carlson, 'Academic Entrepreneurship and Engineering Education'; Noble, *America By Design,* 136–40; McMahon, *The Making of a Profession,* 71–8; Servos, 'The Industrial Relations of Science'; Wickenden, *A Comparative Study of Engineering Education,* 253–66; Jackson, *Present Status and Trends of Engineering Education in the United States*

126 UTA, A68-0006/069, Jackson Report file, 'Report on the Faculty of Applied Science and Engineering University of Toronto'

127 UTA, A68-0006/069, Jackson Report file, 26 July 1940, Report of Committee on Curriculum, Report by sub-committee; Jan. 1941, Interim Report; 27 Jan. 1941, 'Memorandum to Dr Cody re Interim Report of Committee on Curriculum'; 6 Mar. 1941, Cody to Jackson

128 UTA, A74-0008/015, Mitchell Tributes file, 'Resolution of the Senate Respecting the Late Brigadier-General C.H. Mitchell ... November 14, 1941'; 'Charles Hamilton Mitchell,' American Society of Civil Engineers, *Memoirs,* Memoir 1158, prepared by C.R. Young

129 UTA, A74-0008/015, lectures file

130 A74-0008/1, 1919–1940 file, various letters from Haultain, esp. 18 Nov. 1929 and 20 Nov. 1930, Haultain to Young, and 7 Nov. 1934, Haultain to J.R. Cockburn; also 'Diary re Haultain's Anti-Mitchell Activities,' rough notes by C.R. Young

131 UTA, A67-0007/075, 7 May 1926, Mitchell to Falconer

132 *UTPR,* 1927/28, 11, registrar's report of the occupations of parents

Chaper 4

1 *UTPR*, 1939/40, 24; UTA, A74-0008/001, 1941 file, 3 Nov. 1941, 'Committee on War Adjustments of Instruction and Examinations'
2 *Torontonensis*, 1940, 302; 1941, 215
3 *Torontonensis*, 1941, 211–15; 1945, 238–45; Granatstein, *Canada's War,* 100–1
4 Avery, *The Science of War,* 43–4; McKillop, *Matters of Mind,* 522–24; *UTPR,* 1940/41, 29–30
5 UTA, A68-0006/069, Jackson Report file, 20 Nov. 1940, Jackson to Cody; 6 Mar. 1941, Cody to Jackson; Applied Science Deanship file, 10 Mar. 1941, Jackson to Cody; 17 Mar. 1941, Cody to Jackson; 21 Apr. 1941, Mackenzie to Cody
6 Ibid., Applied Science Deanship file, 21 Oct. 1940, Challies to Cody; Christie, *What Does an Engineer Do?,* unpaginated photocopy
7 UTA, A74-0008/001, 1941 and 1942 files, various correspondence
8 Ibid., 1942 file, 16 Dec. 1942, Young to Lea; 1943 file, 11 Jan. 1943, Young to Lea; 13 Jan. 1943, 'Faculty of Applied Science and Engineering – Notice to All Years'; 21 Jan. 1943, Lea to Young
9 *UTPR,* 1942/43, 26–8
10 *UTPR,* 1943/44, 28–30
11 *UTPR,* 1940/41, 23; *Torontonensis,* 1942, 215; Avery, *The Science of War,* 47, 83
12 Avery, *The Science of War,* 102–4
13 Avery, *The Science of War,* 107–10
14 *UTPR,* 1940/41, 122; Eggleston, *Scientists at War,* 194
15 Eggleston, *Scientists at War,* 168 and *National Research in Canada,* 168–70; 'Ceramics – A New Course for School-Men,' 22
16 *The Varsity,* 4 Oct. 1943; Pidgeon, 'New Methods for the Production of Magnesium'; Wilson, 'Magnesium: Production and Technology'
17 UTA, A74-0008/001, 1941 file, 30 Apr. 1941, 'Memorandum of the Active Participation'; A77-0005/020, file SER Financial Sub-Committee
18 UTA, A74-0008/001, 1943 file, 1 July 1943, Price to Young
19 UTA, C.R. Young, 'Some Observations on the Future Development of the Faculty,' 28 Sept. 1943; A74-0008/001, 1944 file, 27 Jan. 1944, 'Final Report of Sub-Committee on Humanistic-Social Studies'
20 UTA, A74-0008/001, 1944 file, numerous documents
21 *UTPR,* 1943/44, 28–30; *The Varsity,* 30 Sept. 1943
22 UTA, A74-0008/001, 1945 file, 'Memorandum on the Proposed Establishment of an Undergraduate Course in Engineering and Business, 27 Jan. 1945
23 FASE Calendar, 1944/45 and 1945/46
24 Keshen, 'Getting it Right the Second Time Around,' 65–6

25 UTA, A74-0008/001, 1944 file: 19 Jan. 1944, Senate to Secretary of FASE, including copy of report
26 Ibid., 1944 file, 12 Apr. 1944, Wilson to Registrar (copy to Young)
27 Ibid., 1944 file, 16 Nov. 1944, Young to Smith, with accompanying confidential draft 'Suggested Plan of Organization ...' by W.J.T. Wright
28 *UTPR*, 1945/46, 10
29 Bliss, *Northern Enterprise*, 466; 'Prominent Engineer Appointed to University's Board of Governors'
30 UTA, A68-0006/063, 21 June 1945, Smith to George Drew; 21 June 1945, Smith to C.D. Howe; Memo, 4 June 1945, 'Ajax Visit'; Memo, 7 June 1945, 'Defence Industries Limted Property Ajax'
31 UTA, A68-0007/016 (02), 22 Jan. 1947, Smith to Young
32 *UTM*, Nov. 1945, 31
33 'Operation Ajax,' 147–8
34 *UTPR*, 1945/46: 33
35 *UTPR*, 1946 to 1949
36 *UTPR*, 1946/47: 32
37 Heisey, 'The Ajax Years,' 45
38 'Ajax Engineers Invade Varsity Campus'
39 UTA, FASE Calendars, various years
40 Patterson, *Pathway to Excellence*, 3–10; B.E. Etkin, unpublished memoir
41 UTA, FASE Calendars, 1944/45, 1946/47
42 UTA, FASE Calendars, various years
43 Engineering Society, *Transactions and Yearbook*, 59 (1945), 76; UTA, 'New Mechanical Building,' printed pamphlet; Bureau of Architecture and Urbanism, *Toronto Modern Architecture 1945–1965*, 26, 46
44 UTA, FASE Calendars, various years
45 Bissell, *Halfway up Parnassus*, 43; UTA, Oral History Interviews of B. Etkin, J. Gow, and G.R. Slemon
46 UTA, A75-0026/003, various clippings, esp. *Monetary Times*, Mar. 1962, 61; Eggleston, *National Research in Canada*, 57, 299–302
47 UTA, A83-0036/003 (PUH), 9 May 1950, Tupper to Smith; *UTPR*, 1950/51, 56–58; 1951/52, 61; 1952/53, 56–7; 1953/54, 61–2
48 American Society for Engineering Education, 'Report of the Committee on Evaluation of Engineering Education,' 94
49 *UTPR*, as above; UTA, A83-0036/003 (PUH), 1 Mar. 1954, Smith to Phillips; various informal interviews by author
50 *UTPR*, various years
51 *UTPR*, 1954/55, 1–18; 1955/56, 1–12; 1956/57, 3; UTA, 5 June 1956, 'Report of the Plateau Committtee to the Senate'

52 'Report of the Committee on Evaluation of Engineering Education,' 79–81; Chant, 'Factors Affecting the Trends in Engineering Education'; Grayson, *The Making of an Engineer,* 168–70, 175–6

53 Seely, 'Research, Engineering, and Science'

54 Wayman, 'William Howard Rapson'

55 UTA, A71-0008, Committee Reports, Report No. 1816 'Interim Report, Committee on Development,' Apr. 1956

56 Ibid.; *UTPR,* 1955/56, 70

57 UTA, A71-0008, Committee Reports, Report No. 1879, 16 May 1957

58 Calculated from *UTPR* Research reports, various years; *UTPR,* 1955/56, 71

59 Various informal interviews by author

60 *UTPR,* Reports on Research, various years; various informal interviews by author

61 UTA, A77-0005/016 and 017, SER files; /020, SER Finance sub-committee file, various annual reports; A85-0033/002, Research in Faculty file, 17 Apr. 1958, Sinclair to McLaughlin; 20 Feb. 1962, 'Second Report of the Special Committee to Study Research in the Faculty'

62 UTA, A73-0025/053 to 055, DRB files; *UTPR,* 1954/55, 77, 1955/56, 62, 1956/57, 74, 1957/58, 25; A83-0036/018 (PUH), Computers file

63 Eggleston, *National Research in Canada,* 360–1

64 *UTPR,* 1957/58, 25 and 157

65 UTA, A71-0008, Committee Reports, Report No. 1986, 'Report of the Special Committee to Study the Faculty,' 15 Sept. 1958; A85-0033/002, Research in Faculty file, 17 Apr. 1958, Sinclair to McLaughlin

66 Calculated from *UTPRs,* various years

67 UTA, A71-0008, Committee Reports, Report No. 1986, 'Report of the Special Committee to Study the Faculty,' 15 Sept. 1958

68 Patterson, *Pathway to Excellence,* 72–7; UTA, A71-0008, Committee Reports, Report No. 1835, 'Committee on Development,' 25 Sept. 1956

69 FASE Calendar, 1957/8

70 *UTPR,* 1955/56, 72; 1956/57, 60; 1957/58, 49; UTA, A77-0005/011, Atomic Energy file, various correspondence; A78-0008/007, Atomic Energy file, 24 June 1959, McLaughlin to Edey, and other papers; UTA, Oral History interview with Gordon Slemon; Bothwell, *Canada Since 1945,* 159

71 *UTPR,* 1956/57, 4

72 *UTPR,* 1955/56, 2; Patterson, *Pathway to Excellence,* 94–5

73 *Toike Oike,* 12 Mar. 1958; Levine, *A Century of Skill and Vigour,* 37, 44, 45; A.J. Paul LaPrairie, 'The Lady Godiva Memorial Band and the Skule Cannon,' Memo prepared for the Engineering Society, n.d., personal communication to author

74 *The Varsity*, 24 Sept. 1954
75 *The Varsity*, 27 Sept. 1954
76 *UTPR*, 1954/55, 75
77 Levine, *A Century of Skill and Vigour*, 60; *The Varsity*, 28 Sept. 1955, and 3 Oct. 1956; Donahue, 'A Hundred Years of Mischief'
78 UTA, A77-0005/011, Sopron students file, various papers, especially memos by James Gow, 23 Feb. 1972 and W. Szenci, 18 Feb. 1972
79 Various informal interviews conducted by the author, Jan. to Apr. 1999; Rossiter, *Women Scientists in America*, 67–8
80 Myers, *North of the Border*, 38–41, 172
81 *UTPR*, 1958/59, 44
82 UTA, FASE Calendars, various years
83 *UTPR*, 1958/59, 43–44; 1951/52, 33; UTA, A77-0008/035, Engineering and Business file, 6 Mar. 1961, Lord to McLaughlin (with attachment, Mar. 1959, Hooper to Lord); A78-0008/016, Canadian Universities General file, 3 Jan. 1962, McLaughlin to Holbrook
84 UTA, FASE Calendar, 1959/60, 40–1
85 Porter, 'Industrial Engineering in Retrospect and Prospect'
86 UTA, FASE Calendars, various years; Allcut, *Principles of Industrial Management*
87 Author's interview with Arthur Porter
88 Ball, 'A Short History of Engineering Science'
89 UTA, A77-0008/035, Eng. Sci. Course Committee file, 19 Mar. 1957, V.G. Smith to McLaughlin, and other papers
90 Various informal interviews by author
91 Ball, 'A Short History of Engineering Science,' 3; *UTPR*, 1962/63, 69
92 UTA, A78-0008/036, Ford Foundation file, clippings from *The Financial Post*, 9 Feb. 1963, and *The Globe and Mail*, 7 Feb. 1963
93 Magat, *The Ford Foundation at Work*, 32–3, 179
94 UTA, A78-0008/036, Ford Foundation file, 6 Jan. 1960, Trautman to McLaughlin; 6 Jan. 1960, Borgmann to McLaughlin
95 UTA, A73-0019/001, Ford Foundation General file, typescript, 25 Apr. 1963, RRM, 'History of the Ford Foundation Grant ...'; 30 Mar. 1962, McLaughlin to Borgmann; 8 Jan. 1963, McDonald to Bissell; A78-0008/036, Ford Foundation file, 31 Jan. 1962, McLaughlin to Borgmann
96 A73-0019/001, Equipment file, 10 Jan. 1967, Report No. 24, Collins to Ham
97 *UTPR*, 1962/63, 67; 1958/59, 45–6
98 *URPR*, various years, 'Research Funds' in list of benefactions
99 Calculated from lists of publications in *UTPR*, various years
100 Eggleston, *National Research in Canada*, 392

101 Axelrod, *Scholars and Dollars*, 23–4; Morris, *Canadian Engineering Education*, 12
102 Vincenti, *What Engineers Know*; Seely, 'Research, Engineering, and Science,' 367–86 discusses this phenomenon in the United States, and offers different explanations for its occurrence.
103 Calculated from UTPRs, various years; FASE, Annual Report for 1975/76, graph of enrolment, 102 gives different numbers.
104 Axelrod, *Scholars and Dollars*, 96–8, 141
105 Morris, *Canadian Engineering Education*, 12; *UTPR*, 1953/54, 61–2
106 'History of the Institute of Biomedical Engineering, 1962–1987,' unpublished manuscript, Institute of Biomedical Engineering, 2; 'Men in the Middle Zone,' 3
107 UTA, A85-0033/010, IBE file, 20 Sept. 1961, Porter to McLaughlin; author's interview with Arthur Porter
108 UTA, A85-0033/010, IBE file, 'Minutes of the First Meeting of the Council of the Institute of Bio-medical Electronics of the University of Toronto,' 2
109 Ibid., Minutes of Council Meeting, 5 June 1967
110 UTA, A82-0029/001, Mining file, 19 Dec. 1965, R.R. McLaughlin, 'Memorandum to Mr. Henry Borden ...,' including committee recommendation of 1 Mar. 1965; H.R. Rice, 'Memorandum re. Proposals ...,' 2 Mar. 1965
111 *UTPR*, 1966/67, 81
112 *UTPR*, 1965/66, 81; UTA, A78-0008/006, Faculty Study Committee file, various documents, especially 13 Nov. 1964, Ham to Scott
113 FASE Calendars, 1965/66 and 1966/67
114 'Shock Skulemen as Dean Decides Cut Out Jackets,' *The Varsity*, 30 Sept. 1958; various informal interviews by author

Chapter 5

1 Bissell, *Halfway up Parnassus*, 123–36
2 Bissell, *Halfway up Parnassus*, 130
3 Bissell, *Halfway up Parnassus*, 117–21; Haist Rules printed in *University of Toronto Staff Bulletin*, Oct. 1967, 15–22; UTA, Oral History Interview with Ben Etkin
4 UTA, A71-0008, Council Minutes, Report No. 1879, 16 May 1957
5 UTA, A78-0008/006, Faculty Study Committee file, 27 Nov. 1961, McLaughlin to council
6 Ibid., 29 Mar. 1962, Ham to McLaughlin; A78-0008/005, Committee of 1st Year file, 'Report for the 1963–64 Session' (Report No. 2231)
7 UTA, A78-0008/005, Committee of 1st Year file, 30 Jan. 1967, Craig to Council, with attachments

8 Etkin, 'A Case History of Academic Change,' in B. Etkin, 'Speeches and Writings 1938–1979,' unpublished collection held in UTIAS Library; UTA, A71-0008, Council Minutes, Report No. 2405, 21 Mar. 1968

9 UTA, A71-0008, Council Minutes, Reports No. 2413, 2420, 2470, 2489, 2500, 2511, 2523, 2534, 2539, 2543, 2544, 2550, 2560, 2561; also A78-0008/005, Task Force Study file, 'Progress Report from the Curriculum Task Force,' May 1969

10 UTA, A85-0033/002, Special Committee on Curriculum file, various student submissions

11 UTA, A71-0008, Council Minutes, Report No. 2499, Special Committee on Structure of the Faculty and Council, 23 Jan. 1970

12 Jasen, 'The Student Critique of the Arts Curriculum'

13 'Engineers Want Council Seats,' The Varsity, 9 Oct. 1968; UTPR, 1969/70, 14

14 Levine, A Century of Skill and Vigour, 62–3

15 UTA, A73-0025/106, file 4, 7 Dec. 67, 'Student Demonstration – Sit In, Confidential Interim Report'; The Varsity, various articles, 20, 21, 22, 24 Nov. 1967

16 'Ryerson student heckles Dow march,' The Varsity, 22 Nov. 1967, 3

17 'Petitioners Pursue Faulkner's Resignation,' The Varsity, 24 Nov. 1967

18 UTA, UC Student Handbook, 1968–69, 1; The Varsity, 19 Jan. 1968

19 Bissell, Halfway up Parnassus, 144; 'Meeting Accepts Bissell's Statement,' and 'Skulemen Turn Out in Force,' The Varsity, 3 Oct. 1969, 1, 3; Toike Oike, 9 Oct. 1969, 2, 5

20 'Skulemen Turn out in Force,' The Varsity, 3 Oct. 1969

21 UTPR, 1967/68, 17

22 UTA, A78-0008/005, Committee of 1st Year file, 'Report for the 1963–64 Session'; 30 Jan. 1967, Craig to Council, with attachments, and miscellaneous other documents; UTPR, 1970/71; 10 Oct. 1968, Ham to Gow; A82-0029/002, Experimental Teaching Unit file, numerous papers

23 UTA, A85-0033/006, Clean Air Car Race file, numerous clippings and papers; Hooper, 'How We Came to Where We Are'

24 Bissell, Halfway up Parnassus, 181

25 Etzkowitz and Kemelgor, 'The Role of Research Centres'; Bissell, Halfway up Parnassus, 82

26 UTPR, 1969/70, 15; 1970/71, 17; UTA, A78-0008/011, Haultain Building file, 18 Apr. 1969, Foster to Ham; /004, Presidential Advisory Committee on Environmental Studies file; A82-0029/005, Environmental Engineering files; UTA, SGS Calendar 1971/72

27 UTA, A85-0033/012, IHPST file; A78-0008/006, Faculty Study Committee file; Author's interview with Arthur Porter

28 UTPR, 1966/67, 28–9; UTA, A78-0008/014, Materials Science file

29 UTPR, 1969/70, 15; UTA, A82-0029/002, Transportation Engineering file, various papers, especially 30 June 1969, Pickersgill to Bissell

30 UTPR 1970/71, 17; A78-0008/014, Systems Building Centre file, 'Proposal to Gain Support for the Systems Building Centre ...,' Feb. 1971

31 UTA, A85-0033/006, SLOWPOKE file, various papers; A78-0008/007 and / 011, Nuclear Engineering files; A78-0006/006, Nuclear Engineeering file

32 UTA, A71-0008, Council Minutes, Report No. 2407, 1 Apr. 1968; A85-0033/ 008, Cockburn Bequest file; /011, CCED file

33 UTPR, 1969/70, 15

34 FASE, AR, 1972/73, 1

35 UTA, A78-0008/004, Presidential Committee on Environmental Studies file; A85-0033/003, Co-operative Program on Environmental Engineering file; A89-0029/005, Environmental Engineering file; FASE, AR, 1977/78, 102

36 UTA, A85-0033/003, Co-operative Program in Environmental Engineering file, various reports and memos

37 UTA, A86-0022/001, Social Impact of Technology file, various papers

38 FASE, AR, 1978/79, 8; 1977/78, 9; UTA, A85-0033/003, 3 Apr. 1977, Etkin to Evans; 7 June 1978, Etkin to Executive Committee; 17 July 1978, Ham to Etkin

39 Axelrod, *Scholars and Dollars*, 141; Fleming, *The Expansion of the Educational System*, 316–21; Bissell, *Halfway up Parnassus*, 78–9

40 Axelrod, *Scholars and Dollars*, 141–80

41 FASE, AR, 1972/73, 76 and 1980/81, 132

42 Calculated from budgets in UT 'bluebooks,' UT Financial Services

43 FASE, AR, 1976/77, 112, Fig.2b

44 FASE, AR 1980/81, 10 and 133, Fig.2b; statements of restricted funds in UT 'greybooks,' 1979, 1980, UT Financial Services

45 FASE, AR, 1978/79, 76; UT 'greybooks,' 1979, 1980, UT Financial Services

46 FASE, AR, 1980/81, 10, and 133, Fig 2b

47 MacElhinney, 'The Engineering Society,' 27; Levine, *A Century of Skill and Vigour*, 29

48 FASE, AR, 1975/76, 93; Miglin, 'The Recent Years,' 87–90

49 'Toike Oike Editor Asked to Resign,' *The Varsity*, 29 Sept. 1965, 1

50 'Engineers Drool: Pro Stripper Goes Nude,' *The Varsity*, 29 Oct. 1973; can be compared with 'Reporter Goes for Big Money,' *The Varsity*, 31 Oct. 1969 and 'CIN 203 Women Invade, Disrupt Engineers' Annual Slave Auction,' 23 Oct. 1970; beginning in 1974, only the *Toike Oike* covered the event; the *Varsity* took no notice – see *Toike Oike*, Dec. 1974, and *The Trawna Moon*, 28 Oct. 1976, 10–11.

51 UTA, A85-0033/006, Sandford Fleming Fire file, various papers, especially

16 Feb. 1977, Memo to the President, 'Summary Report on Sandford Fleming Fire'

52 UTA, A78-0008/011, Sandford Fleming file, various letters, esp. n.d. (c.1974), final draft of letter, Etkin to Connell, re: Sandford Fleming renovation

53 FASE, AR, 1979/80, 11; 1980/81, 13

54 A68-0007/016 (02), 11 Mar. 1949, Smith to Young; 10 Mar. 1949, Nicholson to Smith; 4 Apr. 1949, Young to Smith; 1 Apr. 1949, Tracy to Young

55 UTA, A71-0011/011(03), 19 Nov. 1957, Dunlop to Woodside; 4 Dec. 1957, McLaughlin to Dunlop

56 UTA, A78-0008/016, Canadian Universities General file, 27 Jan. 1970, Ham to Gow

57 UTIAS, Stangeby files, 10 Nov. 1976, Stangeby to Committee; 1 Dec. 1976, Stangeby to Mills

58 UTIAS, Stangeby files, 21 Oct. 1991, Stangeby to Etkin; UTA A85-0033/003, PEY file, 28 Feb. 1979, Scott to Etkin; FASE, AR 1978/79, 7

59 Ibid., 22 Nov 1979, Slemon to Scott, and 13 Feb. 1980, Slemon to various

60 FASE, AR, 1980/81, 8

61 Worthington, 'Engineering Alumni Association,' 129

62 FASE, AR, 1981/82, 15

63 FASE, AR, 1979/80, 7

64 FASE, AR, 1982/83, 8, 69; UTA, A94-0034, various papers

65 FASE, AR, 1980/81, 123

66 UT 'greybooks,' various years, UT Financial Services

67 Bird, *Industrial Policy in Ontario*; Ontario, 'The Technology Challenge: Ontario Faces the Future'

68 'BILD: This is what was done in the first year,' Ontario government pamphlet, n.d. (c.1982); FASE, AR, 1982/83, 8, 28–9

69 *Ontario Universities: Options and Futures*, 27

70 Courchene and Telmer, *From Heartland to North American Region State*, 109–13

71 *Competing in the Global Economy, Report of the Premier's Council*, Vol. 1, 212

72 'Recommendation 11,' *Competing in the Global Economy, Report of the Premier's Council*, Vol. 1, 210; also Courchene and Telmer, *From Heartland to North American Region State*, 109–13

73 FASE, AR, 1986/87, 2–3, 5; Abbott and Jones, 'Anatomy of a Competition'

74 FASE, AR, 1991, 6

75 UT 'bluebook' figures: 1981 – $5.6M, 1990 – $24.8M; in FASE, ARs, 1980 – $7.1M (from graph), 1990 – $29.6M

76 The following is based on unpublished data provided by the Office of Statistics, Records, and Convocation, UT

77 Based on author's interviews with a sample of 1970s female graduates
78 FASE, AR, 1990, 1
79 FASE, AR, 1986/87, 6
80 FASE, AR, 1991, 1, 9
81 FASE, AR, 1981/82, 74–5
82 FASE, AR, 1984/85, 4
83 FASE, AR, 1986/87, 15; AR, 1989, 14; AR, 1990, 15–16
84 The section that follows, on the current affairs of the Faculty, is based on a number of interviews, annual reports from the Faculty, and a series of planning reports prepared by Dean Charles and the staff of the dean's office in 1994, 1997, and 1999.

A NOTE ON SOURCES

This history is based almost entirely on the extensive collection of papers pertaining to the Faculty of Applied Science and Engineering held at the University of Toronto Archives. A wide variety of material was consulted: official Faculty records such as council minutes (from the inception of the School of Practical Science), school calendars, and correspondence files; some less official material deposited by the alumni association, the student society, and various students and academic staff; and a large collection of pamphlets and clippings. All of this was valuable, although some of the more recent material is perhaps still a little too unculled to be readily usable. Of particular note are the research files of C.R. Young, the Faculty's first historian, in both his personal papers and the papers from his deanship. The research files of Robin Harris, who worked for many years compiling material for a university history he never finished writing, also contain a valuable selection of material. There is much more held in the University Archives than could be used for this study.

WORKS CONSULTED

Abbreviations:

UTP   University of Toronto Press
UTM   University of Toronto Monthly
FASE   Faculty of Applied Science and Engineering

Abbot, Mark, and Joseph Jones, in association with the Impact Group. 'Anatomy of a Competition: Ontario Centres of Excellence Program April 1986 – March 1987', March 1998 (unpublished report done for Ontario Ministry of Industry, Trade, and Technology)
'Ajax Engineers Invade Varsity Campus.' *UTM* 48, 2 (Nov. 1947), 41
Alexander, W.J., ed. *The University of Toronto and its Colleges, 1827–1906*. [Toronto]: University Library, 1906
Allcut, Edgar Alfred. 'Heat Insulation for Buildings.' *The Engineering Journal* 20, 1 (Jan. 1937), 1–8
– *Principles of Industrial Management*. Toronto: I. Pitman, 1932
American Society for Engineering Education. 'Report of the Committee on Evaluation of Engineering Education.' *Journal of Engineering Education* 46, 1 (Sept. 1955), 25–60
'An Act Respecting the University of Toronto and University College,' Assented to 15 April 1901, 1 Edw. VII. *Statutes of Ontario*, ch. 41, 192
Anderson, G.R. 'University Exhibits New Lighting Methods.' *UTM* 27, 4 (Jan. 1927), 156–8
Angus, R.W. 'Kreitner's Diagram for Water-Hammer Problems.' *Mechanical Engineering* 57, 12 (1935), 781–2
– 'The New Laboratories of the University of Toronto for Steam, Gas and Hydraulic Work.' *Applied Science* old ser. 22, new ser. 3, 4 (Feb. 1910), 127–52

'Arthur Philemon Coleman.' *Transactions of the Royal Society of Canada* ser. 3, 33 (1939), 125

Averill, Harold, and Gerald Keith. 'Daniel Wilson and the University of Toronto.' In Eliabeth Hulse, ed., *Thinking with Both Hands: Sir Daniel Wilson in the Old World and the New.* Toronto: UTP, 1999

Avery, Donald H. *The Science of War: Canadian Scientists and Allied Military Technology during the Second World War.* Toronto: UTP, 1998

Axelrod, Paul. *Scholars and Dollars: Politics, Economics, and the Universities of Ontario, 1945–1980,* The State and Economic Life no. 4. Toronto: University of Toronto Press, 1982

– *Making a Middle Class: Student Life in English Canada during the Thirties.* Montreal and Kingston: McGill-Queens University Press, 1990

Axelrod, Paul and John G. Reid, eds. *Youth, University and Canadian Society: Essays in the Social History of Higher Education.* Montreal and Kingston, McGill-Queen's University Press, 1989

Bain, J. Watson. 'A Master's Course in Chemical Engineering.' *UTM* 17, 8 (May 1917), 305–8

Ball, Don. 'A Short History of Engineering Science at University of Toronto.' [Toronto]: [FASE], November 1970

Ball, Norman R. *Mind, Heart, and Vision: Professional Engineering in Canada 1887 to 1987.* Ottawa: National Museum of Science and Technology/National Museums of Canada, 1987

'Banquet to Principal Galbraith.' *UTM* 1, 5 (Jan. 1901), 148–57

Benson, Nathaniel A. 'SPS 77 Years Young.' *University of Toronto Alumni Bulletin* (Autumn 1954), 23–6

Berger, Carl. *Honour and the Search for Influence: A History of the Royal Society of Canada.* Toronto: UTP, 1996

Bird, Richard. *Industrial Policy in Ontario.* Ontario Board of Industrial Leadership and Development. Toronto: Ontario Economic Council, 1985

Bissell, Claude Thomas. *Halfway up Parnassus: A Personal Account of the University of Toronto, 1932–1971.* Toronto: UTP, 1974

Bliss, Michael. *Northern Enterprise: Five Centuries of Canadian Business.* Toronto: McClelland and Stewart, 1987

Bothwell, Robert, Ian Drummond, and John English. *Canada Since 1945: Power, Politics, and Provincialism.* Toronto: UTP, 1981

Bureau of Architecture and Urbanism. *Toronto Modern Architecture 1945–1965.* Toronto: Coach House Press, 1987

Burwash, N. 'The Development of the University, 1887–1904.' In W.J. Alexander, ed., *The University of Toronto and its Colleges,* 57–70

Calvert, Monte A. *The Mechanical Engineer in America, 1830–1910: Professional Cultures in Conflict.* Baltimore: Johns Hopkins University Press, 1967

Carlson, W. Bernard. 'Academic Entrepreneurship and Engineering Education: Dugald C. Jackson and the MIT-GE Cooperative Engineering Course, 1907–1932.' *Technology and Culture* 29, 3 (1988), 536–67

'Ceramics – A New Course of School Men.' *UTM* 26, 1 (Oct. 1925), 22–3

Chant, R.E. 'Factors Affecting the Trends in Engineering Education.' *Engineering Journal* 48, 1 (Jan 1965), 29–31

Christie, Alexander Graham. *What Does an Engineer Do?* New York: Vantage Press, 1963

Clark, A. L. *The First Fifty Years: A History of the Science Faculty at Queen's University 1893–1943.* Kingston [Ont.]: School of Mining [Queen's University], 1943

Conway, Jill K. *True North: A Memoir.* Toronto: A.A. Knopf Canada, 1994

Courchene, Thomas J., and Colin R. Telmer. *From Heartland to North American Region State: The Social, Fiscal and Federal Evolution of Ontario: An Interpretive Essay,* U of T Centre for Public Management, monograph series on public policy, no. 6. Toronto: University of Toronto Faculty of Management, 1998

Cox, R.C. *Engineering at Trinity.* Dublin: School of Engineering, Trinity College Dublin, 1993

Dictionary of Canadian Biography. 14+ vols. Toronto: UTP, 1965

Donahue, Pat. ' A Hundred Years of Mischief.' *Graduate: The University of Toronto Alumni Magazine* 13, 2 (Nov./Dec. 1985), 6–10

Drummond, Ian M. *Progress without Planning: The Economic History of Ontario from Confederation to the Second World War.* Toronto: UTP, 1987

Eggleston, Wilfrid. *National Research in Canada: The NRC, 1916–1966.* Toronto: Clarke Irwin, 1978

– *Scientists at War.* Oxford: Oxford University Press, 1950

Ellis, W. Hodgson. 'Chemical Notes on the so-called Sudbury Coal.' *Proceedings of the Canadian Institute* new ser. 1 (1895–98), 67–8

– 'John Galbraith.' *UTM* 15, 1 (Nov. 1914) 6–13

– 'Tannin in Cloves.' *Proceedings of the Canadian Institute,* 3rd ser. 4, 2 (1887), 214–15

– 'The Analysis of Milk.' *Proceedings and Transactions of the Royal Society of Canada* 5, sec. III (1885–87), 35–8

– 'The University and Industrial Research.' *Applied Science* old ser. 27, new ser. 10, 5 (June 1916), 121–5

– 'The Faculty of Applied Science.' In W.J. Alexander, ed., *The University of Toronto and its Colleges,* 180–3

Engineering Society, University of Toronto, *Transactions and Year Book,* 59 (1945)

Enros, Philip C. 'The University of Toronto and Industrial Research in the Early Twentieth Century.' In Richard A. Jarrell and Arnold E. Roos, eds., *Critical Issues in the History of Canadian Science, Technology, and Medicine*, 155–66. Thornhill and Ottawa: HSTC Publications, 1983

– The 'Bureau of Scientific and Industrial Research and School of Specific Industries': The Royal Canadian Institute's Attempt at Organizing Industrial Research in Toronto, 1914–1918.' *HSTC Bulletin* 7, 1 (Jan. 1983), 14–26

Etzkowitz, Henry and Carol Kemelgor. 'The Role of Research Centres in the Collectivisation of Academic Science.' *Minerva* 36, 2 (1998), 271–81

Evans, A. Margaret. *Sir Oliver Mowat.* Toronto: UTP, 1992

Finlay, R.D. 'The Origins of Mechanical Engineering Education in Canada'. In Andrew H. Wilson, ed., *From Steam to Space: Contributions of Mechanical Engineering to Canadian Development*, 204–16. Ottawa: Canadian Society for Mechanical Engineering, 1996

Fleming, W.G. *The Expansion of the Educational System.* Ontario Educative Society, no. 1. Toronto: UTP, 1994

Ford, George and Marjorie Thompson. *Sons of Martha: University of Alberta, Faculty of Engineering, 1913–1988.* Edmonton: Faculty of Engineering at the University of Alberta, 1988

Friedland, Martin. *History of the University of Toronto.* (work in progress)

Frost, Stanley Brice. *McGill University: For the Advancement of Learning, Volume I 1801–1895.* Montreal: McGill-Queen's University Press, 1980

Galbraith, John. 'Address – Dean Galbraith.' *Applied Science* old ser. 22, new ser. 2, 4 (Feb. 1909), 170–85

– 'On the Conservation of Energy and the Nature of Force.' *Canadian Journal of Science, Literature, and History* new ser. 15, 6 (1877), 491–508

– 'Technical Education: Address Delivered by Professor Galbraith at the Opening of the Engineering Laboratory at the School of Practical Science, Toronto, February 24th 1892.' *Applied Science* 5 (1891–2), 91–9

Gidney, R.D. and W.P.J. Millar. *Inventing Secondary Education: The Rise of the High School in Nineteenth-Century Ontario.* Montreal and Kingston: McGill-Queen's University Press, 1990

– *Professional Gentlemen: The Professions in Nineteenth-Century Ontario.* Toronto: University of Toronto Press, 1994

Gingras, Yves. *Physics and the Rise of Scientific Research in Canada.* Montreal and Kingston: McGill-Queen's University Press, 1991

Granatstein, J.L. *Canada's War: The Politics of the Mackenzie King Government, 1939–1945.* Toronto: UTP, 1975

Grayson, Lawrence P. *The Making of An Engineer: An Illustrated History of Engineer-*

ing Education in the United States and Canada. New York: John Wiley & Sons, Inc., 1993

Hall, A. Rupert. *Science For Industry: A Short History of the Imperial College of Science and Technology.* London: Imperial College, 1982

Harris, Robin S. *A History of Higher Education in Canada 1663–1960.* Toronto: UTP, 1976

Harris, Robin S. and Ian Montagnes, eds. *Cold Iron and Lady Godiva: Engineering Education at Toronto 1920–1972.* [Toronto]: UTP, [1973]

Haultain, H.E.T. 'The University of Toronto and the Mineral Industry.' *Applied Science* old ser. 24, new ser. 6, 4 (Aug. 1912), 125–31

Haultain, H.E.T., and F.C. Dyer. 'Ball Paths in Tube Mills.' *Transactions of the Canadian Institute of Mining and Metallurgy* 25 (1922), 276–92

Heisey, Alan. 'The Ajax Years.' In Robin S. Harris and Ian Montagnes, eds., *Cold Iron and Lady Godiva,* 73–83

Hershfield, C., and G.W. Heinke. 'Civil Engineering Education in Canada, Present and Future.' *Engineering Journal* 53, 1 (1970), 7–11

Hodgins, J. George, and Ontario. Dept. of Education. *Documentary History of Education in Upper Canada: From the Passing of the Constitutional Act of 1791 to the Close of Rev. Dr. Ryerson's Administration of the Education Department in 1876.* Toronto: Warwick Bros. & Rutter, 1894

Hooper, F.C. 'How We Came to Where We Are.' In *UTME 1890–1990' One Hundred Years of Mechanical Engineering at the University of Toronto.* [Toronto]: Privately Printed, [n.d.]

Hughes, P.B. 'The Faculty.' In Robin S. Harris and Ian Montagnes, eds., *Cold Iron and Lady Godiva,* 3–22

Hugill, Peter J. and D. Bruce Dickson, eds. *The Transfer and Transformation of Ideas and Material Culture.* College Station TX: Texas A&M University Press, 1988

Hull, James P. and Philip C. Enros. 'Demythologizing Canadian Science and Technology: The History of Industrial R&D.' *Canadian Issues* 10, 3 (1988), 1–21

Humphries, Charles W. *'Honest Enough to Be Bold': The Life and Times of Sir James Pliny Whitney.* Toronto: UTP, 1985

'Initiations', *Transactions and Yearbook of the University of Toronto Engineering Society,* 36 (1922-23), 107

Jackson, Dugald C. 'Trends in Engineering Education.' *Science* 92, no. 2383 (August 30, 1940), 183–9

– *Present Status and Trends of Engineering Education in the United States: A Report.* New York City: Engineers' Council for Professional Development Committee on Engineering Schools, [1939]

Jarrell, Richard A. *The Cold Light of Dawn: A History of Canadian Astronomy.* Toronto: UTP, 1988

Jasen, Patricia. 'The Student Critique of the Arts Curriculum in the 1960s.' In Paul Axelrod and John G. Reid, eds., *Youth, University and Canadian Society*, 247–71

Jones, L.E. 'Robert William Angus (1873–1960)', University of Toronto Department of Mechanical Engineering Technical Publication series TP7003, Sept. 1970

Katz, Michael B. and Paul H. Mattingly, eds. *Education and Social Change: Themes from Ontario's Past.* New York: New York University Press, 1975

Keshen, Jeff, 'Getting it Right the Second Time Around: The Re–Integration of Veterans of World War II.' In Peter Neary and J.L. Granatstein, eds., *The Veterans Charter*, 62–84

Kline, Ronald. 'Construing "Technology" as "Applied Science": Public Rhetoric of Scientists and Engineers in the United States, 1880–1945.' *Isis* 86, 2 (1985), 194–221

Langton, H.H. *James Loudon and the University of Toronto.* Toronto: UTP, 1927
– *Sir John Cunningham McLennan: A Memoir.* Toronto: UTP, 1939

Laudan, Rachel. *From Mineralogy to Geology: The Foundations of a Science, 1650–1830, Science and its Conceptual Foundations.* Chicago: University of Chicago Press, 1987

Lawr, Douglas. 'Agricultural Education in Nineteenth–Century Ontario: An Idea in Search of an Institution.' In Michael B. Katz and Paul H. Mattingly, eds., *Education and Social Change*, 169–92

Levi, Charles Morden. 'Where the Famous People Were? The Origins, Activities, and Future Careers of Student Leaders at University College, Toronto, 1854–1973.' PhD Thesis, York University, 1998

Levine, Barry G. *A Century of Skill and Vigour.* Downsview, Ont.: B.G. Levine, 1985

Lockett, Wilfred G. 'The Lesson of the Quebec Bridge.' *Scientia Canadensis* 11, 2 (1987), 63–89

Loudon, James. 'Affiliated Institutions.' In W.J. Alexander, ed., *The University of Toronto and its Colleges*, 201–5
– 'Buildings and Equipment.' In W.J. Alexander, ed., *The University of Toronto and its Colleges*, 206–17
– 'Presidential Address.' *Proceedings and Transactions of the Royal Society of Canada* 2nd ser. 8 (1902), app. A, xlix–lix

Loudon, W.J. *Studies of Student Life*, vol. 1. Toronto, Macmillan, 1923

Magat, Richard. *The Ford Foundation at Work: Philanthropic Choices, Methods, and Styles.* New York and London: Plenum Press, 1979

MacElhinney, W.G. 'The Engineering Society.' In Robin S. Harris and Ian Montagnes, eds., *Cold Iron and Lady Godiva*, 23–36

McBride, W.A.E. 'History of the Chemistry Department.' (Unpublished manuscript, 1999), ch.5, 20

McKillop, A.B. *Matters of Mind: The University in Ontario 1791–1951.* Toronto: UTP, 1994

– 'Marching as to War: Elements of Ontario Undergraduate Culture, 1880–1914.' In Paul Axelrod and John G. Reid, eds., *Youth, University and Canadian Society*, 75–93

McLaughlin, R.R. 'Some New Rubber Derivatives.' PhD Thesis, U of T, 1926

McMahon, A. Michal. *The Making of a Profession: A Century of Electrical Engineering in America.* New York: IEEE Press, 1984

McMath, Robert C., Jr., *et al. Engineering the New South: Georgia Tech, 1885–1985.* Athens, Ga.: University of Georgia Press, 1985

'Men in the Middle Zone.' *Canada's Health and Welfare* 18, 9 (Nov. 1963), 3; 8

Miglin, Eric J. 'The Ajax Years.' In Robin S. Harris and Ian Montagnes, eds., *Cold Iron and Lady Godiva*, 84–7

Millard, J. Rodney. *Master Spirit of the Age: Canadian Engineers and the Politics of Professionalism 1887–1922.* Toronto: UTP, 1988

Mills, Judith Eileen. *University of Toronto Doctoral Theses 1968–1975: A Bibliography.* Toronto: Published for the School of Graduate Studies University of Toronto by UTP, 1977

Mills, Judith Eileen and Irene Dombra. *University of Toronto Doctoral Theses, 1897–1967: A Bibliography.* Toronto: Published for University of Toronto Library by UTP, 1968

Mitchell, C.H. 'The Future of Applied Science.' *UTM* 20, 2 (Nov. 1919), 57–65

Moriarty, Catherine. *John Galbraith 1846–1914: Engineer and Educator: A Portrait.* Toronto: FASE, University of Toronto, 1989

Morris, Glenn A. *The Evolution of Engineering Education in Canada.* Ottawa: Canadian Council of Professional Engineers, 1990

Mouré, F.A. 'Outline of the Financial History of the University.' In W.J. Alexander, ed., *The University of Toronto and its Colleges*, 71–7

Munroe-Blum, Heather, (Office of Research and International Relations, University of Toronto). 'Growing Ontario's Innovation System: The Strategic Role of University Research.' Report to the Ontario Ministry of Training, Colleges and Universities, December 1999

Myers, B.R. *North of the Border: A Story Resulting from Two Years in Canada.* New York: Vantage Press, 1963

Neary, Peter and J.L. Granatstein, eds. *The Veterans Charter and Post-World War II Canada.* Montreal and Kingston: McGill-Queen's University Press, 1998

Noble, David F. *America By Design: Science. Technology, and the Rise of Corporate Capitalism.* Oxford: Oxford University Press, 1977

'Old School 1891–1901.' *Transactions and Year Book of the University of Toronto Engineering Society* 36 (1922–23), 79–92

Oliver, Richard, ed. *The Making of an Architect – 1881–1931: Columbia University in the City of New York.* New York: Rizzoli, 1981

Ontario Universities: Options and Futures. Toronto: Commission on the Future Development of the Universities of Ontario, 1984

Ontario. Board of Industrial Leadership and Development. 'BILD: This is What was Done in the First Year.' Toronto: BILD, 1982

– Innovation and Technology Division. *The Technology Challenge: Ontario Faces the Future: A Discussion Paper.* [Toronto]: Innovation and Technology Division Ministry of Industry and Trade, 1984

– Premier's Council. *Competing in the New Global Economy.* Toronto: the Council, 1988

'Operation Ajax: From Shell Plant to University.' *UTM* 47, 6 (Mar. 1947), 147–9

Parkin, J.H. 'The Toronto Aerodynamic Laboratory.' *UTM* 24, 1 (Oct. 23), 25–6

Patterson, Gordon Neil. *Pathway to Excellence: UTIAS – The First Twenty–Five Years.* [Toronto]: Institute for Aerospace Studies University of Toronto, 1977

Pedder, J.F., 'School Night at Hart House.' In *Transactions and Yearbook of the University of Toronto Engineering Society* 36 (1922–3), 104–7

Pidgeon, L.M. 'New Methods for the Production of Magnesium.' *Transactions of the Canadian Institute of Mining and Metallurgy* 47 (1944), 16–34

Porter, Arthur. 'Industrial Engineering in Retrospect and Prospect' [Inaugural Lecture, 15 February 1962, FASE, University of Toronto]. [Toronto]: FASE, 1962

'Prominent Engineer Appointed to University's Board of Governors.' *UTM* 45, 2 (Nov. 1944), 46

Reid, A.M. 'The Twenties.' In Robin S. Harris and Ian Montagnes, eds., *Cold Iron and Lady Godiva,* 52–64

Report of the Royal Commission on the University of Toronto. Toronto: Printed by order of the Legislative Assembly of Ontario by L.K. Cameron, 1906

Richardson, R.A. and B.H. MacDonald. *Science and Technology in Canadian History: A Bibliography of Primary Sources to 1914.* Thornhill: HSTC Pubs, 1987

Richardson, W. George. *Queen's Engineers: A Century of Applied Science 1893–1993.* Kingston, Ont.: Queen's University Faculty of Applied Science, 1992

Rosebrugh, T.R. 'The Analytics of Transmission Calculations.' *Transactions of the American Institute of Electrical Engineers* 49, 4 (1930), 1419–31

Rosebrugh, T.R. and W. Lash Miller. 'Mathematical Theory of the Changes of

Concentration at the Electrode Brought About by Diffusion and Chemical Reaction.' *Journal of Physical Chemistry* 14 (1910), 816–84

Ross, Alexander M. *The College on the Hill: A History of the Ontario Agricultural College, 1874–1974.* Vancouver: Copp Clark, 1974

Ross, Alexander M. and T. A. Crowley. *The College on the Hill: A New History of the Ontario Agricultural College, 1874–1999,* 2nd ed. Toronto: Dundurn Press, 1999

Ross, Peter M. 'The Establishment of the Ph.D. at Toronto: A Case of American Influence.' In Michael B. Katz and Paul H. Mattingly, eds., *Education and Social Change,* 193–214

Rossiter, Margaret W. *Women Scientists in America: Before Affirmative Action, 1940–1972.* Baltimore: Johns Hopkins University Press, 1995

Royal Society of London. *Catalogue of Scientific Papers 1800–1900.* London: C.J. Clay, 1867–1925

Schull, Joseph. *Edward Blake: The Man of the Other Way.* Toronto: Macmillan, 1975

Seeley, Bruce E. 'Research, Engineering, and Science in American Engineering Colleges: 1900–1960.' *Technology and Culture* 34, 2 (1993), 344–86

– 'The Diffusion of Science into Engineering: Highway Research at the Bureau of Public Roads, 1900–1940.' In Peter J. Hugill and D. Bruce Dickson, eds., *The Transfer and Transformation of Ideas and Material Culture,* 143–62

Servos, John W. 'Changing Partners: The Mellon Institute, Private Industry, and the Federal Patron.' *Technology and Culture* 35, 2 (1994), 221–57

– 'Engineers, Businessman, and the Academy: The Beginnings of Sponsored Research at the University of Michigan.' *Technology and Culture* 37, 4 (1996), 721–62

– 'The Industrial Relations of Science: Chemical Engineering at MIT, 1900–1939.' *Isis* 71, 259 (1980), 531–49

Silversides, Brock. *Gateway to the North: A Pictorial History of Prince Albert.* Saskatoon: Western Producer Prairie Books, 1989

Simmins, Geoffrey. *Fred Cumberland: Building the Victorian Dream.* Toronto: UTP, 1997

– *Ontario Association of Architects: A Centennial History 1889–1989.* Toronto: Ontario Association of Architects, 1989

Sinclair, Bruce. 'Inventing a Genteel Tradition: MIT Crosses the River.' In Bruce Sinclair, ed., *New Perspectives on Technology and American Culture,* 1–18. Philadelphia: The American Philosophical Society, 1986

Smith, V.G. 'Reactive and Fictitious Power.' *Transactions of the American Institute of Electrical Engineers* 52, 3–4 (1933), 748–51

Stacey, C.P. *Arms, Men and Governments: The War Policies of Canada 1939–1945.* Ottawa: Minister of National Defense, 1970

Stewart, Edward Emslie. 'The Role of the Provincial Government in the Development of the Universities of Ontario, 1791–1964.' DEd Thesis, University of Toronto, 1970

'They Will Direct the Ajax Division.' *UTM* 46, 2 (Nov. 1945), 31

Thistle, Mel. *The Inner Ring: The Early History of the National Research Council of Canada.* Toronto: UTP, 1966

Torontonensis. 68 vols. Toronto: Students' Administrative Council of the University of Toronto, 1898–1966

'Town Planning Course in February.' *UTM* 23, 4 (Jan. 1923), 158–9

Trudel, Jean-Louis, 'Born in War: Canada's Postwar Engineers and Toronto's Ajax Division', *Scientia Canadensis,* 50 (1999), 3–27

University of Toronto Roll of Service 1914–1918. Toronto: UTP, 1921

Veysey, Laurence R. *The Emergence of the American University.* Chicago: University of Chicago Press, 1965

Vincenti, Walter G. *What Engineers Know and How They Know It: Analytical Studies from Aeronautical History.* Baltimore: Johns Hopkins University Press, 1990

Walden, Keith. 'Hazes, Hustles, Scraps, and Stunts: Initiations at the University of Toronto, 1880–1925.' In Paul Axelrod and John G. Reid, eds., *Youth, University and Canadian Society,* 94–121

– 'Respectable Hooligans: Male Toronto College Students Celebrate Hallowe'en.' *Canadian Historical Review* 68 (1987), 1–34

Wallace, W. Stewart. *A History of the University of Toronto 1827–1927.* Toronto: UTP, 1927

Wayman, Morris. 'William Howard Rapson (1912–1997), Pioneer.' *Canadian Chemical News* 49, 7 (July/Aug. 1997), 15–16

Weatherhead, Arthur Clason. 'The History of Collegiate Education in Architecture in the United States.' PhD Dissertation, Columbia University, 1941

Westman, L.E. 'The Department of Chemistry.' *UTM* 21, 6 (Mar. 1921), 253–5

White, Richard. *Gentlemen Engineers: The Working Lives of Frank and Walter Shanly.* Toronto: UTP, 1999

Wickenden, William E. *A Comparative Study of Engineering Education in the United States and Europe,* Bulletin of the Investigation of Engineering Education, 16. New York: Society for the Promotion of Engineering Education, 1929

Williams, Trevor I. *A Short History of Twentieth Century Technology, c.1900–c.1950.* Oxford: Oxford University Press, 1982

Wilson, Philip D. 'Magnesium: Production and Technology.' *Mining and Metallurgy* 24, 2 (1943), 70–1

Worthington, W.R. 'Engineering Alumni Association.' *Applied Science* old ser. 27, new ser. 10, 5 (June 1916), 129

Wright, C.H.C. 'History of the Applied Science Buildings.' *Applied Science* old ser. 22, new ser. 2, 4 (Feb. 1909), 159–62

Wright, R. Ramsay and W.J. Alexander. 'The Arts Faculty.' In W.J. Alexander, ed., *The University of Toronto and its Colleges*, 78–99

Young, Clarence Richard. 'Emil Andrew Wallberg Contructor and Adventurer.' [Toronto]: FASE, [1951]

– *Early Engineering Education at Toronto 1851–1919*. Toronto: UTP, 1958

INDEX

Abbreviations:

FASE: University of Toronto Faculty of Applied Science and Engineering
SPS: School of Practical Science
UC: University College
UT: University of Toronto
WWI: First World War
WWII: Second World War

Abrams, John: role in IHPST, 222
Academic staff: in 1880s, 32; in
   1890s, 45–6; in early 1900s, 66–7;
   development of departments, 66;
   post-WWI, 98; outsiders hired
   (1920s), 112; renewal in 1930s,
   131–2; at Ajax campus, 162; post-
   WWII, 164; increases planned in
   1950s, 174; rapid expansion 1955–
   60, 184; salaries raised, 184; summer supplements for, 184–5;
   increases in 1960s, 199–200; lower
   teaching loads, 199–200; and
   reforms (1960s), 208, 210, 212; rising proportion of full professors,
   229–30
Access to Opportunities Program
   (ATOP), 262
Adams, Frank, 94

Admission standards: raised 1922,
   105; raised 1950, 173
Advanced students, instruction for
   (1933), 129
AECL, *see* Atomic Energy Canada
   Limited
Aerodynamics: wind tunnel and
   research (1917), 93
Aeronautical Engineering: new wind
   tunnel laboratory (1923), 121–2;
   option in mechanical engineering,
   122; re-introduced, 132–4; instruction in civil engineering, 165; new
   department of, 166; moved to engineering physics, 182
Ajax campus, 158–62; reasons for, 158;
   selection of site, 158–9; construction and operation, 161; enrolment,
   161–2; classroom, 161; student activ-

ities, 161–2; academic staff, 162; dormitories, 162, 163; closed, 167

Allcut, E.A.: SER-funded research (1920s), 108; appointed, 112; research in 1930s, 134; department head, 164; DRB grants in 1950s, 179; advocate of industrial engineering, 191–2

Allward and Gouinlock, 169

Alumni, Engineering: form association, 74; provide graduate student scholarships, 110, 241; request Jackson Report, 139; and new faculty council, 211; in FASE affairs, 240–1; medal and hall of distinction, 270–7

Alumni, UT: delegation to Ontario government (1901), 51

American Society for Engineering Education: Grinter Report, 173

Analytical and Applied Chemistry: program, 21; dispute over teaching, 25–27; curriculum, 28, 64; continues, 64; terminated, 103

Anderson, G.R., 61, 63, 84; and FASE physics department, 126–8; retires, 131

Andrews, D.G.: and reactor simulator, 183; appointed, 184

Angus, R.W.: appointed, 46; professor of mechanical engineering, 66; role in new laboratory, 66; aerodynamics research, 93; SER-funded research (1918), 95; research in 1920s, 108; and engineering physics, 129; still influential, 132; research in 1930s, 134; retires, 164; and wind tunnel, 165

Applied Chemistry: teaching department of, 25–7, 103, 195

Applied Mechanics: teaching department of, 66, 195; moves to Electrical Building, 100

Applied Physics: see Physics, SPS/ FASE

Architects: Kivas Tully (original SPS), 16; Darling and Pearson (Thermodynamics), 64–6; Darling and Pearson (Electrical), 99; Page and Steele (Wallberg), 167–8; Allward and Gouinlock (Mechanical), 169; Page and Steele (Galbraith), 192

Architecture: SPS course introduced, 43; room in SPS, 44; students request separate degree, 70; general development of education in, 100–2; pressure to reform, 102–3; appointment of Adrian Berrington, 102; BArch degree, 102; five-year course, 103; renamed School of Architecture, 103; separates from FASE, 169

Ardagh, A.G.: and research, 58; shell testing (WWI), 92

Armstrong, William: at College of Technology, 10

Arthur, E.A.: appointed, 112; inventory of historic buildings, 135, 137

Assaying and Mining Geology: program, 21; curriculum, 28

Atomic Energy Canada Limited (AECL): develops CANDU reactor, 182–3; FASE procures AECL-type reactor, 183; funds for research (1960s), 198; and Slowpoke reactor, 223

Babington, F.W., 29

Baby boom, 174

Bahen, John: chairs Dean's Advisory

Board, 259; co-chairs campaign cabinet, 261
Bahen-Tannenbaum Chairs in Civil Engineering, 261
Bain, J.W.: appointed, 46; research, 58; in WWI, 92, 93; opposes chemistry teaching by Faculty of Arts, 103; and engineering physics, 129; still influential, 132; research in 1930s, 135; retires, 164
Bequests and benefactions: Wallberg, 125; Cockburn, 223; Pratt, 254; Rogers, 266
Berrington, Adrian: appointed, 102; death, 112
Bissell, Claude: comments on 1954 initiation incident, 186; reflects on student protests, 207, 213, 219–20; Convocation Hall meeting (1969), 215–6; FASE students support, 215–6; role in IHPST, 221–2
Blake, Edward: and College of Technology, 8–12; becomes premier of Ontario, 9; views on UT, 9–12
Borgmann, Carl: and Ford Foundation, 196
Boswell, M.C.: and research, 58–9; in WWI, 93; SER-funded research (1918), 95; research in 1930s, 135
Bovey Commission: recommends private sector support, 245
Breckenridge, J.G.: research in WWII, 155
Buildings: original SPS, 16–17, 20–21, 22, 23; UC, 11, 21; expanded SPS (1890), 40–1, 48; UT Biology, 39–40; UT Chemistry, 47–8; Chemistry and Mining, 51–53; Mill, 51, 124; Thermodynamics, 64–6; Electrical, 99–100; addition to Mill, 123; inad-

equacy of in 1930s, 123; Wallberg Memorial, 163, 167–9; Mechanical, 163–4, 168, 169; Galbraith, 192–3; old engineering, demolished, 205–6; Pratt, 254, 255; Mining renovation, 254–5; new government funds for, 259–60; Bahen Centre for Information Technology, 265; see also Architects
Bureau of Scientific and Industrial Research, 93
Burt-Gerrans, J.T.: in WWI, 93
Burton, E.F.: comments on SPS physics teaching, 63; role in establishing course in engineering physics, 126–31

Cambridge University, 7, 13; Cavendish laboratory, 60
Campaign cabinet, 261
Canadair Limited: provides nuclear reactor, 184
Canadian Engineering Accreditation Board: and curriculum, 228, 243
Canadian government: see Government of Canada
Canadian Industries Limited, 159
Canadian Officer's Training Corps (COTC): founded, 88; FASE participation in (WWI), 88–90; bonus to students (WWI), 90; re-established, 148; academic credits for (WWII), 148
Canadian Transportation Commission, 222
Canadian War Mission in Washington (WWI), 92
Cass-Beggs, D.N.: appointed, 132, 164
Centre for Biomaterials (Dentistry), 263

Centre for Chemical Process Metal-
lurgy, 249
Centre for Nuclear Engineering, 242
Centre for Technology and Social
Development, 243
Centres of Excellence: conceived,
246; established, 246–8; newspaper
clipping, 247; additional space for,
254–5; consolidation of, 257; Photonics Research Ontario, 258
Ceramics engineering: introduced,
121; terminated, 173
Chapman, E.J., 17, 21, 24, 32, 35, 37
Chapman, Freddie: comments on
SPS initiations, 118
Charles, Michael: appointed vice-
dean, 248; appointed dean, 257;
deanship, 257–67; peer review of
FASE, 257, 263, 266; establishes
advisory board, 257; FASE at end of
deanship, 264–5
Chemical Engineering: course introduced, 64; department created,
103; changes name, 103–04; PhD
degrees in, 111; SER grants to
(1940s), 178; and nuclear engineering, 184; and environmental
engineering, 228
Chemistry, department of (Faculty of
Arts): teaching FASE students, 103;
proposes teaching FASE students,
103–4
Chemistry teaching: dispute over
(1880–82), 24–7
Cherriman, J.B., 14
Christie, A.G.: recollections c.1900,
71; offered deanship, 151
Civil Engineering: re-structured, 121;
united, 173; takes engineering
drawing instructors, 190; and envi-

ronmental studies, 220; and joint
program in transportation studies,
222; and Systems Building Centre,
223; and environmental engineering, 228; structures laboratory, 237
Class of 2T3, 105–6
Clean air car race, 218–9, 219
Cockburn, J.R.: appointed, 66; volunteers for overseas service in WWI,
90; bequest to FASE, 223–4
Cockburn Centre for Engineering
Design: established, 223–4, 228
Cody, H.J.: favours joint engineering
physics course, 128; and Dugald
Jackson, 139–40; seeks new FASE
dean, 151
Coleman, A.P.: appointed to SPS, 45
College of Technology, 3, 8–10, 13–
14; closes, 16–17
Columbia University: architecture
education at, 102
Committee on Development (1955–
7): struck, 176; recommendations,
176–7, 181; importance of, 181;
curriculum reform, 208–9
Committee on First Year, 209
Committee on University Governance, 226
Common first year: ends, 105; importance of, 181; partially re-introduced, 181–2; established, 204;
relaxed, 256
Composite Committee on Curriculum, 210
Computation Centre, UT: FASE role
in, 179
Computer Engineering: program
established, 256; popularity of, 262
Computer Science, department of:
new facilities in Sandford Fleming

building, 237; close relations with FASE, 256

Computer Systems Research Group, 222

Convocation Hall: protest meeting at (1969), 215–6

Cornell University: inspection of laboratories, 40; architecture education, 101–2

COTC: *see* Canadian Officer's Training Corps

Croft, H.H., 17, 20, 21, 24, 26

Crooks, Adam, 12–13, 18

Curriculum, SPS/FASE: 1878, 21–2; 1880s, 27–9; evening classes, 28–9; mechanical engineering introduced, 42–3; architecture course introduced, 43; optional fourth year, 43–4; mining engineering introduced, 45; sanitary option introduced, 45; mechanical renamed mechanical and electrical, 45; chemical engineering introduced, 64; revised 1909–11, 68–70; electrical and mechanical separated, 68; three-year course terminated, 68–9; non-technical instruction, 69, 105, 116; metallurgical engineering introduced, 69; revisions to architecture course, 102–3; analytical and applied chemistry course terminated, 103; Gull Lake survey camp, 104; pressure to reform, 104–5; science instruction in, 104–5; revised 1922–23, 105; physical training, 113; ceramics engineering introduced, 121; aeronautical engineering introduced, 122; engineering physics introduced, 130–1; aeronautical engineering re-intro-

duced, 132–4, 156; mining geology introduced, 134; humanistic-social studies, 155–6; engineering and business introduced, 156–7; ceramics engineering terminated, 173; questioned in 1950s, 175; science and mathematics in, 175; committee on development and, 176, 181, 208–9; practical subjects questioned in 1950s, 182; nuclear option added, 184; reduction in engineering drawing, 182, 190, 203; engineering and business terminated, 190–1; industrial engineering introduced, 191–2; becomes non-Galbraithian, 192; mining engineering terminated, 202–3; increase in humanities, 203, MEng introduced, 203; increasing mathematics in, 204; computer programming in first year, 209; engineering graphics, 209; revised structure (1967–71), 209–10; semester system, 210; first-year seminars, 217; geological engineering and applied earth science, 226; computer engineering introduced, 256; environmental engineering introduced, 263–4; language across the curriculum introduced, 264; Jeffrey Skoll BASc/MBA, 265; *see also* Common first year, Non-technical instruction, and Engineering Drawing

Curriculum Task Force, 210

Currie, Marion: first female academic staff member, 189

Currie, I.G.: and continuing education, 243

Curzon, Miss E.M.: applies for admission, 73

Dalton, I.R.: early biomedical electronics research, 200
Daniel, William: co-chairs campaign cabinet, 261
Darling and Pearson, 64, 99
Dawson, John William, 18
Dawson, William Bell, 18
Dean's Advisory Board, 257, 261
Defence Industries Limited, 159
Defence Research Board (DRB): founding grant to UTIA, 166; funds for research (1950s), 178–9; funds for research (1960s), 198; and UTIAS, 200
Degrees: CE, 30; requirements for diploma, 42; BASc, 44, 50, 55; PhD (UT), 55; end of SPS diploma, 68–9; BArch, 102; MASc, 110; establishment of PhD, 110–11; MBA following BASc, 191; MEng, 203; Jeffrey Skoll BASc/MBA, 265
Department of National Defence (WWII), 153
Departments: origin of, 66; teaching departments, 66; graduating departments, 66; organized around specialties, 121; teaching departments of Physics, 127; see also individual department names, Teaching departments
Depression: effect on FASE, 123–5; employment of FASE graduates during, 124; research curtailed, 125
Development office, 261
Dow Chemical: protest against recruitment by, 214–5
Downsview airport: UTIA at, 166
DRB, see Defence Research Board

Duff-Berdhal Commission, 208
Dunbar, W.B.: appointed, 112, 132; retires, 190
Dunlop, W.J.: and co-op education, 238
Dyer, F.C.: research with H.E.T. Haultain, 108

École Polytechnique de Montréal: student massacre at, 254
Electrical Engineering: separate department, 58; popularity post-WWI, 99; research contracts (1970s), 231; new facilities in Sandford Fleming building, 237; and computer engineering program, 256–7; department re-named Edward S. Rogers Sr. Department of Electrical and Computer Engineering, 266
Ellis, O.W.: SER-funded research (1920s), 108; appointed, 112
Ellis, William Hodgson: at College of Technology, 10; appointed, 20; c.1880, 25; and chemistry teaching dispute (1880–82), 26–7; appointed professor of applied chemistry, 26–7; teaches evening classes, 29; on SPS council, 35–7; and research, 56; c.1900, 59; appointed dean, 80–1; and industrial research, 94; changes chemistry departments, 103
Endowed chairs, 260–1
Energy studies: chair in, 228
Engineering Alumni Association: see Alumni, engineering
Engineering and Business: development of course in, 155–7; opposed by FASE alumni, 156; short life of,

169–71; questioned in 1950s, 182; terminated, 190–1
Engineering computer facility, 242
Engineering Drawing, 27–8, 66, 71, 182; department terminated, 190; importance of, 190, 203
Engineering Physics: introduction of course in, 125–31; resistance to in FASE, 126–7; at McGill University, 128; at University of Alberta, 128; graduating class of 1938, 130; importance of Faculty of Arts in, 130–1; renamed Engineering Science, 193
Engineering Science, FASE program in: new name for Engineering Physics, 193; growing importance of at FASE, 193–4; national recruitment for, 262–3
Engineering science, see Science, engineering
Engineering Society, 73–4
Engineering: course at original SPS, 21
Enrolments, student: early 1880s, 22–3; 1887, 30–2; 1890s, 43, 45, 49; early 1900s, 53, 64; 1911, 70, 76; in WWI, 88, 90, 91; post-WWI, 98; 1923–30, 107; 1930s, 123, 124; post-WWII, 157–8, 163–4; at Ajax campus, 160; 1950s, 174; expected increases in 1960s, 174, 176; graduate in 1950s, 180; graduate in 1960s, 199; 1980s, 249, 255; 1990s, 262–3
Environmental Engineering: FASE collaborative graduate program in, 227–8; undergraduate program in, 263–4
Environmental Science and Engi-neering: UT graduate program in, 220
Environmentalism: and clean air car race, 219; and research institutes, 220
Ethnicity, of student body (1980s-90s), 251–2
Etkin, Ben: appointed, 164; aeronautics instruction, 165–7; appointed dean, 226; background, 226; and Committee on University Governance, 226; at UTIAS, 227; role in establishing PEY, 238–9; and installation of Jim Ham, 239; in 1999, 265
Evans, John: and Sandford Fleming building re-construction, 237
Evening classes at SPS (1880s), 28–9
Experimental Teaching Unit, 217; audio-visual materials in, 217

Faculty council: restructured, 210–12
Faculty of Applied Science and Engineering: created 1906, 47; created 1900, 50; in new UT, 54–5
Faculty of Law: and university federation, 34
Faculty Study Committee (1961), 209
Falconer, Sir Robert: comments on WWI, 88; and WWI research, 93, 94; seeks new FASE dean, 96; and C.H. Mitchell, 96–7; and architecture reforms, 102; encourages outside hiring, 112
Fay, C.R., 116
Federation Act of 1887, 34
Fellowships and scholarships: alumni association, 109–10, 241; shortage of, 138, 180–1; Ford Foundation, 196–7, 199; new fundraising, 261; Rogers donation, 266

Financial affairs, FASE: concern over in 1970s, 229–32; external sources, 240; alumni liaison, 240–1; appeal to students, 240

Fire, Sandford Fleming Building, 235–37

First World War: at FASE, 87–95; enduring importance of, 97, 105, 113

Ford Foundation, grant to FASE, 195–8; background, 196; R.R. McLaughlin's role, 196; distribution of funds, 196–8; fellowships, 196–7; equipment purchased, 197–8; addition to Wallberg building, 198; importance to FASE, 198

Ford Motor Company: and Ford Foundation, 196; donation to environmental sciences and engineering program, 220

Foster, Sir George, 94

Franklin, Ursula: appointed, 222; teaches social impact of technology, 228

Friedland, Martin: comments on 1954 initiation incident, 186

Fundraising: new campaign, 261; development office created, 261; for all aspects of FASE, 261

Galbraith, John, 39–86 passim; background, 18–19; and James Loudon, 18–19; appointed first professor of engineering, 19; c.1880, 20; teaches evening classes, 29; teaching loads (1880s), 32; appointed principal of SPS, 35; in 1888 class photograph, 35; on SPS council (1889), 35–7; equipping laboratory (1890), 40; and academic diver-

gence from UT, 55–63; and research, 56; teaching c.1908, 57; and physics teaching (1904), 61–3; and professional education, 63; dean of FASE, 63; and Engineering Society, 73; death, 80; views on engineering education, 81–6; views on research, 83; achievements, 83, 86; c.1908, 85; legacy secure, 87; lingering influence of, 127, 132; views on consulting, 143; building named after, 192; continuity with era of, 267

Germany: PhDs from, 24, 45

Gilchrist, Lachlan: and engineering physics, 129

Gillespie, Peter: and research, 60; SER-funded research (1918), 95; SER grants in 1920s, 108; appointed department head, 121; death, 131

Gilley, J.R.: and Ajax campus, 159–61

Governance of FASE: reforms (1969–71), 210–12; faculty council restructured, 210–12

Government of Canada: financial support for research, 223, 258; Canadian Foundation for Innovation, 260

Government of Ontario: see Ontario government

Gow, Jim, 164: Faculty secretary, 194

Gradilude, 241

Graduate studies: origins of, 109–10; growth of post-WWI, 110–11; scholarships for, 110; in 1930s, 137–8; development of in 1950s, 179, 180–1; impact of Ford Foundation grant on, 199; growth in 1960s, 199;

MEng introduced, 203; in environmental studies, 220

Graduating class: 1888 photograph of, 35

Graydon, W.F.: appointed, 164; and Convocation Hall protests, 215–6

Grinter Report: K.F. Tupper and, 173

Guess, George A.: appointed, 69, 84; SER-funded research (1918), 95; retires, 164

Guggenheim Aeronautical Laboratory, 165

Gull Lake survey camp, 104

Haist Rules, 208

Hall of Distinction, 270–7

Ham, Jim: appointed, 164; and research in 1950s, 175; DRB grants in 1950s, 179; appointed dean, 205–6; curriculum reform, 209; faculty council, 211; student participation, 213–4; student-staff relations, 217; and IHPST, 221; Slowpoke reactor, 223; appointed dean of Graduate Studies, 226; appointed president of UT, 226, 239; course in social impact of technology, 228

Harcourt, Richard, 51

Harris, Premier Mike: government supports research, 258

Harvard University, 6, 8

Haultain, H.E.T.: appointed, 67; and iron ring ceremony, 67; engineering background, 67; personal eccentricities, 67; concern over mining curriculum, 70; with Invalided Soldier's Commission (1917), 91–2; SER grants in 1920s, 108; ore-crushing research, 108; retires, 132; superpanner and infra-sizer, 134–5; views on C.H. Mitchell, 145

Heinke, Gary: appointed dean, 248; Task Force on Professional Image and Women in Engineering, 254; Committee on Women in Engineering, 254; and hiring female academic staff, 254; changes under summarized, 257; in 1999, 265

High schools, 4

History, department of: and joint chair in history of technology, 221

History of technology and engineering: course in, 222

Hodgins, J. George, 8

Hodgins Commission Report, 8–9, 12, 16, 37

Hoeppner, D.W.: director, Cockburn Centre for Engineering Design, 228

Hogg, T.H.: offered deanship, 151

Hooper, Frank: appointed, 164; DRB grants in 1950s, 179; curriculum reform, 209; and faculty council, 211; and clean air car race, 218

Howe, C.D.: at school dinner (1939), 148; and Ajax campus, 159

Huber, D.G.: curriculum reform, 209

Huggins, Mark: appointed, 164; and Systems Building Centre, 223

IBM: donates computer equipment, 242, 256

IHPST, see Institute for the History and Philosophy of Science and Technology

Iler, R.K.: first FASE PhD, 111

Industrial Cellulose Research Limited: and W.H. Rapson, 176

Industrial Engineering: defined, 191–2; program in introduced, 191;

department of, 193; Arthur Porter occupies chair in, 193; and joint program in transportation studies, 222; and environmental engineering, 228; amalgamated with mechanical engineering, 263

Industrial partnerships: and committee on development (1957), 181; in 1960s, 198; Dean Slemon seeks, 241–2; benefits of, 242; innovations foundation, 242; and continuing education, 242–3; Ontario government promotes, 245; industrial chairs, 248; co-operative R&D grants, 248; in 1980s, 248; appointment of vice-dean for, 248; proliferate in 1990s, 258–9, 261

Industrial research: in WWI, 93–4

Initiations, student, 76, 114; violence in, 116–18, 186–7; opposition to, 117–18; in 1950s, 185–7; constructive, 186–7

Institute for the History and Philosophy of Science and Technology: founded, 221; teaching FASE students, 221–2

Institute of Aerospace Studies: *see* University of Toronto Institute of Aerospace Studies

Institute of Biomaterials and Biomedical Engineering, 263

Institute of Biomedical Electronics: founded, 200–1; early development, 201–2; re-named Institute of Biomaterials and Biomedical Engineering, 263

Institute of Environmental Studies, 220, 227–8

Interdisciplinary institutes: proliferate in 1960s, 220–3

Jackson, Dugald: studies FASE, 139–41; background, 139–40; views on engineering education, 140; recommendations to FASE, 140; consulted by H.J. Cody on new dean, 151

Jackson, K.B.: and engineering physics course, 127–31; department head, 132; role in FASE, 194–5; retires, 194

Jackson Report (1940): resistance to, 140; influence of, 156, 169

Jeffrey Skoll BASc/MBA, 265

Jervis, R.E.: appointed, 184; and Slowpoke reactor, 223

Johnson's Wax fund: and Institute of Biomedical Electronics, 202

Joint Program in Transportation Studies, 222

Jones, L.E.: appointed, 164; FASE archivist, 224; contribution to FASE, 224; son's convocation, 225

Jones, P.H.: and environmental studies, 220; and environmental engineering, 227

Kennedy, D.J.L.: and curriculum reform, 209–10

Kenney, T.C.: advocates restructured council, 212

King's College, 5

Kingston School of Mining and Agriculture: provincial aid to, 49

Kubbinga, W.H.: and school cannons, 114, 185

Laboratories: at UC, 29, 32, 33; engineering in expanded SPS in 1890s, 40, 44–5; blowpipe and assaying, 47; inadequacies of in 1908, 64;

new (1908–9), 64–6; heat labora-
tory, 68; structural materials test-
ing, 100; wind tunnel, 122; new
structural, 237
Lady Godiva, 185, 234, 252–3
Laing, A.T.: appointed, 46; and
research, 58; SER grants in 1920s,
108
Langstaff farm: considered as new
FASE site, 176
Language across the curriculum, 264
Lawrence Scientific School, 8
Leaving class pledge, 241
Leggett, R.: appointed, 132, 164
Library: new facilities (1982), 237
Lord, G.R.: appointed, 132; chairs
committee on development, 176;
professional practice, 178; with
Ontario Conservation Authority,
178
Loudon, James, 14–17, 42; background, 14–15; ideas on science
teaching, 14, 16; appointed chair
of mathematics at UC, 14–15;
recommendations for SPS, 15–17;
science teaching at UC, 16; recommends John Galbraith, 18; at SPS,
21, 24; teaching SPS students, 27,
29; and physics laboratory, 29, 33;
gone from SPS board, 37; and provincial aid to Queen's University,
49; and Ontario government, 52;
and research ideal, 55–6; named
UT president, 56; and J.C. McLennan, 60; and physics teaching dispute (1904), 61–3; view of John
Galbraith, 84
Loudon, T.R.: appointed, 66; volunteers for overseas service in WWI,
90; on committee for advanced stu-

dents (1933), 129; and aeronautics
instruction, 132–4, 156; and University Air Training Corps (WWII), 150;
department head (aeronautical),
164; aeronautics instruction, 165–7;
and G.N. Patterson, 165; department head (civil), 173; retires, 182

Macallum, A.B.: and NRC, 94
Macdonald, Sandfield: government
of proposes college of technology,
7–10
MacFarlen, Walter: graduating class
photograph (1888), 35; SPS
diploma (1888), 36
MacGill, Elsie, 120
Mackenzie, C.J.: acting head of NRC,
152; offered deanship, 152
Madill, H.H.: in COTC (WWI), 89–
90; head of architecture, 131; in
COTC (WWII), 150
Materials Research Centre, 222
McAndrew, W.J.: injured in 1954 initiation incident, 186
McCharles prize: to H.W. Price, 136
McConnell, A.W.: role in COTC, 89–
90; volunteers for overseas service
in WWI, 90
McDougall, William: teaches evening
classes at SPS, 29
McGill University: engineering physics at, 128
McIntosh, W.G.: appointed, 112, 132
McLaughlin, R.R.: appointed, 132;
research in WWII, 135; department
head, 164; appointed dean, 174;
and PhD, 174; DRB grants (1950s),
179; and nuclear reactor, 183–4;
comments on 1954 initiation incident, 186; and Ford Foundation

grant; retires, 204, 210; assessment of career, 204–5; and curriculum reform, 209; and faculty study committee, 209; opposed to co-op education, 238

McLennan, J.C.: early academic work, 60–1; awarded PhD, 61; teaching SPS students, 61; role in teaching dispute (1904), 61–3; helium research in WWI, 93; on NRC advisory council (WWI), 94; proposes joint courses with FASE, 126

Mechanical and Electrical Engineering, 32–3

Mechanical Engineering: separate course introduced, 41–2; work experience required in, 42; separate department, 68; research in post-WWII, 177; takes engineering drawing instructors, 190; clean air car race, 218–9; Cockburn Centre for Engineering Design, 224; and environmental engineering, 228; energy conversion laboratory, 228; BILD funds, 245; amalgamated with industrial engineering, 263

Mechanics institutes, 4

Medicine: students in, 21–2

Mellon Institute, 93

Metallurgical Engineering (Metallurgy): course introduced, 69; NRC research funds to (1950s), 180; renamed Metallurgy and Materials Science, 203; program re-named materials engineering, 263

Mickle, G.R.: appointed, 46; resigns, 67

Military enlistment: in WWI, 89, 90; in WWII, 148, 150

Military registration: in WWI, 91

Miller, Lash: and chemistry research, 58–9

Mining Engineering: course introduced, 45; professional practice in, 177; traditional importance of, 202–3; lack of research in, 202–3; enrolment in, 203; program and department terminated, 202–3

Miss Purity, 219

Mitchell, Charles Hamilton: appointed dean, 81, 97; background, 96; war service, 96–7; consulting work, 96–7; on UT Senate and Board of Governors, 96; improves internal management, 100; and architecture program, 102; and research, 109; comments on PhD, 111; teaches economics and finance, 116; comments on geology program, 134; and Wickenden report, 138–9; advocates general engineering, 139; retires, 141, 151; death, 141; legacy of, 141–45; deferred to department heads, 141; importance of consulting, 143; Haultain's views of, 145; in study c.1940, 144; as an outsider, 171–2

Montgomery, R.J.: appointed, 121; optical glass research in WWII, 155

Moody, N.F.: background, 201–2; appointed, 201–2; and early Institute of Biomedical Electronics, 202

Morrison, C.F.: appointed, 132; department head, 173; professional practice, 178

Mowat, Oliver, 12–13, 16

Mustard, J. Fraser: and Bovey Commission, 245; and Centres of Excellence, 247

Myers, R.B.: comments on Canadian engineering education c.1960, 189

National Network of Centres of Excellence, 249, 258

National Research Council: founded in WWI, 94; funds for wind tunnel (1923), 122; and UTIA research, 166; funds for research (1950s), 179–80; summer supplements, 185; funds for research (1960s), 198; funds for UTIAS, 200; negotiated development grants, 222; funds for research (1970s), 230; see also National Science and Engineering Research Council

National Resources Mobilization Act (1940): effect on FASE, 149–50

National Science and Engineering Research Council (NSERC): research chairs, 248, 249, 255, 260; co-operative R&D grants, 248; funds for research (1980s), 243–4; financial aid to new structures laboratory, 237; ongoing aid to research, 258

New Left Caucus, 215

Newcombe, J.A.: appointed, 112

Non-technical instruction: in 1880s, 28; in 1909, 69; in 1922, 105; competition between humanities and vocational subjects, 105; in 1920s, 116; in WWII, 155–6; Jackson Report and, 140, 156; SPEE position on, 156; C.R. Young's success with, 169–71; increasing humanities in, 203–4; social impact of technology, 228, 243; language across the curriculum, 264

Nortel Chairs in Electrical and Computer Engineering, 261

NRC, see National Research Council

NSERC, see National Science and Engineering Research Council

Nuclear engineering: early development of, 182–4; Centre for Nuclear Engineering, 242

Nuclear reactor: sub-critical purchased and installed, 182–4; simulator, 183; Slowpoke, 223

Ontario Association of Architects: demand reforms to FASE program, 102

Ontario Clay Products industry: and ceramics engineering, 121

Ontario College of Agriculture, 4

Ontario Conservation Authority: and G.R. Lord, 178

Ontario government: promotes economic development, 3–5, 7, 12; establishes College of Technology, 7–12; establishes SPS, 12–13; pays for SPS, 17, 24; and chemistry teaching dispute (1880–82), 26–7; initiates architecture course, 43; refuses aid to UT, 49; delegation of SPS students to (1901), 50–1; provides aid to UT and SPS, 51–2, 53–4; supports SPS Physics department, 61–2; funds for UT research, 94; funds for Electrical Building (post-WWI); funds for ceramics research, 121; funds for Mill Building addition, 123; reduces grant to UT (1932), 124–5; assists in purchasing 'west campus', 174; new university funding formula, 200; generous to universities in 1960s,

226; reduction of university grants in 1970s, 229–30; financial aid to re-build Sandford Fleming building, 237; funds for research (1980s), 244–8; develops industrial policy, 244–6; BILD, 245; funds for research (1990s), 258; funds for expanding infrastructure, 259–60; Ontario Innovation Trust, 260; Access to Opportunities Program, 262

Ontario Hydro-Electric Power Commission: supports work of H.W. Price, 125

Ontario Research and Development Challenge Fund (ORDCF), 258

Page and Steele, 167–8, 192

Parkin, J.H.: shell testing (WWI), 92; early aerodynamics research, 93; SER grants in 1920s, 108; appointed, 112; and aerodynamics research (1920s), 122; resigns, 133; early research at FASE, 165

Patterson, Gordon N.: background, 165; and E.F. Burton, 165; international career, 165–6; appointed professor of aerodynamics, 166; founds UTIA, 166; commitment to research, 166–7; summer supplements for UTIA staff, 184–5; in 1964, 200

PEST: original name for PEY, 239

Peterson, Premier David: establishes premier's council, 245; and Centres of Excellence, 247

PEY, see Professional Experience Year

Phillips, M.J.: appointed, 189

Phillips, W.E.: and Ajax, 159

Photonics Research Ontario, 258

Physics, SPS/FASE department of: John Galbraith establishes, 61–63; as a teaching department, 66; role in FASE, 126–8; G.R. Anderson in, 126–8; K.B. Jackson in, 127–31; renamed Applied Physics, 131–2; role in FASE, 194; terminated, 194

Physics, UT department of: in 1904 teaching dispute, 60–63; attempts to establish joint programs with FASE, 126; role in establishing engineering physics, 126–31; radar research in WWII, 154

Physics teaching: 1904 dispute over, 60–3

Pickersgill, Jack: and joint program in transportation studies, 222

Pidgeon, L.M.: magnesium research in WWII, 155; appointed, 164; DRB grants (1950s), 179

Pierre Lassonde Chair in Mining Engineering, 261

Pike, W.H.: appointed at UC, 24; dispute over teaching SPS students, 24–27, 47, 103; John Galbraith's opinion of, 81

Pitts, Arnold: radar research in WWII, 154

Porter, Arthur: appointed, 193; background, 193; head of industrial engineering, 193; and Institute of Biomedical Electronics, 202; and IHPST, 222

Pratt, Lorne: bequest to FASE, 254

Pratt, Lucille: bequest to FASE, 254

Premier's council: establishes Centres of Excellence, 246; University Research Initiatives Fund, 248–9

Price, H.W.: appointed, 66; SER grants in 1920s, 108; work on frequency regulator, 125, 136; department head, 132; retires, 164

Professional education, 63, 138, 177, 190–1, 204; bond between staff and students, 213, 217; continuing education, 242–3

Professional Experience Year (PEY): origins of, 237–40; growth of, 249, 259

Professional practice: C.H. Mitchell and, 143, 177; importance of maintaining, 177; in civil and mining, 177; growth of in 1950s, 178

Publications: SPS transactions, 58; scientists and engineers contrasted, 58–60; professional and industrial journals, 108–9; in-house, 108–9; see also Research

Pulp and Paper Centre, 249

Queen's University: provincial aid to (1890s), 49; and G.A. Guess, 69

Rapson, W.H.: research in 1930s, 135; and research in 1950s, 175–6; at Industrial Cellulose Research Limited, 176; pulp and paper laboratory, 198

Research Enterprises Limited: in WWII, 155; and W.E. Phillips, 159

Research institutes: in 1960s, 200; proliferate, 220; interdisciplinary, 220–3

Research: early adoption of at UT, 55–6; PhD degree adopted, 56; Galbraith and, 56; at SPS/FASE in 1890s, 56–60; scientific at UT, 58; early aerodynamics, 93; in WWI, 93; SER established, 93–5; industrial, 93–4; SER-funded research in

1918, 95; expansion of in 1920s, 107–12; SER grants in 1920s, 107–8; publication of in 1920s, 108–9; practical emphasis of, 109; at U.S. engineering experimental stations, 109; and graduate students, 109–10; aerodynamics in 1920s, 122; in 1930s, 134–8; scientific fundamentals, 135; during WWII, 154–5; G.N. Patterson and, 165–7; early aerophysics, 166–7; growing importance of in 1950s, 175; fundamentals (1950s), 175; committee on development favours, 176–7; at FASE in 1950s, 177–80; factors impeding development of, 177–8; DRB grants for, 178–9; committee to study, 180; nuclear, 184; impact of Ford Foundation grant, 198; rising funds in 1960s, 198–9; funds from U.S. Air Force, 198; funds for in 1970s, 230–2; contracts in 1970s, 230–2; NSERC funds for in 1980s, 243–4; funds from federal government, 243–4; Centres of Excellence, 246–8; growing importance of, 249, 255; in 1990s, 257–9; applications, 259; spin-off companies, 259

Returned soldiers (WWI): special arrangements for, 97–8

Roentgen, J.C.: McLennan replicates experiment of, 60

Rogers, Loretta: donation to FASE, 266

Rogers, Ted: donation to FASE, 266

Rogers, Edward S. Sr., 266

Rosebrugh, T.R.: transfers to SPS, 30; appointed, 45; lecturer in electrical engineering, 46; and

research, 58–9; head of electrical
engineering 68; SER-funded
research (1918), 95; comments on
joint courses, 126; retires, 132;
advanced mathematics in research,
135

Ross, George: and SPS laboratory
expansion, 33, 40; and architecture
course, 43; receives student delegation (1901) as premier, 51

Ross, R.A., 94

Royal Canadian Institute, 93–4

Royal Commission on the Quebec
Bridge, 81

Royal Commission on the University
of Toronto, 54

Royal Flying Corps: and FASE, 91–2

Runnalls, O.J.C.: appointed, 228; and
Centre for Nuclear Engineering,
242

Ryerson, Egerton, 8

SAC (Students Administrative Council): FASE students oppose, 215–6

Scholarships, see Fellowships and
scholarships

School dinners, 72, 74

School for Continuing Education:
FASE takes over from, 242–3

School nights (skule nites), 114, 115,
120, 262

School of Engineering Research
(SER): origins in WWI, 93–5; funds
from UT, 94; projects funded in
1918, 95; grants in 1920s, 107–8;
and graduate students, 110; in
Depression, 125; funding resumes
1935, 131; projects funded in
1930s, 134–5; war-related research
in WWII, 155; grants in 1940s, 178

School of Practical Science: 3–63
passim; bill to create, 12–13; origins and meaning of name, 13;
construction of building, 16–17;
independence of, 17, 35–7; school
crest, 17; courses taught at (1878),
20–21; UC science instruction at,
22–3; fees (1880s), 27; curriculum
and timetable (1880s), 27–9; photograph of original lecture hall, 31;
academic staff (1880s), 32; expansion of, 33, 40–2; diploma, 36;
becomes FASE, 54–5; research at,
56–60

Science, engineering: defined, 137;
developing, 137; established, 199

Science: teaching at UC, 7, 16, 22

Scott, Hildegarde E.: first female
graduate of FASE, 73

Scott, David: role in establishing PEY,
239

Second World War: at FASE, 147–57;
importance of engineering in, 150;
pressures on FASE, 153–4; shortage
of instructors at FASE, 153–4;
research in, 154–5

Sedra, A.S.: and computer engineering, 256–7; as provost, 265; and
Academic Priorities Fund, 265

SER, see School of Engineering
Research

Sheffield Scientific School, 8

Sinclair, G.: and research, 175

Slemon, Gordon: appointed, 164;
and research, 175; and Honeywell
simulator, 183; curriculum reform,
209; appointed dean, 240; seeks
external funding, 240; linkages
with industry, 241; innovations
foundation, 242; in office, 244;

deanship ends, 248; changes under summarized, 257; in 1999, 265

Slowpoke reactor, 223

Smith, E.A.: appointed, 112

Smith, Sidney: and Ajax campus, 159; expects enrolment increases, 174; and work placements, 237

Smith, V.G.: appointed, 132; advanced mathematics in research, 135

Smith, I.W.: and clean air car race, 218–9; and Cockburn Centre for Engineering Design, 224; retires, 228

Social impact of technology: course in, 228

Society for the Promotion of Engineering Education (SPEE): Wickenden Report and FASE, 138–9; and non-technical instruction, 156–7

Solandt, O.M.: and UTIA, 166; and Arthur Porter, 193

Sopron, University of: students to FASE, 188

Sputnik: effect on engineering education, 199

St Michael's College: and university federation, 34

Stangeby, Peter: role in initiating PEY, 238

Stern, E.W.: appointed fellow in engineering, 32

Stevenson, Adlai: protest against, 207

Stewart, George B.: John Galbraith's mentor, 19; father of Louis B., 42

Stewart, Louis B.: 42; appointed lecturer in surveying, 37; and research, 56, 60; Saturday instruction, 70; and John Galbraith, 84; department head, 121; retires, 131

Stoicheff, Boris: appointed, 164

Student activities: Engineering Society, 73–4; UC Lit, 73; athletics, 74; clubs, 74; YMCA, 74; military drill, 74; hallowe'en pranks, 74; dances, 74, 120; school dinner, 74, 'at homes', 74, 75; scraps, 76; initiations, 76, 114, 116–8, 185–7; elections, 76–7; Toike Oike, 77, 234, 252; brute force committee, 77; restrictions on, 77; early protests and strikes, 78; petitions, 78–9; Toike Oikestra, 79, 80; after WWI, 113–4; cannon, 114, 142, 185; green ties, 114; school nights (skule nites), 114, 115, 120, 262; FASE students become distinct, 116–8; tie-clipping, 117; soph-frosh banquets, 117–8; theatre nights, 117–8; gymnastics, 133; at Ajax campus, 161–2, 185; Engineers' Ball (Cannon Ball), 185; Lady Godiva Memorial Band, 185, 235; decline of traditional activities, 232; excessive ribaldry in, 232–5; shinerama, 232, 233; slave auction, 234; ribaldry challenged, 252–3; and female enrolment, 252–3; see also Student protests

Student body: 1890–1914, 71–3; women in, 72–3, 119–20, 145, 149, 188, 221, 252, 265; in 1940, 145; in 1950s, 187–9; international, 188; 1980s, 249–52; ethnic diversity in, 250–52

Student life: 1890–1914, 70–80; 1919–39, 112–20; at Ajax, 161–2; 1950s, 185–7; 1960s activism, 212–16; 1970s, 232–5; 1980s, 252–3

Student protests (1960s): at UT, 207–

8; reasons for absence at FASE, 213;
FASE students demand institutional participation, 213; FASE students oppose student left, 214;
against Dow Chemical, 214–5;
against president Bissell, 215–6
Student-Staff relations: changes
(1967–72), 216–20; first-year seminars, 217; secondary school liaison,
217; teaching innovation, 217–8;
clean air car race, 218–9
Students (SPS/FASE): in 1880s, 27–8;
delegation to Ontario government,
50–1; *see also* Enrolments, Student
activities, Student body, and Student life
Surveying: at original SPS, 21;
dropped from first year, 182, 204;
as teaching department, 195
Systems Building Centre, 222–3

T-program: introduced, 256
Teaching departments: defined, 66;
teaching departments of Physics,
127; history and significance of,
195; terminated, 195; *see also* Engineering Drawing, Applied Chemistry, Applied Mechanics
Teaching fellows, 32, 42, 46
Technical education, 4, 5, 12, 28–9
Thomas, E. Llewellyn: and Institute
of Biomedical Electronics, 201–2
Timetable: c.1880, 27–9; c.1900, 70–
1; post-WWI, 98; 1920s, 115
Toike Oike, 77, 234, 252–3; *see also* Student activities
Toronto Architectural Guild: and SPS
course, 43
Toronto Mechanics Institute, 9
Toronto Reference Library, 236–7

Toronto School of Medicine: and university federation, 34
Town planning, 102
Tracy, G.F.: appointed, 132, 164;
department head, 164; early biomedical research, 200
Training Centre Battalion, 150
Trass, Olev: and re-structuring council, 212
Treadgold, W.M.: appointed, 66;
department head, 132, 164
Trinity College: and university federation, 34
Tully, Kivas, 16, 40
Tupper, K.F.: appointed dean, 169;
background, 171–3; aerodynamics
research, 172; with Turbo Research
in WWII, 172; at atomic energy
project, 173; administrative
changes by, 173; resigns, 173
Turbo Research: and K.F. Tupper, 172

Undergraduate studies: remain
important, 255–6, 260; *see also* Curriculum
University Air Training Corps
(WWII), 150
University College, 3; student discipline at (1870s), 5; early civil engineering instruction at, 7; in 1870s,
11; relations with SPS, 12, 16–17,
22–7, 29; and university federation,
34; ends affiliation with SPS, 34
University Naval Training Division
(WWII), 150
University of Alberta: engineering
physics at, 128; G.N. Patterson studies at, 165
University of Toronto: relations with
Ontario government (1860s), 4–5;

College Avenue gates, 6; reforms at, 7; relations with SPS, 12–17, 24, 30; establishes CE degree 1884, 30; federation of, 34–7; affiliation with SPS, 34–7; financial affairs (1890–1906), 47–63

University of Toronto Act, 54

University of Toronto Institute of Aerophysics (UTIA): founded, 165–7; early graduate seminar at, 179; takes over undergraduate aeronautics teaching, 182; research funds from U.S. government, 184–5; and Ford Foundation grant, 198; moves to Dufferin Street, 198; research at (1960s), 200; renamed UT Institute of Aerospace Studies, 200

University of Toronto Institute of Aerospace Studies, 200; research funds from U.S. military, 200, 231; and joint program in transportation studies, 222

University of Toronto/FASE relations: after 1906, 63; in student life, 77–80; John Galbraith's role in, 83–4; UT funds to SER, 94–5; Falconer and academic staff, 112; academic, 115–6; FASE students become distinct, 116–18; perception of FASE students, 118; Engineering Physics, 126–31; Jackson Report, 140; WW II research, 154–5; Ajax campus, 157–60; humanities instruction, 169–71; expansion in 1950s, 176; 1954 initiation incident, 186–7; Haist rules, 208; student protests, 214–16, 220; interdisciplinary institutes, 220–3; finances (1970s), 229–30; and

computer science, 256; technical writing, 264; academic priorities fund, 264–5; Jeffrey Skoll BASc/MBA, 265

University of Toronto/SPS relations: affiliation with UT, 34–37; biology department, 39–40; chemistry teaching, 40; BASc degree, 44; generally 1895–1906, 47–63; chemistry department, 47; teaching connections, 47, 49; SPS fees to UT, 49; land rent payments to UT, 53; academic divergence (1890–1906), 55–63; and research, 55–63; physics teaching dispute (1904), 60–63

University of Waterloo: co-op program at, 238

University reform, 6–7; at UT (1870s), 7; and research ideal, 55–6

University Science Students Regulation (WWII), 153

Utility, 6, 13, 49, 51–2, 55, 109, 135

Vanderburg, W.H.: and Centre for Technology and Social Development, 243

Venn, Doug: and clean air car race, 218–9

Venter, Ron: as vice-dean, 257

Veterans (WWII): accommodation of, 158; and Ajax campus, 158–62; gone by 1951, 174

Veterinary medicine: students in, 21–2; and chemistry teaching, 26

Victoria College: and university federation, 34; and A.P. Coleman, 45

Wallberg, E.A., 125

Wallberg, Ida Marie: bequest to FASE, 125

Wardell, A.: appointed, 132; retires, 190

Wartime Bureau of Technical Personnel, 153

Wayman, Morris: and course on social impact of technology, 228, 243

Whitney, J.P.: aid to UT, 53–4

Williams, C.G.: appointed, 132

Wilson, Daniel, 42; chairs SPS board, 23–4; teaches evening classes at SPS, 29; and UC laboratory, 33; gone from SPS board, 37; opinion of John Galbraith, 84

Wilson, W.S. (Colonel): in COTC (WWII), 150; importance to FASE, 194; retires, 194

Wiren, R.C.: appointed, 132

Women: first female graduate of FASE, 73; at UT (1884–1911), 73; students at FASE in 1920s, 119–20; students at UT in 1920s, 119; students at FASE in 1930s, 145, 149; continuing low enrolment of, 188; on academic staff, 188–9; rising enrolment of in 1970s, 221, 252; rising enrolment of in 1980s and 1990s, 252, 265; ongoing concerns over, 252–4; deterrents to enrolment, 252–3; École Polytechnique de Montréal massacre, 254

Wood, C.S., 15–16

Woodside, president: and co-op education, 238

Work experience requirement, 42, 71, 115; abandoned, 237

Wright, C.H.C., 35; appointed lecturer in architecture, 43, 45; and J.C. McLennan's experiment, 60; role in COTC, 90; lack of architecture experience, 102; retires, 131; father of W.J.T. Wright, 190

Wright, George: explosives research in WWII, 155

Wright, R. Ramsay, 17, 24, 37

Wright, W.J.T.: teaches technical English, 116, 204; in COTC (WWII), 150; and Ajax campus, 159–61; department head, 164; retires, 190; connection to John Galbraith, 190

Yale University, 6, 8

York University, and joint program in transportation studies, 222

Young, C.R.: appointed, 66; role in COTC (WWI), 89; role in establishing engineering physics course, 128–31; appointed dean, 152; curriculum reforms in WWII, 155–7; and Ajax campus, 157–60, 170; retires, 169; assessment of career, 169–71; as FASE historian, 171; higher admission requirements, 173; and work placements, 237